# WATER AND ELECTROLYTE METABOLISM

SOLE DISTRIBUTORS FOR THE UNITED STATES OF NORTH AMERICA:

D. VAN NOSTRAND COMPANY, INC.

*120 Alexander Street, Princeton, N. J. (Principal office)*

*257 Fourth Avenue, New York 10, N.Y.*

SOLE DISTRIBUTORS FOR CANADA:

D. VAN NOSTRAND COMPANY (CANADA), LTD.

*25 Hollinger Road, Toronto 16*

SOLE DISTRIBUTORS FOR THE BRITISH COMMONWEALTH EXCLUDING CANADA:

D. VAN NOSTRAND COMPANY, LTD.

*358 Kensington High Street, London, W. 14*

SYMPOSIUM ON

# WATER AND ELECTROLYTE
# METABOLISM

AMSTERDAM 1960

*organised by*

*The Netherlands Society of Clinical Chemistry,*
*Het Genootschap ter Bevordering van Natuur-, Genees- en Heelkunde*
*te Amsterdam*
*and The Netherlands Society for General Pathology*

*edited by*

## C. P. STEWART

*Department of Clinical Chemistry, Royal Infirmary, Edinburgh, Great Britain*

*and*

## TH. STRENGERS

*Clinical Laboratory, O.L. Vrouwe Gasthuis, Amsterdam, The Netherlands*

ELSEVIER PUBLISHING COMPANY

AMSTERDAM — LONDON — NEW YORK — PRINCETON

1961

*Library of Congress Catalog Card Number 60–12360*

Some of the lectures presented at the Symposium on Water and Electrolyte Metabolism have been published already in *Clinica Chimica Acta*. Papers to which this applies are indicated in the Table of Contents (page *v*) by an asterisk. Reference is given to the appropriate pages in *Clinica Chimica Acta*.

*With 132 illustrations and 24 tables*

PRINTED IN THE NETHERLANDS BY

N.V. DRUKKERIJ G. J. THIEME, NIJMEGEN

# CONTENTS

* This paper has been published already in *Clin. Chim. Acta*, 5 (1960).

# INTRODUCTION

C. P. STEWART

*Department of Clinical Chemistry, Royal Infirmary, Edinburgh (Great Britain)*

The fact that so many of us are here this morning—well over 400 have enrolled —is an indication of how well-justified has been the enterprise of the three sponsoring Societies in organising this symposium. We, and the many others who cannot be present but will later read our "Proceedings" are grateful to them.

I am somewhat in a quandary as to the precise form my "Introduction" should take. I conceive the duty of the introducer to be threefold—to say something in general, but preferably sensible, terms about the subject of the symposium; to avoid stealing the thunder of the main contributors who are to follow; and to speak just so long that any late arrivals are in time for the first paper of the symposium proper, whilst those already present have not become impatient or bored.

Invariably the transition from one year to another, and more especially from one decade to another, is the signal for a flood of prophecies by people who tell us what we must expect during the time ahead. Among the crop which, last week, appeared in the British press and radio or television programmes was one which suggested that the focal point of scientific research would shift during the coming decade from nuclear physics to biology and in particular to the fundamental physical and chemical phenomena which constitute life. Such a move has, in fact, been discernible for some time, and the striking progress of organic chemists not only in unravelling the structure of protein and nucleic acids, but in showing how these latter substances control the reproducibility and the reproduction of the cellular matter, have already pointed the way.

But organic and organised cellular structure is not all; movement and change are also characteristics of living matter. As HOPKINS said, in an address to the British Association for the Advancement of Science as long ago as 1913: "Life is the expression of a particular dynamic equilibrium which obtains in a polyphasic system". And again: "The cell constitutes a system which can maintain itself in dynamic equilibrium with its environment." Although HOPKINS was, at this time, emphasising the importance of specific catalysis in orderly sequence, he went out of his way to quote the dictum of PAUL EHRLICH: *"Corpora non agunt nisi liquida"*.

I stress the essential role of water because, in wonder at the magnificent achievements of the organic chemists, there is a perceptible tendency to ignore it or at least to take it for granted. We, here, know that water, along with particular inorganic ions in particular amounts, is absolutely necessary for the complex interactions of the organic substances which constitute living matter, but which without such interactions do not live.

Yet we do not know the precise functions of the ions; why they are required by the cell in such definite quantities; how (or why) these essential ions are individually toxic and how by some mutual antagonism these toxicities may be cancelled out; how the cell maintains the correct ion concentrations (its "internal environment") in the face of a very different and variable external medium; or indeed many other things of fundamental importance.

It is right, and a necessary stimulus to further progress that we should from time to time take stock of our present knowledge and herein lies the value of our symposium today and tomorrow. During these discussions our speakers will consider water and electrolytes in relation to the diseased as well as to the healthy person, the pathological as well as the physiological factors. This too is right for both approaches must interest us whatever our professional label may be. The abnormal often yields evidence which elucidates the normal, and conversely the study of disease is inevitably and enormously facilitated by a knowledge of the processes occurring in health.

# THE MOVEMENTS OF WATER AND SALTS THROUGH NATURAL MEMBRANES

I. M. GLYNN

*Physiology Department, University of Cambridge (Great Britain)*

Today and tomorrow we shall be hearing about the movements of water and electrolytes in a number of different tissues, both normally and in disease. In this introductory lecture I thought it would be a good idea to look at water and electrolyte movements from the point of view of a single cell. To start with, it will be better not to name the cell, as once one calls it a nerve cell, or a muscle cell, or a red cell, a number of special features are introduced which complicate the picture.

Our generalised cell, then, will contain a solution of proteins and salts, and, at the pH that is likely to exist within the cell—say somewhere between 6 and 7 (HILL[1])—the protein will have a net negative charge. The cell will be bathed in a solution containing, probably, less protein—none at all if the cell is a unicellular animal living in the sea or a pond—and containing salts in different relative concentrations from those inside. If the cell membrane were freely permeable to water and salts, this pattern could not be maintained. The inequality of protein on the two sides of the membrane would lead to an osmotic inflow of water, and the salts would take up a Donnan distribution which would increase the osmotic flow still further and would be different from the observed distribution of ions. What I want to do is to talk about the features of the cell membrane that enable the characteristic pattern to be maintained.

Consider first the problem of water movements. The obvious question here, clearly, is: is there osmotic equilibrium across the membrane, or is cell volume maintained by the active pumping of water out of the cell against an osmotic gradient? In an amoeba, or other unicellular organism living in a pond, it is fairly clear that osmotic equilibrium cannot exist and the animal must, directly or indirectly, pump out water. In large multicellular animals the question whether the cells are in osmotic equilibrium is, rather surprisingly, still not quite settled, though it seems very likely that most of them are.

One way of testing whether osmotic equilibrium exists is to make a list of the solutes present on each side of the membrane, together with the concentrations in which they are found, and then to calculate the total number of osmotically active particles on the two sides and see whether they are the same. The difficulty with this method is that the list may be incomplete or, conversely, may include some solutes which are breakdown products of larger, and therefore osmotically less active, molecules. The method has been applied to red cells by HILL[2] in 1930, and more recently by DRABKIN[3], and to rat muscle by CONWAY AND HINGERTY[4].

A more direct method is to measure the freezing point depression of tissue homogenates. CONWAY AND MCCORMACK[5] froze tissues in liquid oxygen, then ground them to a powder, suspended the powder in isotonic saline, and measured the freezing point depression of the solution obtained. A complication of this method is that, with many tissues, the freezing point depression increases steadily with time—apparently as a result of autolysis (CONWAY AND GEOGHEGAN[6]), so that to find the original freezing point depression it is necessary to measure the rate of increase and extrapolate to zero time. CONWAY AND McCORMACK measured the freezing point depression of homogenates of liver, kidney, diaphragm, and abdominal muscle, in both rat and guinea pig. Their experiments, together with those of BRODSKY et al.[7], and others, are reviewed critically by DICK[8], who comes to the somewhat cautious conclusion that "the assumption of osmotic equality does not seem to be unequivocally contradicted by any of the evidences so far available".

Yet another way of testing whether osmotic equilibrium exists is to measure the change in volume which occurs when cells are immersed in hypo- or hypertonic solutions. A difficulty here, apart of course from the practical difficulty of measuring the volume change, is that as water enters or leaves the cell the intracellular concentration changes, and therefore the extent to which the osmotic behaviour may be expected to depart from *ideal* also changes. If behaviour at infinite dilution according to the Boyle – Van 't Hoff law is given by

$$\pi V = nRT$$

then behaviour in more concentrated solutions can be described by

$$\pi V = \phi nRT$$

where $\phi$ is simply an arbitrary "osmotic coefficient" inserted to make the results fit. At infinite dilution $\phi$ tends to 1. Protein solutions tend to have high osmotic coefficients, probably because of the large size of the protein molecules compared with the molecules of solvent, and at high concentrations the osmotic coefficients change markedly with change in concentration. PONDER[9] has made a thorough study of the volume changes of red cells in solutions of different strengths, and finds that, though they swell in dilute solutions and shrink in concentrated solutions, both the swelling and the shrinking are less than would be predicted if the cells were ideal osmometers. But red cells contain about 30% of haemoglobin and, from the osmotic behaviour of haemoglobin *in vitro*, DICK AND LOWENSTEIN[10] have calculated the change in osmotic coefficient to be expected as the intracellular concentration changes, and claim that this change in coefficient can account for most of the deviation from ideal behaviour observed by PONDER.

There are, of course, various situations in the animal body where a cell membrane separates fluids of different tonicity. Not all secretions are isotonic with the plasma. The cells lining the salivary ducts, for example, cannot be isotonic with both plasma and saliva; similarly, the cells lining the bladder and ureters must, more often than not, have a tonicity different from that of the urine. But in this sort of situation no osmotic problem need arise provided that the surface of the cell presented to the lumen is impermeable to water. A more complicated situation must exist in the mammalian kidney where, when a hypertonic urine is being secreted, the net effect is that water is transferred from a stronger to a weaker solution against an osmotic gradient. At first sight this would seem, necessarily, to involve a water pump rather than a salt pump, but WIRZ, HARGITAY AND KUHN[11] have put forward an ingenious theory which not only gets round this difficulty but also makes sense of some otherwise puzzling features of the anatomy of the kidney tubule. Dr. WIRZ's theory is discussed elsewhere in this volume (p. 100).

Turning now to the maintenance of the salt distribution, the problem is clearly a good deal more complicated. It is not possible to postulate that the high internal potassium and the low internal sodium are maintained by impermeability of the membrane to these ions: most cell membranes are not impermeable to sodium and potassium. Nor has it been possible to explain the ion distribution in terms of ion binding in the cell interior, although several attempts to do so have been made. There is very little doubt that small amounts of sodium and potassium do occur in a bound state inside certain cells: EDDY AND HINSHELWOOD[12] have demonstrated potassium binding in some bacteria; GOLD AND SOLOMON[13] gave evidence of a slowly exchanging sodium fraction in red cells; there are several pieces of evidence suggesting ion binding in mitochondria—in particular GAMBLE[14] has recently shown that rat liver mito-chondria bind potassium in preference to sodium even when their membranes have been disrupted with the surface-active agent digitonin. Nevertheless, except in bacte-ria, it seems that the total quantity of ions bound represents only a small fraction of the amount present in the cell. In nerve and muscle fibres, the mobility and diffusion of sodium and potassium ions appear to be of the same order as in free solution. Mobility and diffusion can be measured by adding radioactive sodium or potassium intracellularly, either by injection or by immersing the tissue for a short period in a solution containing the labelled ion, and then observing the rate at which the radio-activity diffuses through the cytoplasm or moves under the influence of an applied electric field[15-17]. A possible criticism of these experiments is that the added ions might behave differently from ions already present, but this seems rather unlikely as most flux measurements show that intracellular sodium and potassium behave as single compartments[18-21]. Apparent deviation from single compartment behaviour in frog muscle[22-24] seems to be due to slight differences in diameter or permeability among the population of fibres, as HODGKIN AND HOROWICZ[25] find that single fibres do not show this deviation. It is anyway very difficult to explain the low sodium concentration on the ion-binding hypothesis unless a large fraction of the cell water is bound, which there is evidence against[2], and which would upset the osmotic equilibrium. There is other evidence against the ion-binding theory (see reviews [26-30]), but this will do for the present.

We are therefore left with only one alternative—that the distribution of sodium and potassium depends on the activity of the membrane, which must be able to move one or both of these ions against electrical or concentration gradients or a combination of the two. If the membrane pumped sodium out, the inside of the cell would be left negatively charged; this would lead to a gain of potassium and loss of chloride, and at equilibrium the Nernst relationship:

$$\frac{K_i}{K_o} = \frac{Cl_o}{Cl_i} = \exp EF/RT$$

should hold. In red cells the potential cannot be measured, but the potassium ratio is about 20 and the chloride ratio about 1.4, so the explanation will not work. It is necessary to postulate the pumping in of potassium as well as the pumping out of sodium, and this fits in with observations that depriving the cells of glucose or poison-ing them with fluoride leads to a slowing of potassium influx as well as of sodium efflux[31-34]. In nerve and muscle the chloride ratio is difficult to determine, as it is not easy to get an accurate figure for internal chloride, but the potential can be measured. Under physiological conditions the potential is generally found to be slightly lower than would be expected from the potassium ratio[35-38] (but cf.[27]), but this in itself is not good evidence for the active accumulation of potassium, as the potential measurements may be slightly out, for example through junction potentials. In nerve, however, anoxia and metabolic inhibitors strongly inhibit potassium influx as well as sodium efflux, so here too it seems that both fluxes are active[16,21,39-41]. There is also evidence in nerve and in red cells that active sodium efflux and active potassium influx are linked together, since sodium efflux is reduced by lowering the external potassium concentration, and the effect cannot be explained by a change in membrane potential[16,34,42,43]. As similar behaviour is found in frog muscle[20,44-46], it seems likely that, in this tissue also, active extrusion of sodium is linked to an active uptake of potassium, though there are no published data showing the effects of metabolic inhibitors on potassium influx.

Whatever the mechanism that is responsible for the sodium–potassium exchange, it seems to occupy a very small fraction of the membrane surface. Some years ago cardiac glycosides—substances like digoxin and strophanthin—were shown to inhibit the active movements of sodium and potassium in red cells without affecting respiration or glycolysis[47]; detailed study of the effects of cardiac glycosides on the active and passive fluxes of sodium and potassium suggested that they acted on the pump mechanism[48]. At low concentrations their behaviour was such that it seemed reasonable to assume that a single molecule of glycoside could affect only one carrier site and, since appreciable inhibition could be obtained at concentrations so low that relatively few molecules were present, it was possible to get an estimate of the number of carrier sites on the cells. The estimate was of course an upper limit. as not every inhibitor molecule could be assumed to be sitting on a carrier site. From the effects of low concentrations of scillaren A, one of the squill glycosides, it was calculated that the number of sites on each cell responsible for the active influx of potassium could not be more than about one thousand[48]. This low figure does not demand an impossibly high turnover, but it does suggest that very little of the total area of the membrane is involved, as, though we have no very clear idea how big a site is, on any reasonable estimate a thousand of them will not cover much space.

In this connection, it is interesting that rather similar results have been obtained in experiments on the exchange of both chloride and glycerol across the red cell membrane. EDELBERG[49] showed that chloride entry could be appreciably slowed by quantities of tannic acid sufficient to cover less than 1% of the surface, and JACOBS AND CORSON[50] found that glycerol entry was markedly inhibited by minute amounts of copper ions. I think it is important to bear these results in mind when one comes to consider how the membrane might function in terms of its chemical constituents. Chemical analyses of the cell membrane, and the majority of the physical methods of investigation, give information about the structure of the membrane as a whole, but if only one very small bit of membrane is responsible for the permeability to a particular substance, the information may be irrelevant.

The active movements of sodium and potassium require energy, and this energy is provided by the metabolism of the cell. In nerve, muscle, the nucleated red cells of birds and reptiles and probably in most tissues, the energy comes from aerobic metabolism[6,41,51]. In mammalian red cells, which lack the cytochrome system, the energy appears to come from glycolysis[31,32,52]. Since some cells use oxidative energy, and some energy from glycolysis, it seems a little unlikely that active transport is linked to any particular stage in the glycolytic or respiratory sequences; but the mechanisms in the two sorts of cell could conceivably be different, and a number of workers, in particular CONWAY[53,54], have sought to link active ion movements with the electron transfer associated with the cytochrome system. In favour of this "redox theory", CONWAY[27] and CAREY, CONWAY AND KERNAN[55] point out that active extrusion of sodium in frog muscle is inhibited by cyanide, which knocks out the cytochrome system, but not by dinitrophenol, which is thought to dissociate oxidation from ATP synthesis. Indeed CAREY, CONWAY AND KERNAN find a small increase in the rate of sodium extrusion when dinitrophenol is present. There is, however, some disagreement, as yet unexplained, between the effects of cyanide and dinitrophenol described by CONWAY and his co-workers and those found by KEYNES AND MAISEL[56] and by FRAZIER AND KEYNES[57]. Under conditions in which net sodium extrusion is taking place, FRAZIER AND KEYNES find that the ratio of sodium expelled to oxygen used is considerably greater than would be expected on the simple "redox theory." In nerve and nucleated red cells, which of course lack the large store of phosphagen present in muscle, both cyanide and dinitrophenol inhibit active movements.

If active transport is not linked to any of the individual steps in glycolysis or respiration, it seems reasonable to suppose that glycolysis and respiration are required merely as sources of ATP, and that it is the ATP that provides the energy for ion pumping. The same conclusion is suggested by the fact that dinitrophenol inhibits ion pumping in nerve and nucleated red cells, which depend on oxidative energy, but not in mammalian red cells, which depend on energy from glycolysis[16,33,51,52]. If ATP does provide the energy, then under conditions in which ATP synthesis is stopped, one might expect the decline of active movements to be related to the fall in ATP content. Such observations have been made in squid axons by CALDWELL[58,59], and in red cells by DUNHAM[60] and WHITTAM[61]. More clear cut evidence that ATP can provide the energy for ion transport, comes from experiments in which ATP has been added intracellularly to cells lacking any other energy supply. In squid axons poisoned with cyanide, CALDWELL AND KEYNES[62] found that sodium efflux was partially restored by injecting ATP or arginine phosphate. (Arginine phosphate and ATP are thought to be in equilibrium in the axon through the action of arginine phosphoryl transferase, just as in vertebrate muscle creatine phosphate and ATP are thought to be in equilibrium through the Lohmann reaction.) If the ATP was hydrolysed by boiling before being injected into the axon, efflux was not restored.

In red cells intracellular injection is not possible, but ATP may be made to enter the cells by making use of the "reversible haemolysis" described by SZÉKELY, MÁNYAI, AND STRAUB[63] in Hungary and by TEORELL[64] in the United States. If red cells are lysed by mixing them with a large volume of water, and then washed, the ghosts obtained are highly leaky; but if the cells are lysed in a relatively small volume of water, and tonicity is then restored by the addition of salt, the ghosts have relatively impermeable membranes and, in the presence of suitable substrates show active accumulation of potassium. In the absence of added substrates no accumulation occurs. GÁRDOS[65] showed that if the cells are lysed not in water but in an ice-cold $10\%$ solution of the acid sodium salt of ATP, then after "reversal" they contain about 4 mg of ATP per ml and can accumulate potassium without any further addition of substrate.

I. M. GLYNN

In view of all this evidence it seemed worth while to look at the ATP-ase activity associated with the cell membrane. Such ATP-ase activity has been described in squid axons by LIBET[66] and in red cell membranes by CLARKSON AND MAIZELS[67], HERBERT[68] and CAFFREY et al.[69].

During the past fifteen months, Dr. DUNHAM and I have been investigating the

TABLE I

THE EFFECT OF STROPHANTHIN ON THAT PART OF THE ATP-ASE ACTIVITY OF RED CELL GHOSTS
THAT REQUIRES THE PRESENCE OF SODIUM AND POTASSIUM

| Na concentration (mM) | K concentration (mM) | Activity (mM P/l cells/h) |
|---|---|---|
| 0 | 0 | 0.75 |
|   |   | 0.78 |
| 0 | 16 | 0.82 |
|   |   | 0.84 |
| 16 | 0 | 0.73 |
|   |   | 0.83 |
| 16 | 16 | 1.34 |
|   |   | 1.37 |
| In the presence of $10^{-4}$ strophanthin | | |
| 16 | 16 | 0.78 |
|   |   | 0.85 |

Conditions of experiment: Duration 1 h, pH 7.0, temp. 37.2 °. Mg, concn. 0.5 mM; Cysteine 1 mM; ATP 1.5 mM; "Tris" was added to make the total cation concentration 162 mM in all samples. (Data from E. T. DUNHAM AND I. M. GLYNN, 1960—in preparation)

ATP-ase activity of red cell ghosts. The activity seems to be of two kinds, both activated by magnesium ions. One kind occurs in the absence of both sodium and potassium and, provided magnesium is present, is greatly activated by small amounts of calcium; when the ratio of calcium to magnesium is made too high, inhibition occurs. This part of the ATP-ase is unaffected by strophanthin, and there is no reason to connect it with active transport. The other kind requires the presence of both sodium and potassium and, for optimal activity, the ratio between them must be neither too high nor too

TABLE II

THE EFFECT OF POTASSIUM CONCENTRATION ON THE INHIBITION OF RED CELL ATP-ASE
BY A LOW CONCENTRATION OF STROPHANTHIN

| K concentration (mM) | Total glycoside-sensitive activity (mM P/l cells/h) | Activity in the presence of $5 \times 10^{-8}$ strophanthin (mM P/l cells/h) | Inhibition (%) |
|---|---|---|---|
| $1/4$ | 0.188 | 0.027 | 86 |
| $1/2$ | 0.364 | 0.134 | 63 |
| 1 | 0.619 | 0.290 | 53 |
| 2 | 0.778 | 0.498 | 36 |
| 4 | 0.855 | 0.686 | 20 |
| 8 | 0.926 | 0.782 | 15 |
| 16 | 1.02 | 0.823 | 19 |
| 32 | 1.04 | 0.964 | 7 |

Conditions of experiment: Duration 1 h, pH 7.2, temp. 37.2°. Na concentration 60 mM; Mg concentration 0.5 mM; "Tris" to make up 160 mmoles. 1 mmole of cysteine and 1.5 mmoles of ATP were present. At its highest, the glycoside-sensitive activity accounted for 50% of the total ATP-ase activity. (Data from E. T. DUNHAM AND I. M. GLYNN, 1960—in preparation) low. This part of the ATP-ase is completely inhibited by strophanthin (Table I), as has also been reported by POST[70]. There is, furthermore, a remarkable resemblance between the effects of very low concentrations of cardiac glycosides on this fraction of the ATP-ase on the one hand, and on the active potassium influx in intact red cells on the other (*cf.* Fig. 1 and Table II). In both cases the percentage inhibition is high at low potassium concentrations, and decreases as the potassium concentration is raised, so that the overall effect is that the low concentration of glycoside appears to increase the Michaelis constant for potassium. One way of interpreting this result is to

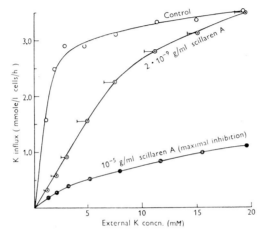

Fig. 1. The influence of potassium on the inhibitory effect of a very low concentration of scillaren A. Haematocrit *ca.* 3%. Cells were incubated with the test solutions for 3 h, [42]K was added, and the amount of [42]K which entered during the next hour was measured. The lowest curve represents maximal inhibition at each K concn. The short horizontal lines indicate the greatest error that could arise from the small increase in K concn. produced by the addition of [42]K. (From GLYNN[18]).

assume that the potassium ions and the glycoside molecules compete for the same site, but there are difficulties with this hypothesis.

Now consider two separate sets of properties of the red cell membrane. On the one hand we know from the experiments I mentioned earlier that the membrane can pump potassium in and sodium out, and that the two movements are linked so that one cannot occur without the other. The energy for these active movements certainly comes from glycolysis, and is probably made available as ATP. The active movements can be completely inhibited by cardiac glycosides, which do not interfere with ATP production, and at low concentrations of cardiac glycoside the inhibition can be reversed in a characteristic way by raising the potassium concentration. On the other hand, we have in the membrane an enzyme system which splits phosphate from ATP; which requires the presence of both sodium and potassium, neither alone being adequate; which can be inhibited by cardiac glycosides; and which, at low cardiac glycoside concentrations, shows the same reversal of inhibition as the potassium concentration is increased. One cannot help wondering whether the systems responsible for the two sets of properties are not the same—in other words: is the part of the ATP-ase that is sensitive to cardiac glycosides somehow responsible for the active exchange of sodium and potassium?

If this suggestion is right, then one would expect similar ATP-ase activity to be found in association with other cell membranes and, in particular, with nerve and muscle membranes. Unfortunately nothing is known of the effects of sodium and potassium on the squid axon preparation studied by LIBET, but in homogenates of crab nerve SKOU [71] has found two ATP-ases, one of which shows a very similar activation by sodium and potassium to that found by DUNHAM and me in the strophanthin-sensitive fraction of the red cell ATP-ase. Whether the nerve ATP-ase is similarly inhibited by cardiac glycosides, and, if it is, whether the inhibition can be reversed by potassium is not known. The dificulty in trying to find out the properties of ATP-ases associated with cell membranes is that it is only in exceptional cells—red cells and giant axons—that the membrane can be separated from the rest of the cell; and even in a giant axon whose axoplasm has been extruded, the membrane has a neurilemma adhering to the outside and probably still has mitochondria inside.

So far I have restricted my remarks entirely to the movements of ions into or out of cells. I want to finish by saying something about the movement of ions across cells. If cells are arranged to form a sheet, and the two faces of the cell have different transporting properties, then a net active movement from one side of the sheet to the other is possible. Such polarisation of cells, as it is sometimes called, may be reflected in the microscopic appearance—as, for example, in the brush border of cells of the proximal kidney tubule—or there may be no obvious visible difference between the two faces of the cell. Transfer of one sort of ion across a cellular membrane will lead to the setting up of an electrical potential which, if the permeability is right, will in turn lead to the transfer of ions of opposite charge. The net result will be that equal numbers of positive and negative ions are transported, but measurement of the electrical potential across the membrane may give a clue to which ion is actively moved. For example, in sheep the lining of the rumen possesses the power of taking up large quantities of sodium chloride. (The purpose of this absorption seems to be to regain salt secreted in the very copious saliva.) Though both sodium and chloride are absorbed, measurements of the potential across the rumen lining by DOBSON AND PHILLIPSON [72] show that it is only necessary to postulate active transport of sodium—the electrical gradient is sufficient to account for the chloride movement.

Another membrane that transports sodium chloride and that has been subjected to detailed study, in particular by Professor USSING and his associates in Copenhagen, is frog skin. Frogs, living in fresh water, tend to become depleted of salt, but possess the power of taking it up through the skin. Since the concentration of salt in the animal is much higher than it is in the pond, the absorbtion is clearly active; and since, when salt is being absorbed, there is a potential across the skin positive on the inside, it looks as though sodium transport is the primary event. That this is indeed so was shown by the elegant experiments of USSING AND ZERAHN [73] and of KOEFOED-JOHNSEN, USSING AND ZERAHN [74]. They put a piece of frog skin between two similar salt solutions, and arranged a counter-E.M.F. so that the potential across the skin was kept at zero. The current that had to be passed to hold the potential at zero was found to be exactly equivalent to the difference between the large flux of sodium from the outer to the inner face of the skin (measured with $^{24}$Na) and the small flux of sodium in the opposite direction (measured with $^{22}$Na). The net chloride movement through the skin at zero potential must have been zero. When the skin was treated with adrenaline, the relationship between current and net sodium flux broke down for a short time, apparently because chloride was secreted outwards, possibly from mucus glands.

Behaviour exactly like that of frog skin, but without the complicating effect of adrenaline, has recently been described in frog bladder by LEAF, ANDERSON AND PAGE[75]: sodium chloride is taken up from the urine and this uptake presumably helps to maintain body salt.

Animals living in sea water, or eating a very salty diet, are faced with the opposite problem—the problem of getting rid of excess salt. In fish this seems to be done by so-called "chloride secreting cells" in the gills, and in many marine birds there is a salt-secreting gland on the beak. It is said that the black-footed albatross can secret from its gland a 0.8–0.9 $M$ salt solution at a rate of over half a millilitre a minute[76]. Whether the secretion of salt is primarily a secretion of sodium or of chloride is not known.

Recent work by KOEFOED-JOHNSEN AND USSING[77] suggests that the mechanism responsible for transporting sodium across frog skin may be the same as that responsible for the exchange of sodium and potassium across cell membranes. It has been known for some time[78] that for sodium transport to occur, it is necessary that potassium ions be present in the solution in contact with the inner face of the skin, even though potassium is not itself transported. KOEFOED-JOHNSEN AND USSING found that, in the absence of penetrating anions, the outer face of the skin behaves like an almost ideal sodium electrode whereas the inner face behaves like a potassium electrode. Direct measurements of the change in potential across the thickness of the skin by ENGBAEK AND HOSHIKO[79], using micro-electrodes, showed that the potential charge occurred in two jumps. Taking all these observations together, KOEFOED-JOHNSEN AND USSING suggest that the outer surface of the cells of the stratum germinativum allows passive movements of sodium but not of potassium; the inner surface allows passive movements of potassium but not of sodium; and that a pump at the inner surface pumps potassium into the cells in exchange for sodium. The system as a whole carries out sodium transport.

This is a very ingenious theory. It will be interesting to see whether a similar explanation will be found to account for salt absorption or secretion in the other tissues I have mentioned. It will be even more interesting if a more sophisticated version can account for the more elaborate events which occur in the kidney tubule. On the other hand, it is rather unlikely that sodium movements can always be explained in terms of sodium–potassium exchange. In the sea lettuce *Ulva lactuca*, SCOTT AND HAYWARD[80] find that sodium and potassium movements can be inhibited independently. In the gills of *Eriocheir*, KOCH[81] finds that sodium and potassium are pumped indiscriminately. And, of course, even where it is possible to explain salt transport in terms of a sodium–potassium exchange pump, this only brings us back to the problem: how does this pump work?

SUMMARY

The penetration of water and salts through cell membranes and membranes composed of sheets of cells is discussed. The way in which energy from metabolism is made available for the active transport of ions is considered, and some new work is reported suggesting that the active movement of sodium and potassium ions across the red cell membrane is intimately linked with the splitting of adenosine triphosphate by the membrane.

*References p. 12–13*

REFERENCES

[1] A. V. HILL, *Proc. Roy. Soc. (London) B*, 144 (1955) 1.
[2] A. V. HILL, *Proc. Roy. Soc. (London) B*, 106 (1930) 477.
[3] D. L. DRABKIN, *J. Biol. Chem.*, 185 (1950) 231.
[4] E. J. CONWAY AND D. HINGERTY, *Biochem. J.*, 40 (1946) 561.
[5] E. J. CONWAY AND J. I. MCCORMACK, *J. Physiol. (London)*, 120 (1953) 1.
[6] E. J. CONWAY AND H. GEOGHEGAN, *J. Physiol. (London)*, 130 (1955) 438.
[7] W. A. BRODSKY, J. W. APPELBOOM, W. H. DENNIS, W. S. REHM, J. F. MILEY AND I. DIAMOND, *J. Gen. Physiol.*, 40 (1956) 183.
[8] D. A. T. DICK, *Intern. Rev. Cytol.*, 8 (1959) 387.
[9] E. PONDER, *Hemolysis and Related Phenomena*, Grune and Stratton, New York, 1948.
[10] D. A. T. DICK AND L. M. LOWENSTEIN, *Proc. Roy. Soc. (London) B*, 148 (1958) 241.
[11] H. WIRZ, B. HARGITAY AND W. KUHN, *Helv. Physiol. Acta*, 9 (1951) 196.
[12] A. A. EDDY AND C. HINSHELWOOD, *Proc. Roy. Soc. (London) B*, 136 (1950) 544.
[13] G. L. GOLD AND A. K. SOLOMON, *J. Gen. Physiol.*, 38 (1955) 389.
[14] J. L. GAMBLE JR., *J. Biol. Chem.*, 228 (1957) 955.
[15] A. L. HODGKIN AND R. D. KEYNES, *J. Physiol. (London)*, 119 (1953) 513.
[16] A. L. HODGKIN AND R. D. KEYNES, *J. Physiol. (London)*, 128 (1955) 28.
[17] E. J. HARRIS, *J. Physiol. (London)*, 124 (1954) 248.
[18] E. J. HARRIS AND G. P. BURN, *Trans. Faraday Soc.*, 45 (1949) 508.
[19] R. D. KEYNES, *J. Physiol. (London)*, 114 (1951) 119.
[20] R. D. KEYNES, *Proc. Roy. Soc. (London) B*, 142 (1954) 359.
[21] R. CREESE, *Proc. Roy. Soc. (London), B*, 142 (1954) 497.
[22] E. J. HARRIS, *Trans. Faraday Soc.*, 46 (1950) 872.
[23] E. J. HARRIS, *J. Physiol. (London)*, 120 (1953) 246.
[24] E. J. HARRIS, *J. Gen. Physiol.*, 41 (1957)169.
[25] A. L. HODGKIN AND P. HOROWICZ, *J. Physiol. (London)*, 145 (1957) 405.
[26] R. D. KEYNES AND R. H. ADRIAN, *Discussions Faraday Soc.*, No. 21 (1956) 265.
[27] E. J. CONWAY, *Physiol. Revs.*, 37 (1957) 84.
[28] I. M. GLYNN, *Progr. in Biophys. and Biophys. Chem.*, 8 (1957) 241.
[29] I. M. GLYNN, in J. COURSAGET (ed.), *The Method of Isotopic Tracers Applied to the Study of Active Ion Transport*, Pergamon Press, London, 1958, p. 46.
[30] I. M. GLYNN, *Intern. Rev. Cytol.*, 8 (1959) 449.
[31] J. E. HARRIS, *J. Biol. Chem.*, 141 (1941) 579.
[32] T. S. DANOWSKI, *J. Biol. Chem.*, 139 (1941) 693.
[33] M. MAIZELS, *J. Physiol.*, 112 (1951) 59.
[34] I. M. GLYNN, *J. Physiol. (London)*, 134 (1956) 278.
[35] G. LING AND R. W. GERARD, *J. Cellular Comp. Physiol.*, 34 (1949) 383.
[36] J. W. MOORE AND K. S. COLE, *Federation Proc.*, 14 (1955) 103.
[37] R. H. ADRIAN, *J. Physiol.*, 133 (1956) 631.
[38] A. L. HODGKIN, *Proc. Roy. Soc. (London) B*, 148 (1957) 1.
[39] W. O. FENN AND R. GERSCHMANN, *J. Gen. Physiol.*, 33 (1949) 195.
[40] A. M. SHANES, *J. Gen. Physiol.*, 33 (1950) 643.
[41] A. M. SHANES, *Federation Proc.*, 10 (1951) 611.
[42] E. J. HARRIS AND M. MAIZELS, *J. Physiol. (London)*, 113 (1951) 506.
[43] T. I. SHAW, *J. Physiol.*, 129 (1955) 464.
[44] H. B. STEINBACH, *J. Biol. Chem.*, 133 (1940) 695.
[45] H. B. STEINBACH, *Proc. Natl. Acad. Sci. U.S.*, 38 (1952) 451.
[46] J. E. DESMEDT, *J. Physiol. (London)*, 121 (1953) 191.
[47] H. J. SCHATZMANN, *Helv. Physiol. Acta*, 11 (1953) 346.
[48] I. M. GLYNN, *J. Physiol. (London)*, 136 (1957) 148.
[49] R. EDELBERG, *J. Cellular Comp. Physiol.*, 40 (1952) 529.
[50] M. H. JACOBS AND S. A. CORSON, *Biol. Bull.*, 67 (1934) 325.
[51] M. MAIZELS, *J. Physiol.*, 125 (1954) 263.
[52] M. MAIZELS, *Symposia Soc. Exptl. Biol.*, 8 (1954) 202.
[53] E. J. CONWAY, *Science*, 113 (1951) 270.
[54] E. J. CONWAY in J. COURSAGET (ed.), *The Method of Isotopic Tracers Applied to the Study of Active Ion Transport*, Pergamon Press, London, 1958, p. 1.
[55] M. J. CAREY, E. J. CONWAY AND R. P. KERNAN, *J. Physiol. (London)*, 148 (1959) 51.
[56] R. D. KEYNES AND G. W. MAISEL, *Proc. Roy. Soc. (London) B*, 142 (1954) 383.
[57] H. S. FRAZIER AND R. D. KEYNES, *J. Physiol. (London)*, 148 (1959) 362.
[58] P. C. CALDWELL, *J. Physiol. (London)*, 132 (1956) 35P.
[59] P. C. CALDWELL, *Biochem. J.*, 67 (1957) 1P.

[60] E. T. DUNHAM, *Federation Proc.*, 16 (1957) 33.
[61] R. WHITTAM, *J. Physiol.*, 140 (1958) 479.
[62] P. C. CALDWELL AND R. D. KEYNES, *J. Physiol. (London)* 137 (1957) 12P.
[63] M. SZÉKELY, S. MÁNYAI AND F. B. STRAUB, *Acta Physiol. Acad. Sci. Hung.*, 3 (1952) 571.
[64] T. TEORELL, *J. Gen. Physiol.*, 35 (1952) 669.
[65] G. GÁRDOS, *Acta Physiol. Acad. Sci. Hung.*, 6 (1954) 191.
[66] B. LIBET, *Federation Proc.*, 7 (1948) 72.
[67] E. M. CLARKSON AND M. MAIZELS, *J. Physiol.*, 116 (1952) 112.
[68] E. HERBERT, *J. Cellular Comp. Physiol.*, 47 (1956) 11.
[69] R. W. CAFFREY, R. TREMBLAY, B. W. GABRIO AND F. M. HUENNEKENS, *J. Biol. Chem.*, 223 (1956) 1.
[70] R. L. POST, *Federation Proc.*, 18 (1959) 121.
[71] J. C. SKOU, *Biochim. Biophys. Acta*, 23 (1957) 394.
[72] A. DOBSON AND A. T. PHILLIPSON, *J. Physiol. (London)*, 140 (1958) 94.
[73] H. H. USSING AND K. ZERAHN, *Acta Physiol. Scand.*, 23 (1951) 110.
[74] V. KOEFOED-JOHNSON, H. H. USSING AND K. ZERAHN, *Acta Physiol. Scand.*, 27 (1952) 38.
[75] A. LEAF, J. ANDERSON AND L. B. PAGE, *J. Gen. Physiol.*, 41 (1958) 657.
[76] L. Z. McFARLAND, *Nature*, 184 (1959) 2030.
[77] V. KOEFOED-JOHNSON AND H. H. USSING, *Acta Physiol. Scand.*, 42 (1958) 298.
[78] T. R. FUKUDA, *Japan. J. Med. Sci., III Biophys.*, 8 (1942) 123.
[79] L. ENGBAEK AND T. HOSHIKO, *Acta Physiol. Scand.*, 39 (1957) 348.
[80] G. T. SCOTT AND H. R. HAYWARD, *J. Gen. Physiol.*, 37 (1954) 601.
[81] H. J. KOCH, in J. A. KITCHING, *Recent Developments in Cell Physiology*, Butterworths, London, 1954, p. 15.

# DIRECT DETERMINATION OF
# THE BINDING OF ELECTROLYTES BY PLASMA PROTEINS
## WITH SPECIAL REFERENCE TO Ca AND Mg

A. M. van LEEUWEN

*University Department of Medicine, Binnengasthuis, Amsterdam (The Netherlands)*

Cations in the plasma exist in various physicochemical states; these are best known for calcium (Fig. 1). By ultrafiltration two fractions can be separated, the non-filterable one representing protein-bound calcium; with biological methods an ionized and a non-ionized fraction can be distinguished. This differentiation must also apply to the other cations.

The non-filterable fraction will be called the protein-bound fraction, whereas the filtrable fraction is indicated as the free fraction. In the case of calcium the latter contains not only the ionized fraction, but also a small quantity of complex-bound, but diffusible calcium.

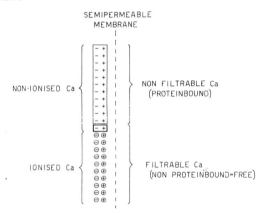

Fig. 1. Schematic representation of the various fractions of plasma Ca. Ca is indicated by a + sign, anions by a — sign.

In 1957, GERBRANDY[1] introduced a method for determining the protein-bound fraction of plasma constituents. It is based on the principle that a correlation must exist between the protein concentration and the concentration of any substance bound by it. GUTMAN AND GUTMAN[2] among others used this principle statistically to calculate protein-bound calcium from a large group of individual samples.

GERBRANDY, however, actively induced a rise in protein-concentration in the venous blood of the forearm by compressing the upper arm with a manometer cuff at a pressure of 90 mm Hg for a period of 7 min. Two blood samples were taken, one just before and one at the end of the compression period. By expressing the rise in concentration of any plasma constituent as a percentage of the increase in total protein concentration, the protein-bound fraction of that substance can be calculated. In accordance with known facts GERBRANDY *et al.*[3] calculated in this way that urea and glucose are not bound, whereas alkaline phosphatase, cholesterol and serum iron are completely bound. For the cations it was found that 8–10% of Na, 35–44% of Ca and about 40% of Mg are bound by plasma proteins. There is a remarkable agreement with the results obtained by other methods. However, this is only true for the mean of the results; the spread is too large to permit the method to be used for the determination of cation-binding in an individual patient. By prolonging venous compression to about 30 min, and by increasing the number of samples taken, the accuracy of the method can be raised considerably. Results obtained by this modification of GER-BRANDY's method are the subject of this communication.

## METHOD

The procedure is as follows: The patient remains in a semi-recumbent position with the arm completely relaxed for the whole period from 10–15 min before the start of venous compression to 10–15 min after its conclusion.

Hemoconcentration is brought about by maintaining the manometer cuff at a pressure of 90–100 mm Hg for about 30 min. From an indwelling needle in a cubital vein, several samples are taken before, 4–6 samples during venous compression, and at least one sample 6–10 min after release of the pressure.

The blood is centrifuged immediately, fluid heparin being used, and the plasma is analysed on the same day. Values are calculated in terms of plasma water.*

Fig. 2 shows the results obtained in a patient suspected of hyperparathyroidism. A steady rise of Hb and total protein concentration during compression is seen, the latter increasing by 70%. Alkaline phosphatase—itself a protein—rises by exactly the same percentage, whereas urea—not being bound—oscillates around its precompression level. Between these extremes are the cations: Ca and Mg rise considerably, whereas Na and K rise only slightly. Ten minutes after release of the pressure all substances have reached precompression levels, with the exception of K which remains at a somewhat higher concentration.

In view of the influence of pH on the cation–protein binding it is important that the pH of the venous blood decreases only slightly—in this case by 0.05 pH unit. This is the result of a decrease in blood flow through the forearm induced by the increase in venous pressure. Evidence of this is the decrease in venous Hb-saturation from 60% to 25%.

Only the results obtained for Ca and Mg are discussed below. They were determined by photometric titration using murexide and eriochrome black respectively as indicators. Total protein was determined by the biuret method.

The calculation of the protein-bound and the free fractions of Ca and Mg is shown in Fig. 3, which is based on results obtained in a normal person. In all, 8 samples were taken, 5 during venous compression. For each sample the Ca concentration found is plotted against the total protein concentration and the same is done for the sum of Ca and Mg. The points appear to lie on a straight line. By extrapolating to zero

---

* The formula $W = 990 - 0.8\,P$ was used, in which $W$ is water content and $P$ is total protein concentration, both in m²/l plasma[10].

protein concentration, free Ca, and also free Ca + Mg are calculated. The slope of the line indicates the binding of electrolyte by protein, which is arbitrarily expressed as mequiv. bound per 100 g protein. By subtracting the values found for Ca from those found for Ca + Mg, the values for Mg are calculated. The influence of the Gibbs-Donnan effect is neglected.

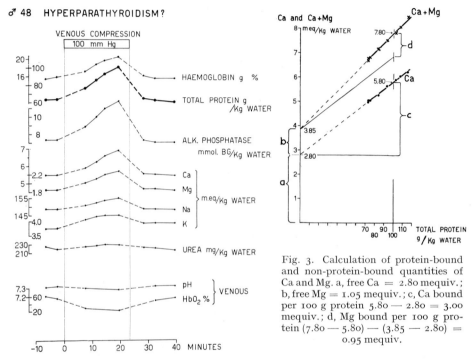

Fig. 3. Calculation of protein-bound and non-protein-bound quantities of Ca and Mg. a, free Ca = 2.80 mequiv.; b, free Mg = 1.05 mequiv.; c, Ca bound per 100 g protein 5.80 — 2.80 = 3.00 mequiv.; d, Mg bound per 100 g protein (7.80 — 5.80) — (3.85 — 2.80) = 0.95 mequiv.

Fig. 2. For explanation see text. The scales for the different substances are so chosen that an equal absolute rise on the graph expresses an equal percentage rise over precompression levels.

VALIDITY OF THE METHOD

When treating the experimental data in the way shown, we have to consider the following points:

*(1) The linear extrapolation to zero protein concentration*

In observations during venous compression we could detect no deviation from linearity over a range from 50 to 120 g of protein as Fig. 4 shows.

Furthermore in compensation dialysis experiments with human plasma under physiological conditions the relation between electrolyte concentration and protein concentration inside the membrane also showed a linear relation over the range 0–60 g of protein. The line goes precisely through the point representing the concentration found in the dialysate and this is actually the free fraction of the electrolyte (Fig. 5). Extrapolation to zero protein concentration therefore seems permissible.

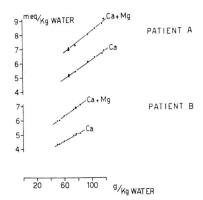

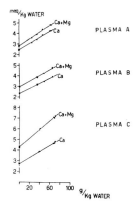

Fig. 4. Venous compression. Results obtained in a patient with renal stones but no abnormality in Ca, Mg and phosphate metabolism (patient A), and in a patient with a nephrotic syndrome (patient B). Both patients had a normal renal function. Parameters as in Fig. 3. T = ± 37°; pH = 7.28–7.35.

Fig. 5. Dialysis experiments with plasma. Electrolyte composition identical with interstitial fluid. Results obtained with compensation dialysis. Plasma A was from a healthy volunteer, plasma B and C were from patients with heart failure, but normal plasma proteins. Parameters as in Fig. 3. T = 37°; pH = 7.30–7.45.

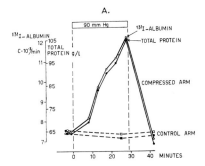

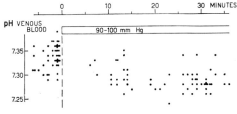

Fig. 7. Decrease in venous pH during venous compression in 36 observations. Mean decrease 0.05; largest individual decrease 0.09.

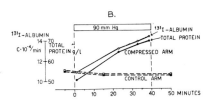

Fig. 6. Experiments with radioactive albumin: A, normal person, ♂ 37, total protein 68 g/l, albumin 40 g/l. B, patient, ♂ 60, hypoalbuminaemia with generalized edema, total protein 53 g/l, albumin 18 g/l. The zero points of protein and radioactivity scales coincide. The open symbols indicate radioactivity, the closed ones total protein concentration.

*(2) The possibility of a change in the composition of total protein during venous compression*

This is important since albumin is known to have a higher binding capacity for Ca and Mg than the globulins. GERBRANDY *et al.* showed electrophoretically that during brief venous compression the albumin concentration rose to exactly the same extent as did the total protein concentration.

We were able to confirm this for venous compression of longer duration with the aid of radioactive albumin (Fig. 6). 16 h after injecting 60 μC of $^{131}$I-labelled albumin we determined the increase in radioactivity during venous compression and compared it with the concomitant increase in total protein. This was done in a normal person and in a patient with hypoalbuminaemia and generalized oedema. We could detect no divergence in the percentage increases of albumin and of total protein.

### (3) The change in venous pH

The pH change during venous compression is shown in Fig. 7. After 23–36 min the mean decrease of the venous blood pH was 0.05 units, and the largest decrease observed in 36 observations was 0.09. This is too small a change to influence signif-icantly the binding of cations by protein[5],[12].

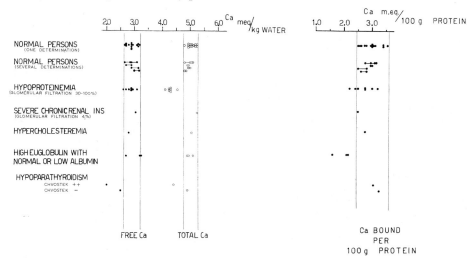

Fig. 8. Values found for free and total Ca in 13 normal persons and a number of patients. The vertical lines in-dicate the extreme values found for free and for total Ca in normal persons.

Fig. 9. Values found for protein-bound Ca in 13 normal persons and a number of patients. The vertical lines indicate the extreme values found in normal persons.

### (4) Neglect of the Donnan-effect

In calculating free Ca and Mg this neglect seems permissible for two reasons. Firstly, the real factor for plasma-interstitial fluid is unknown. Secondly, accepting the highest factor found in *in vitro* experiments, the correction would —at a protein concentration of 70 g/l—decrease the value for free Ca by 0.15 mequiv., and raise the value for bound Ca per 100 g protein by 0.2 mequiv. This is too small a difference to justify the introduction of an inaccurate correction factor.

We therefore conclude that calculation of the protein-bound and free quantities of Ca and Mg as suggested seems acceptable.

### RESULTS

In Fig. 8, the values obtained for free Ca and total Ca in normal persons are compared with those found in a number of patients in a further attempt to check the validity of the method.

For 13 normal male persons, the values for free Ca were found to lie between 2.7 and 3.2 mequiv. The mean value was 2.90 mequiv./kg of plasma water and the spread is only slightly larger than that found for total Ca. Repeated determinations in the same person over a period of 2–3 months all fell within the range found for the normal group as a whole. In 7 patients with hypoproteinaemia and a fair to normal kidney function, the free Ca was found to lie within normal limits, although the total Ca was definitely too low. This is in accordance with the results obtained by other methods. In a patient with severe uraemia, but without bone disease, normal values were expected and, indeed, found. In view of a possible cation binding by plasma lipids, we also investigated a patient with hypercholesterolaemia (cholesterol: 800 mg %), but no abnormalities were found. In 3 patients with a high to extremely high euglobulin

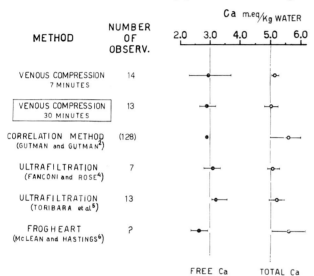

Fig. 10. Comparison of values found for free and total Ca by different methods. Mean values are indicated by a circle, the extreme values connected by a horizontal line. Vertical lines are drawn at 3.00 and 5.00 mequiv./kg water to facilitate comparison. In the observations indicated by "venous compression 7 minutes" the first sample was taken before the start of compression, the second at the end of 7-min compression at 90 mm Hg and a third 10 min after release of the pressure (Group 2 Experiments in GERBRANDY et al.[3]). The number of observations with the correlation method[2] is given between brackets because they have been pooled for the calculation of the regression line from which free Ca was calculated. To allow comparison with the results obtained by venous compression, the values taken from FANCONI AND ROSE[4] are given without correction for Donnan-effect and citrate content. For the same reason, the figures for total Ca concentration given by TORIBARA et al.[5] and by McLEAN AND HASTINGS[6] are calculated for plasma water assuming a protein content of 70 g/l. The free Ca value given for the frog's heart method is derived from ionized Ca values given in the nomogram by McLEAN AND HASTINGS[6] by adding 0.2 mequiv. for citrate[4]. The number of observations from which the nomogram was derived is not stated by the authors.

content (35, 40 and 71 g/l) due to Kahler's disease or liver cirrhosis, and without detectable bone disease, the method indicated normal free Ca, as was expected clinically. Finally, two patients with hypoparathyroidism after thyroidectomy were investigated: the one with a positive Chvostek sign was found to have a free Ca content of 2.0 mequiv./l, the other who showed no signs of nervous hyperexcitability had an almost normal free Ca.

Fig. 9 shows the binding of Ca per 100 g of total protein for the groups mentioned. For normal persons, the mean was found to be 3.0 mequiv./100 g. The patients with a high euglobulin with normal or slightly lowered albumin content show values which are definitely subnormal. This is explained by the fact that euglobulin constitutes in these cases an excessive part of the total, whereas it binds Ca to a lesser extent than albumin. For the same reason a tendency to subnormal values is also seen in hypoproteinaemia.

*References p. 21*

In Fig. 10, our normal values are compared with values for free Ca and total Ca calculated from data obtained by other methods. A comparison is also made with results previously obtained by venous compression of brief duration. It can be seen that modifying the venous compression method in the manner discussed, increased the accuracy considerably but did not change the mean.

The values found by venous compression show a satisfactory agreement with the values found by other methods and it would seem that the normal value for free Ca in plasma is very nearly 3.0 mequiv. per kg of water.

In Fig. 11, our normal values for Mg are compared in the same way with results obtained by ultrafiltration. It can be seen that the mean value and spread are comparable for both methods*.

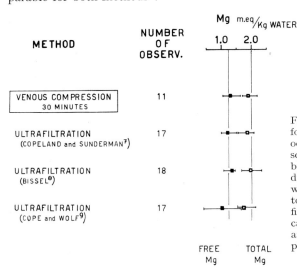

Fig. 11. Comparison of values found for free and total Mg by different methods. Mean values are indicated by squares, the extreme values connected by a horizontal line. Vertical lines are drawn at 1.25 and 2.00 mequiv./kg water to facilitate comparison. The total Mg values given for the ultrafiltration experiments[7-9] are in the case of the experiments of BISSEL and of COPE AND WOLF calculated from plasma concentration assuming a protein content of 70 g/l.

## DISCUSSION

Although the method, for obvious reasons, cannot be used in cases of manifest tetany, it has already given interesting results in the case of hypercalcemia and hypercalcuria. We hope to report on these on a later occasion. The use of the method is however by no means restricted to the study of Ca and Mg as is already evident from the results shown for alkaline phosphatase and urea in Fig. 2. Fig. 12 shows that it is even possible to determine the binding of Na by protein in individual patients. From the slope of the lines we calculated a Na-binding of 15–17 mequiv. per 100 g of protein. Here, however, because of the small percentage differences to be measured the demands on analytical accuracy are very high indeed and the number of reliable observations on Na-binding is still too small to warrant a detailed discussion. Finally it should be stated that the method is not without inconveniences to the patient and in about 40% of the cases a petechial rash develops. 70% of the normal persons—all staff colleagues, to whom I am most grateful—classified the experience as disagreeable.

* Since then another three normal persons were investigated: in two the values fell within the range indicated in Fig. 11, in the third, however, a value of 0.15 for free Mg and 1.20 for total Mg was found.

However, none of the 21 patients complained even when persistently questioned and quite a number indicated of their own will that they were willing to undergo a second venous compression.

This modification of the method of GERBRANDY seems therefore to hold promise for clinical use.

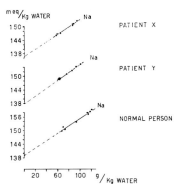

Fig. 12. Correlation between total Na concentrations (vertical axis) and total protein concentrations (horizontal axis) obtained with the aid of venous compression. Patients X and Y were without abnormalities in plasma electrolytes and proteins.

ACKNOWLEDGEMENTS

The results shown are due to the accuracy of the chemical analyses and for this my thanks are due to Miss THOMASSE and Mrs. KAPTEIJN.

SUMMARY

The accuracy of the ultrafiltration *in vivo*-method introduced by GERBRANDY is considerably raised by prolonging the period of venous compression to about 30 min and increasing the number of samples taken. By plotting cation concentrations against concomitant both protein concentrations protein-bound and free cation can be calculated, as the relation between cation and protein concentration is a linear one, pH does not change by more than 0.09 and albumin–protein ratio remains unaltered. The results obtained for Ca and Mg in normal persons and a number of patients with a variety of protein and electrolyte disturbances, were in agreement with the results obtained by others. Preliminary observations indicate that determination of protein-bound Na in an individual patient is also possible.

REFERENCES

[1] J. GERBRANDY, H. B. A. HELLENDOORN, L. A. DE VRIES AND A. M. VAN LEEUWEN, *Scand. J. Clin. & Lab. Invest.*, 10 Suppl. 31 (1957) 272.
[2] A. D. GUTMAN AND E. B. GUTMAN, *J. Clin. Invest.*, 16 (1937) 903.
[3] J. GERBRANDY, A. M. VAN LEEUWEN, H. B. A. HELLENDOORN AND L. A. DE VRIES, *Clin. Sci.*, 19 (1960) 181.
[4] A. FANCONI AND A. G. ROSE, *Quart. J. Med.*, 27 (1958) 463.
[5] T. Y. TORIBARA, A. R. TEREPKA AND PR. A. DEWEY, *J. Clin. Invest.*, 36 (1957) 738.
[6] F. C. McLEAN AND A. B. HASTINGS, *J. Biol. Chem.*, 108 (1935) 285.
[7] B. E. COPELAND AND F. W. SUNDERMAN, *J. Biol. Chem.*, 197 (1952) 331.
[8] G. W. BISSELL, *Am. J. Med Sci.*, 210 (1945) 195.
[9] C. L. COPE AND B. WOLF, *Biochem. J.*, 36 (1942) 413.
[10] C. H. GREENE AND M. H. POWER, *J. Biol. Chem.*, 91 (1931) 183.
[11] CH. W. CARR, *Arch. Biochem. Biophys.*, 62 (1956) 476.
[12] D. D. VAN SLYKE, A. B. HASTINGS, A. HILLER AND J. SENDROY, *J. Biol. Chem.*, 79 (1928)769.
[13] CH. W. CARR, *Arch. Biochem. Biophys.*, 46 (1953) 424.

## DISCUSSION

GLYNN: Are you not dealing with two quite different sorts of ion binding? At body pH, the plasma proteins will have a net negative charge and will therefore be surrounded by positive 'gegen-ions'. If you concentrate the protein you concentrate the 'gegen-ions'. Would this not account for the 'binding' of Na and K you describe? I thought, from the figures you showed it looked as if the ratio of the amounts bound was about the same as the ratio in the plasma. The calcium binding looked quite different, presumably because a specific unionized complex was formed.

VAN LEEUWEN: The term "binding" as used for the relation between small electrolytes and proteins is differently interpreted. Schematically speaking one can distinguish two types: a complex type of binding in which the bound cation no longer contributes to the ionic activity of the surrounding fluid, and an electrostatic "binding" in which the cationic charge balances the negative charge of the protein without the cationic properties being lost. In your question you suppose that the Ca and Mg binding is exclusively of the first, nonionized type, while the Na and K binding is exclusively of the second, ionized type. Probably this is not so. From their *in vivo* dialysis experiments in dogs, GREENE AND POWER[10] calculated that about 10–20% of Ca and Mg was bound in an ionized form by plasma proteins, and that about 10–30% of Na and K was bound in a non-ionized (*i.e.* complex type) manner. From membrane potential measurements on purified protein fractions CARR[11] concluded that $Na^+$ and $K^+$ activity is slightly decreased in solutions containing $\alpha$- and $\beta$-globulin and fibrinogen.

I think therefore that there is no essential difference between the increase in monovalent cations and in divalent cations during hemoconcentration. However, the Donnan effect will affect the change in $Na^+$ and $K^+$ concentration more because they are largely bound in an ionized form. For this reason the Donnan effect cannot be neglected in calculating the amount of Na bound by proteins from hemoconcentration experiments.

VINK: Do you think that the linear relation which you have found between total calcium and total protein of plasma represents an equilibrium state in your ultrafiltration *in vivo* experiments. Have you any idea about the concentration of the negative charges of the protein molecule and do you think they all have the same affinity to the $Ca^{++}$-ion.

VAN LEEUWEN: In answer to the first part of your question I would say: Yes, because there is presumably no change in free $Ca^{++}$ concentration. Accepting the formula given by MCLEAN AND HASTING for the binding of Ca by protein, *i.e.*

$$\frac{[Ca]^{++}\,[Prot]^{--}}{[CaProt]} = K$$

it can be seen that by hemoconcentration both [Ca Prot] and $[Prot]^{--}$ must increase concomitantly and by the same percentage. Therefore no actual shift in the equilibrium occurs.

As to the concentration of the negative valencies of the protein molecule, it is difficult to say how many there are, but from the experiments of VAN SLYKE *et al.*[12] it would follow that at physiological pH, the net negative charge of 100 g of protein of normal composition is equivalent to about 23 mequiv. of cation. Of these, 3 are balanced by Ca, 1.5 by Mg, about 0.5 by K and the remaining 18 by Na, which overcompensates its low percentage binding by a plasma concentration 30 times as high as Ca.

I have no information about differences between the binding sites in their affinity for Ca. Experiments to determine the influence of total Ca concentration on the amount of complex-bound Ca per unit weight of purified protein fraction[13] give no indication in this respect. However, the fact that GREENE AND POWER found part of the protein-bound Ca to be ionized, must in my opinion, indicate the existence of different types of binding sites, when electrostatic adsorption is not accepted.

# THE BEARING OF AGE UPON THE MAINTENANCE OF ELECTROLYTE STABILITY

R. A. McCANCE

*Medical Research Council, Department of Experimental Medicine, University of Cambridge,*
*(Great Britain)*

Stability of the "internal environment" has been a dominating thought in physiology since the time of CLAUDE BERNARD and it applies to every age. The processes and organs concerned have been extensively studied and the various "steady states" which emerge as the result of their activities are the reference line from which the chemical pathologist and the physician judge the abnormalities of disease. Most of the investigations have been made upon adults, and the kidney and the lung are generally regarded as the two vital organs so far as the stability of the electrolytes and the regulation of pH are concerned. We recognise that the function of both organs is directed and co-ordinated to a large extent by a process of "remote control", but there is no need to go into this here. Members of our department, however, have been interested for some time in the physiology of infancy and in connection with this the electrolyte stability of the newly born has naturally been a preoccupation. It has gradually dawned upon us that this stability—the maintenance of these steady states —is not brought about in quite the same way as in adult life and this has led us to explore the effects of age upon it. The present communication is a brief account of some of the findings.

## THE FOETUS

Since the body of a very young foetus may contain over 90% of water and since the osmotic pressure of this fluid is about the same as that of an adult, it is evident that electrolytes must enter into the metabolism of the foetus to as great an extent as they do in the adult; and when, in addition, one considers the volume and composition of the fluids which are outside the "body" but within the foetal membranes, the importance of getting its electrolyte metabolism just right clearly means everything to a foetus which is aiming at a long and happy life *in utero* and after birth. There is strong evidence that the whole of this performance is self-regulated, and that from very early in foetal life the volume and composition of the fluids enclosed within the body and membranes of the foetus are the product of its own metabolism. A moment's thought will dispose of any idea that they can possibly be explained by ultrafiltration or permeability on the part of the placenta. The concentrations of some electrolytes in foetal and maternal plasma are shown in Table I and the comparisons speak for themselves[1].

We have been concerned with the renal function of the foetus. In man, the foetal urine always has a much lower osmolar concentration than the plasma, largely because the urine contains so little sodium and chloride, and this is a legitimate generalisation about the foetal urine of other animals[2,3].

The formation of urine by the developing metanephros has been investigated most completely by ALEXANDER, NIXON, WIDDAS AND WOHLZOGEN[4,5] in the sheep. In this animal there is a large allantoic sac and the urine passes into it so long as the urachus remains functional. The foetus passes most urine about half way through gestation. At this age the glomerular filtration rate is equal to that of the adult per kg of body weight, but only some 60–70% of the filtrate is reabsorbed. This means the passage of a great volume of fluid into and out of the "body" of the foetus, and the

### TABLE I

CONCENTRATIONS OF CALCIUM, MAGNESIUM AND PHOSPHORUS IN
THE SERUM OF MAN, PIG AND RABBIT
The number of observations and their range follow each (average) figure

| Species and age (days) | Ca (mg/100 ml) | Mg (mg/100 ml) | Inorganic P (mg/100 ml) |
|---|---|---|---|
| Human | | | |
| Adult | 8.1 (2) (8.1, 8.1) | 2.2 (2) (2.1, 2.3) | 3.8 (1) |
| Foetus (84–182) | 9.0 (4) (7.9–10.5) | 2.8 (4) (1.9–4.3) | 14.9 (1) |
| Pig | | | |
| Sow | 11.2 (8) (9.8–12.1) | 2.6 (8) (2.2–4.4) | 7.1 (6) (5.9–9.8) |
| Foetus (46) | 17.6 (4) (16.8–18.4) | 3.8 (5) (3.5–4.2) | 13.6 (1) |
| Rabbit | | | |
| Doe | 15.7 (4) (12.0–17.5) | 5.5 (4) (4.1–6.6) | 9.4 (2) (9.1, 9.7) |
| Foetus (21) | 13.0 (3) (10.5–14.3) | 6.9 (3) (6.3–8.0) | 14.4 (1) |

### TABLE II

THE COMPOSITION OF ALLANTOIC FLUID AT VARIOUS GESTATIONAL AGES IN THE PIG

| Foetal age (days) | 20–22 | 46 | 67 | 90 |
|---|---|---|---|---|
| Total osmolar conc. mosmol/l | 256 | 120 | 100 | 225 |
| Na mequiv./l | 114 | 13 | 10 | 6 |
| K mequiv./l | 14 | 5 | 13 | 75 |
| Cl mequiv./l | 70 | 30 | 20 | 75 |
| pH | 7.0 | 5.9 | 6.2 | 5.8 |
| Titratable acid mequiv./l | 5 | 12 | 7 | 10 |
| Ammonia mequiv./l | 0.6 | 6.5 | 2.5 | 5.5 |

authors were not able to settle what happened to the urine after it reached the allantoic sac. They compared, as others had done before them, the composition of the urine and of the allantoic fluid and found both resemblances and differences, so that it was impossible to regard the allantoic sac merely as a receptacle for foetal urine, even if it were large enough, which it is not, to act in this capacity throughout the functional life of the urachus.

We have made similar observations on the pig. This animal has a large and active looking mesonephros until about the 45th day of gestation and pregnancy lasts about 120 days. Table II shows some of the results which have been obtained for the composition of the allantoic fluids at 20–22, 46, 67 and 90 days of gestation. Some of these findings have already been published[6,7] and others are in press[8]. The points to which attention is being drawn at the moment are (a) the acidity of the fluid at and after 46 days. This low pH is due almost entirely to carbonic acid, and the fluids rapidly lose their acidity when they are exposed to the air. (b) The presence of ammonia in the fluids particularly at and after 46 days and (c) the falling concentration of osmolar material in the fluids between 20–22 and 67 days. This is almost entirely due to the falling concentration of sodium, for the concentrations of urea and creatinine tend to rise. MARGARET STANIER has been studying the composition of the urine of the foetal pig at these same gestational ages. She has not yet been able to measure urine flows with great accuracy, but her figures for the composition of the fluids found in the foetal bladder at 45 days of foetal life, when the "urine" is almost entirely the product of the mesonephros, show that they differ greatly from those found in the allantoic fluid at the same foetal age. Later in foetal life, when the metanephros is function-al, the two fluids become more alike but never just the same and there is good evidence that the volume and composition of the allantoic fluids cannot be only the work of the kidney[9,10]. This suggested that the membranes themselves must participate in the formation of the fluids they contain and which are of vital importance to the develop-ing organism; CRAWFORD has recently obtained evidence that there is indeed a sodium "pump" in the chorioallantoic membrane. The results obtained by him in our depart-ment indicate that sodium is actively transferred from the foetal to the maternal side of this membrane, which in the pig covers a large area of the uterine mucosa and acts as the placenta[11]. Evidence was also obtained in this work that the activity of the pump was reduced by a low pH and a high concentration of $CO_2$ on the foetal side and was therefore in all probability a self-regulating mechanism. The work on this membrane is only in its infancy, but it has already shown that the electrolyte stability of the body of the foetus and the welfare of the growing animal depend upon organs and functions which have no place in adult life.

## THE NEWBORN ANIMAL

The kidney of the newborn animal has been shown by many investigators to be functionally immature. There are probably many reasons for this and the net effects on function have been very thoroughly explored. Speaking generally, the concentrat-ing power, the excretion of water, the glomerular filtration rates and the maximum tubular clearances and reabsorptions have all been shown to be well below those of the normal adult. The rates at which these functions mature differ materially among themselves in each species, and the more immature the animal at birth, the weaker the function of the kidney is likely to be. So much is this the case that the kidney of the newly born rat can almost be disregarded as an active regulating organ. Aspects of all this have been reviewed in some detail[12-17]. Yet there is no major change in the volume and composition of the body fluids at the time of birth. Birth may be a functional upheaval for certain organs, but it should produce no threat to electrolyte stability or even to pH and even the rise in the concentration of urea in the plasma during the first days of life (see Fig. 1), small though it is, has been enough to excite comment and investigation. This obvious discrepancy between experience and exper-iment puzzled us for years, although other people did not seem to have been struck by it, and we began to search for the real way in which stability was maintained at this time of life.

Some of the material in the food of a growing animal is always being incorporated into its tissues and does not therefore require excretion by the kidney. The importance of this as an aspect of renal function was pointed out 40 years ago by STRANSKY AND BÁLINT[18], but the importance of it only became apparent when it was investigated quantitatively. Thus we have found out that a newborn piglet may incorporate nine-tenths of the amino acids in its food into its growing tissues. Only a small proportion of the protein N in the milk was converted to excretory end products[16,19]. In spite of this the concentration of urea in the body fluids rose (Fig. 1). Had all the protein N

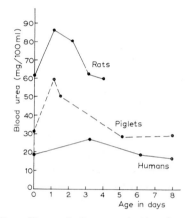

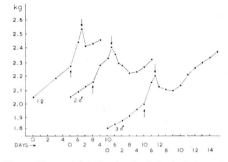

Fig. 1. Changes in the concentration of urea in the blood during early days of life[37].

Fig. 2. The weight charts of 3 infants before, during and after the period of salt administration[32].

been so converted, as it would have been in an adult, the rise would have been astronomical. Anything which upsets the normal growth impulse at this age or accelerates the catabolism of tissue protein may be reflected in a high concentration of urea in the serum. A prolonged and difficult labour[20-23] may do this, and it has been demonstrated experimentally in animals kept without food in a cold environment[8].

The stabilising effects of growth can be demonstrated equally readily in the field of electrolyte and water metabolism. Newborn piglets were given 25 mequiv. of potassium per kg of body weight per 24 h over the first 40 h of their lives (see Table III). Some of the piglets were given this potassium dissolved in water, others in a volume of sow's milk so adjusted that all the animals received the same amount of water as well as potassium[24]. The animals getting the potassium in water did not excrete it fast enough to prevent a major rise in the concentration of potassium in their sera and they became paralysed. The others grew rapidly and incorporated much of the potassium into their cells. The concentrations in the sera rose relatively little although their urine volumes were comparatively small, and the piglets appeared perfectly normal at the end[16,17].

Table IV shows the effect of giving normal and quite reasonable amounts of water unbalanced by food to newborn puppies[25]. These animals differ from piglets in that they tend to excrete water much less freely at this time of life and sodium chloride more freely. The puppies which received milk grew satisfactorily and maintained a perfectly normal internal concentration of sodium and chloride whereas those given water only excreted a relatively small fraction of the quantity which had been administered. They gained considerable weight although they were getting no food, and their body fluids became diluted to an extent which was clearly pathological. It is

### TABLE III

THE EFFECT OF GIVING KCl AND WATER OR KCl AND MILK TO NEWBORN PIGLETS

|  | KCl + water | KCl + milk |
|---|---|---|
| K intake mequiv./kg/24 h | 26 | 27 |
| K retained mequiv./kg/24 h | +2.9 | +10.5 |
| Serum K mequiv./l | 9.3 | 5.9 |
| Signs of toxicity | Paralysed | None |
| Change in body weight g/kg birth weight | —104 | +103 |

### TABLE IV

EFFECT OF FOOD AND GROWTH ON OSMOLAR HOMOEOSTASIS IN THE NEWBORN PUPPY

|  | Water alone | Water and milk solids |
|---|---|---|
| Fluid given   ml/kg birth wt./24 h | 256 | 250 |
| Urine volume   ml/kg birth wt./24 h | 135 | 37 |
| Visible water balance   ml/kg birth wt./24 h | +121 | +219 |
| Serum Na   mequiv./l | 120 | 141 |
| Serum osmolar conc.   mequiv./l | 243 | 310 |
| Gain of body wt g/kg birth wt./24 h | 69 | 178 |

### TABLE V

EFFECT OF FOOD AND GROWTH ON PHOSPHORUS EQUILIBRIUM IN NEWBORN INFANTS

|  |  | 1st day | 2nd day | 7th day |
|---|---|---|---|---|
| P intake | mg/kg/24 h | 0 | traces | 25 |
| P output (urine) | mg/kg/24 h | 0.05 | 3.24 | 0.02 |
|  |  | at birth | at 48 h | 7th day |
| Serum P | mg/100 ml | 6.03 | 7.28 | 6.04 |

### TABLE VI

THE EFFECTS OF ADDING SALT TO THE MILK GIVEN TO BABY 3

|  |  | Before | During | After |
|---|---|---|---|---|
| Serum Cl | mequiv./l | 105 | 119 | 106 |
| Na balance | mequiv./kg/24 h | +2.3 | +14.3 | —5.8 |
| K balance | mequiv./kg/24 h | +3.6 | +3.3 | +1.8 |

probably true to say that many if not most of these effects were appreciated and demonstrated in rather different settings nearly 30 years ago by KERPEL FRONIUS and his associates in Hungary[26-29], but the implications were missed by everyone who read the papers at the time, and by most people since.

Yet one more example of the stabilising effects of growth is provided by a study of the metabolism of phosphate. Table V shows this[30]. During the first 48 h of their lives, these babies were given no food. The serum phosphorus rose somewhat and phosphorus began to be excreted. This rise appears to be due to starvation and the coincidental breakdown of phosphorus from organic combination, and it is shown in a more exaggerated form in the newborn pig. By the seventh day, however, when the intake of phosphorus had been raised by human milk from nothing to 20 mg/day and the infants were *growing*, so much phosphorus was being incorporated into the tissues that the serum phosphorus had fallen and virtually none was being excreted. Other examples of the effects of starvation might be quoted[31].

The only perfect food for the newborn animal is one which can saturate its growth requirements without providing more residual products than the kidney can easily excrete. The addition of sodium chloride to a diet which is otherwise perfect may overcome the ability of the still immature kidney to regulate the volume and composition of the internal environment. Fig. 2 shows the weight charts of 3 premature babies. The lower left hand section of each is a record of their pre-experimental rates of growth. At the first arrow on each record the concentration of sodium chloride in the milk was raised to 0.7% and this resulted in an accelerated gain of weight. This was, however, pathological, and due to an oedematous expansion of the extracellular fluids. Table VI, moreover, shows that the expanding fluids became hypertonic, which no doubt removed water from the cells. Withdrawing the salt at the time indicated by the second arrow led to a rapid loss of weight and a restoration of the earlier growth rates. This effect of sodium chloride has been demonstrated much more dramatically in newborn piglets[16,17,32].

These experiments make it clear that the newly born animal relies upon the integration of food, growth and renal function for the maintenance of its electrolyte stability. The kidney is functionally too immature to maintain stability if most of the ingredients of the diet are not being used for cell growth; and for this to be so, the food must have a composition which saturates in all respects, but only by a small margin, the animal's impulse to grow. Finding concentrations of electrolytes or urea in the serum should lead one to consider the history, growth records and nature of the food consumed before making a diagnosis of defective renal function.

### THE ADULT

For most purposes the adult is still—rightly or wrongly—regarded as the standard of reference. The ways, means and limitations of his capacity to maintain electrolyte stability have been fully tested by physiologists, doctors and even by experience itself. The adult does not have to bother about his kidney when he eats his food or goes to the South Pole, and the functional reserve of the organ is great enough to allow it to cope with the most unexpected eventualities. Apart from the progressive inroads of disease, only an outrageous strain such as a very high altitude or a very hot and humid mine is likely to endanger the stability of an adult's internal environment.
*"Dum vires annique sinunt, tolerate labores"* (OVID, I)[33]

### OLD AGE

Some of the physiological consequences of old age have been painstakingly worked out by SHOCK and his collaborators[34,35]. Some of their findings for the kidney are given in Figs. 3, 4 and 5 and they all show that with advancing age there is a progressive deterioration of renal function and efficiency, and clearly there must in time be a loss

of all reserve. The same is true of the lung, and Table VII, compiled from a paper by
BATES AND CHRISTIE[36], demonstrates that the steady loss of pulmonary elasticity as
the years go on materially reduces the functional capacity of the organ. Yet, unless

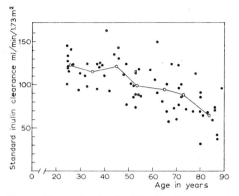

Fig. 3. Change in standard inulin clearance or
glomerular filtration rate with age.
o———o average values[34].

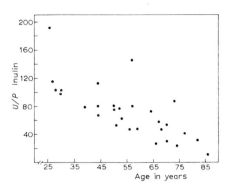

Fig. 4. The relationship between maximum
U/P inulin ratio following pitressin, and age.

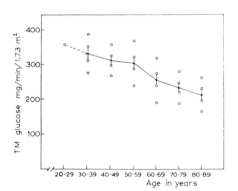

Fig. 5. Decrease in maximal tubular reabsorptive
capacity with age. The slope is drawn to connect
the mean values for each decade. The vertical
lines represent ± one standard error of the
mean, while the open circles define the limits of
± one standard deviation of the distribution.

disease breaks through the weakening reserve of one of the essential organs, electrolyte stability is normally maintained.

How is this done? By a process of integration again, but by one which is very
different from those in early life. "Grow old along with me" (in the words of ROBERT
BROWNING) is what the kidney says to the lung and the heart, the muscles, the brain

TABLE VII

THE EFFECT OF AGE ON THE LUNGS OF NORMAL MEN
After BATES AND CHRISTIE[36]

|  | Mean ages (years) | |
| --- | --- | --- |
|  | 28 | 53 |
| Functional residual capacity (litres) | 29 | 35 |
| Efficiency of gas mixing (as % of perfect efficiency) | 75 | 54 |
| % of $CO_2$ transferred from inspired air to blood | 57 | 31 |

and the appetite. Growth no longer operates as an escape for the man who eats too
much, and indeed eating too much regularly accelerates the ageing processes in a rat's
kidney and leads to premature death[36]. It commonly leads to such obesity in man that
muscular-pulmonary integration fails or heart failure supervenes, to be followed
inevitably by a loss of electrolyte control. At the same time, even the heartiest old
man does not as a rule feel like adventures at high altitudes. His ambitions of the
twenties have gone. His wants are small, or should be; his family has grown up. He
does not need to earn big money in a deep mine to support them. He prefers some
rhythmical activity which he can carry out at his own pace, and perhaps for a modest
wage, and which allows his organs to work together within their joint capacities. His
years should pass unnoticed if his functions keep in step.

"*jam veniet tacito curva senecta pede*" (OVID, I)

## ACKNOWLEDGEMENTS

I am most grateful to the Ciba Foundation and to Dr. NATHAN SHOCK for allow-
ing me to reproduce Figs. 3, 4 and 5. Table VII has been compiled from figures given
by BATES AND CHRISTIE[36] at another Ciba Colloquium. Fig. I was published in the
*Canadian Medical Association Journal* in 1956 and has been reproduced with their
permission. The other figures and certain of the tables have been taken from our own
publications and references are given in the text.

## SUMMARY

The stability of the internal environment has dominated physiological thinking
since the time of CLAUDE BERNARD, and this applies to every age. It is now evident
that stability is maintained within the body of the foetus as effectively as it is in the
body of an adult, although the volume and composition of the body fluids are not the
same for there is more extracellular fluid in the foetus and newborn than there is in the
adult, and the electrolytes, crystalloids and proteins are not necessarily maintained at
the same level. The organs in the adult which are usually regarded as being chiefly
responsible for electrolyte stability and a proper pH in the internal environment are
the kidneys and lungs, integrated with the suprarenal glands, the pituitary, brain
stem and many other tissues in the body. As a generalisation this is true of all ages but
the emphasis to be placed upon the importance of these mechanisms is not the same
in the foetus and in an old man, and the integrated reactions are different. The foetal
kidney may be an important organ in maintaining electrolyte stability but so are the
membranes, fluids and placenta. Food and growth are more important than the kidney
in the newly born when this organ may be functionally very undeveloped, and in old
age the systemic integrations must be far more exact than they need to be in adults.

## REFERENCES

[1] C. ECONOMOU-MAVROU AND R. A. McCANCE, *Biochem. J.*, 68 (1958) 573.
[2] R. A. McCANCE AND E. M. WIDDOWSON, *Proc. Roy. Soc. (London) B*, 141 (1953) 488.
[3] J. W. BOYLAN, E. P. COLBOURN AND R. A. McCANCE, *J. Physiol. (London)*, 141 (1958) 323.
[4] D. P. ALEXANDER, D. A. NIXON, W. F. WIDDAS AND F. X. WOHLZOGEN, *J. Physiol. (London)*,
140 (1958) 1.
[5] D. P. ALEXANDER, D. A. NIXON, W. F. WIDDAS AND F. X. WOHLZOGEN, *J. Physiol. (London)*,
140 (1958) 14.

[6] R. A. McCance and J. W. T. Dickerson, *J. Embryol. Exptl. Morphol.*, 5 (1957) 43.
[7] E. M. Widdowson and R. A. McCance, *Ciba Foundation Colloquia on Ageing*, 4 (1958) 209.
[8] R. A. McCance and E. M. Widdowson, *J. Physiol. (London)*, 151 (1960) 484.
[9] G. B. Wislocki, *Anat. Rec.*, 63 (1935) 183.
[10] R. A. McCance and E. M. Widdowson, *Cold Spring Harbor Symposia Quant. Biol.*, 19 (1954) 161.
[11] J. D. Crawford and R. A. McCance, *J. Physiol. (London)*, 151 (1960) 458.
[12] R. A. McCance, *Am. J. Med.*, 9 (1950) 229.
[13] H. L. Barnett and J. Vesterdal, *J. Pediat.*, 42 (1953) 99.
[14] R. McIntosh, *Arch. Disease Childhood*, 32 (1957) 261.
[15] E. F. Adolph, *Quart. Rev. Biol.*, 32 (1957) 89.
[16] R. A. McCance, *Reflections of a Medical Investigator*, J. B. Wolters, Groningen, 1959.
[17] R. A. McCance, *Arch. Disease Childhood*, 34 (1959) 361, 459.
[18] E. Stransky and A. Bálint, *Jahrb. Kinderheilk.*, 93, 3e Folge, 43 (1920) 350.
[19] R. A. McCance and E. M. Widdowson, *J. Physiol. (London)*, 133 (1956) 373.
[20] R. A. McCance and E. M. Widdowson, *Arch. Disease Childhood*, 29 (1954) 495.
[21] R. A. McCance and E. Colbourn, *Lancet*, 269 (1955) 847.
[22] G. Joppich und H. Wolf, *Klin. Wochschr.*, 36 (1958) 616.
[23] E. Rimbach and A. Bonow, *Zentr. Gynäkol.*, 81 (1959) 1418.
[24] R. A. McCance and E. M. Widdowson, *J. Physiol. (London)* 141 (1958) 88.
[25] R. A. McCance and E. M. Widdowson, *J. Physiol. (London)*, 141 (1958) 81.
[26] E. Kramer, *Jahrb. Kinderheilk.*, N.F., 115 (1927) 289.
[27] E. Kerpel Fronius and F. Leövey, *Arch. Kinderheilk.*, 94 (1931) 9.
[28] E. Kerpel Fronius, *Z. ges. exptl. Med.*, 90 (1933) 676.
[29] J. Csapo and E. Kerpel Fronius, *Z. Kinderheilk.*, 58 (1933) 1.
[30] E. M. Widdowson and R. A. McCance, *Acta Paediat.*, 48 (1959) 383.
[31] R. A. McCance and E. M. Widdowson, *J. Physiol. (London)*, 147 (1959) 124.
[32] R. A. McCance and E. M. Widdowson, *Acta Paediat.*, 46 (1957) 337.
[33] Ovid, *Ars Amatoria*, ii (circa A.D. 1) 669.
[34] N. W. Shock, in A. I. Lansing, *Cowdry's Problems of Ageing*, 3rd ed., Williams & Wilkins, Baltimore, Md., 1952, p. 614.
[35] N. W. Shock, *Ciba Foundation Colloquia on Ageing*, 4 (1958) 229.
[36] D. V. Bates and R. V. Christie, *Ciba Foundation Colloquia on Ageing*, 1 (1955) 59.
[37] R. A. McCance, *Canad. Med. Assoc. J.*, 75 (1956) 791.
[38] G. C. Kennedy, *Ciba Foundation Colloquia on Ageing*, 4 (1958) 250.

## DISCUSSION

STEENDIJK: With reference to the changes occurring in the human body during growth, what, in your opinion is the significance of the sudden fall in the serum phosphate level in adolescence, at about the same time that growth has stopped.

McCANCE: I am afraid I have no information on this.

# THE DEVELOPMENT OF THE WATER METABOLISM REGULATING SYSTEM IN NEWBORNS AND INFANTS

H. RODECK

*Children's Clinic of the Medical Academy, Düsseldorf (Germany)*

The present paper reports briefly on the postnatal development of the hypo-thalamo-neurohypophyseal neurosecretory system, *i.e.* the regulatory system of water metabolism.

Until quite recently it had been generally assumed that the pituicytes under the control of certain hypothalamic nuclei were the site of synthesis of the posterior pituitary hormones. However, tissue culture experiments by HILD[1] have shown that these modified glial cells cannot be considered as the primary site of secretion. As early as 1927/28 TRENDELENBURG AND SATO[2,3,30] were able to detect neurohypophyseal hormones in the hypothalamus and their findings have since been repeatedly confirm-ed. The hypothesis of the secretory activity of some of the hypothalamic nuclei originated about 30 years ago; SCHARRER[4] was the first to suggest that the sites of synthesis of the posterior pituitary hormones were the supraoptic and paraventricu-lar nuclei of the anterior hypothalamus. Subsequently he introduced the term neuro-secretion and suggested intimate connections between the neurosecretory substance and the posterior pituitary hormones. SCHARRER's work was not properly recognized until BARGMANN[5,26], using GOMORI's[6] chromalaun–haematoxylin–phloxin stain, was able to detect selectively the complete neurosecretory system consisting of the supra-optic and paraventricular nuclei of the hypothalamus, the paraventriculo-supraoptico-neurohypophyseal tract and the neural lobe of the pituitary. Stained by GOMORI's method the neurosecretory material in the nuclear cells appears as deep blue or black granules which vary according to the intensity of secretory activity. In the neuro-hypophysis, the neurosecretory material is diffusely distributed in some species; in others, including man, it is found in the vicinity of the blood vessels. Significantly, the amounts of neurosecretory material found are proportional to the hormone content.

While BARGMANN[26] and SCHARRER[4] considered the Gomori-positive material merely as a carrier substance for the hormones, it is now widely assumed ([7-12] and others) that the neurosecretory material and the hormones are identical. Some recent results support this assumption[13].

The functional immaturity of the kidneys at birth is common knowledge. The newborn infant can only concentrate its urine to a certain degree and its fluid intake has therefore to be much greater than that of the adult. The question remains whether the excretion of large amounts of dilute urine by the infant is due to special metabolic conditions, or to the immaturity of the kidneys or of the regulatory system of water metabolism.

Because of the close relationship of the neurosecretory material to, or its identity with the posterior pituitary hormones, it is now possible to investigate the functional state of the neurosecretory system by morphological methods. Such investigations on several species—including man—permit the statement that the neurosecretory system is relatively immature at birth. Small differences exist in mammals from species to species: in the dog and the rat, for instance, neurosecretory activity is seen only after birth, whereas in man signs of activity are already seen during the last months of intra-uterine life. However, despite these differences the immaturity of the neurosecretory system at birth applies quite generally.

The cell bodies in the supraoptic and paraventricular nuclei of the hypothalami of all species investigated (rat, guinea-pig, dog, man) lack the cytological require-ments for neurosecretion and for the production of hormones at the adult level. The cytoplasm of these cells is generally very scanty. Only in human fetuses (7th month of pregnancy) from which the hypothalami were obtained soon after death, did we occasionally find nuclear cells with a clearly developed perikaryon. A few neuro-secretory granules were seen in such cells. Further development in man and animals proceeds gradually: as the cell bodies differentiate, Nissl substance begins to appear followed a little later by the neurosecretory material.

In the neurohypophyses of rats, guinea-pigs and dogs, no neurosecretory granules · can be seen at birth. In human fetuses, however, (7th gestational month) fine dust-like granules are already in their characteristic perivascular position. In other species scanty and diffusely distributed granules can be found in the hypothalamus. The pituicytes show no postnatal development and must be regarded as mature at birth, *i.e.* they behave like glial cells. Our findings[28,29] agree with those of BARGMANN[5] in the dog, DAWSON[14] in the rat, WINGSTRAND[15,16] in the chick, DIEPEN and co-workers[17] in the dog and cat, and BENIRSCHKE AND McKAY[18] and RÄIHÄ AND HJELT[27] in human fetuses and newborns. It follows—for reasons of morphological immaturity—that the neurosecretory system of newborns and infants is not capable of producing significant amounts of neurosecretory substance or posterior pituitary hormones.

HELLER and his co-workers[19-25] have estimated the hormone content in the neurohypophysis of newborns and infants by bio-assay methods and our morpho-logical findings are in agreement with their results. They have shown that the neuro-hypophyses of newborn children and animals contain only a small fraction of the antidiuretic-vasopressor and oxytocic activity which is found in the adult.

Thus, during all the time of neonatal development, the regulatory system (the neurosecretory system), the effector organ (the kidney) and, generally, the conditions of metabolism are in complete harmony. The maturity of the regulatory system cor-responds always to that of the effector organ.

## REFERENCES

1 W. HILD, *Z. Zellforsch.*, 40 (1954) 257.
2 P. TRENDELENBURG, *Klin. Wochschr.*, (1928) 1679.
3 P. TRENDELENBURG AND G. SATO, *Klin. Wochschr.*, (1927) 1827.
4 E. SCHARRER AND B. SCHARRER, *Neurosekretion*, in *Handbuch der mikroskopischen Anatomie des Menschen*, Bd. VI/5, Springer-Verlag, Berlin-Göttingen-Heidelberg, 1954.
5 W. BARGMANN, *Z. Zellforsch.*, 34 (1949) 610.
6 G. GOMORI, *Am. J. Pathol.*, 17 (1941) 315.
7 R. J. BARRNETT, *Endocrinology*, 55 (1954) 484.
8 R. J. BARRNETT AND A. M. SELIGMAN, *Science*, 116 (1952) 323.
9 J. C. SLOPER, *J. Anat. (London)*, 89 (1955) 301.
10 ·J. C. SLOPER, *Nature*, 179 (1957) 148.

11  C. W. M. ADAMS AND J. C. SLOPER, *Lancet*, 268 (1955) 651.
12  C. W. M. ADAMS AND J. C. SLOPER, *J. Endocrinol.*, 13 (1956) 221.
13  H. RODECK, *Z. ges. exptl. Med.*, 130 (1958) 247; 132 (1959) 113; 132 (1959) 122; 132 (1959) 225.
14  A. B. DAWSON, *Anat. Record*, 117 (1953) 620.
15  K. G. WINGSTRAND, *Arkiv. Zool.*, 6 (1953) 41.
16  K. G. WINGSTRAND, *Publ. Staz. Zool. Napoli, Suppl.*, 24 (1954) 25.
17  R. DIEPEN, F. ENGELHARDT AND V. SMITH-AGREDA, *Verh. Anat. Ges., 52. Vers., Münster (Westf.)* 6–9.4.1954, *Erg.-H. Anat. Anz.*, 101 (1954/55) 276.
18  K. BENIRSCHKE AND D. G. McKAY, *Obstet. and Gynecol.*, 1 (1953) 638.
19  H. HELLER, *J. Physiol. (London)*, 102 (1944) 429; 106 (1947) 28; 108 (1949) 303; 115 (1951) 43.
20  H. HELLER, *Arch. Disease Childhood*, 26 (1951) 195.
21  H. HELLER, *J. Endocrinol.*, 8 (1952) 214.
22  H. HELLER, *Neonatal Studies*, 3 (1954) 31.
23  H. HELLER, *Monatsschr. Kinderheilk.*, 106 (1958) 81.
24  H. HELLER AND K. LEDERIS, cited by H. HELLER, *Monatsschr. Kinderheilk.*, 106 (1958) 81.
25  H. HELLER AND E. J. ZAIMIS, *J. Physiol. (London)*, 109 (1949) 162.
26  W. BARGMANN, *Das Zwischenhirn-Hypophysensystem*, Springer-Verlag, Berlin-Göttingen-Heidelberg, 1954.
27  N. RÄIHÄ AND L. HJELT, *Acta Paediatr.*, 46 (1957) 610.
28  H. RODECK, *Neurosekretion und Wasserhaushalt bei Neugeborenen und Säuglingen*, Enke-Verlag, Stuttgart, 1958.
29  H. RODECK AND R. CAESAR, *Z. Zellforsch.*, 44 (1956) 666.
30  G. SATO, *Arch. exptl. Pathol. Pharmakol.*, 131 (1928) 45.

# THE MAINTENANCE OF CIRCULATORY STABILITY
# AT THE EXPENSE OF VOLUME AND ELECTROLYTE STABILITY*

J. G. G. BORST, L. A. DE VRIES, A. M. van LEEUWEN,
G. J. H. den OTTOLANDER and V. CEJKA

*Department of Medicine, University of Amsterdam, Binnengasthuis, Amsterdam (The Netherlands)*

## CONTENTS

On the basis of observations in patients and data from the literature a survey is presented of the factors controlling volume- and osmo-regulation; these are illustrated schematically in Table I (p. 49). The claims made on the kidneys' volume- and osmo-regulatory abilities appear to be conflicting at times. Volume regulation often takes precedence over osmo-regulation, and almost all disturbances in osmo-regulation can be explained in this way. Therefore, osmo-regulation can only be studied in relation to volume regulation. The problem is made still more complex by the fact that volume regulation has no purpose in itself but in all probability only serves to maintain an adequate circulation, which means a circulation adapted to the demands of the organism. All conditions interfering with this vital function lead to compensatory deviations in the volume of the body fluids and sometimes disturb their osmolarity. The evidence on which these conclusions are based will be presented stepwise.

---

\* This paper has appeared already in *Clin. Chim. Acta*, 5 (1960) 887–914.

*References p. 61–62*

I. HYPONATRAEMIA AND HYPERNATRAEMIA AND THEIR RELATION
TO THE CIRCULATING BLOOD VOLUME

In 1936, McCance [1, 2] published the first balance studies on experimental sodium deficiency in man. His subjects were placed on almost salt-free diets; salt loss was induced by sweating. Notwithstanding a liberal water intake the salt depletion was accompanied by a negative water balance, which was reflected in a loss of body weight. In Fig. 1 the weight loss is plotted against the loss of sodium. At first, the sodium loss was followed by an equivalent loss in weight, but on the 5th day, despite

|  | *Before experiment* | *9th day* | *After recovery* |
|---|---|---|---|
| Hb% | 101 | 125 | 93 |
| Cl mequiv./l | 102 | 82 | 102 |
| HCO₃ mequiv./l | 26 | 27 | 24 |
| Na mequiv./l | 148 | 134 | 149 |
| Urea mg/l | 310 | 710 | 250 |

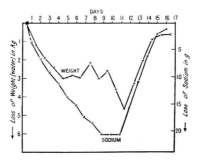

Fig. 1. Subject RBN. Loss of weight and sodium. The two scales are constructed so that a loss of 1 kg in body weight corresponds to a loss of 3.4 g of sodium which is the approximate amount contained in 1 l of extracellular fluid (blood values are converted to mequiv.). Courtesy McCance [1, 2].

the continuous loss of sodium, the weight ceased to fall. The blood sodium and chloride levels were found to be depressed on the 9th day. The circulating blood volume must have been seriously decreased; the rise in haemoglobin level points to a haemoconcentration corresponding to a 40% reduction in the circulating blood plasma volume. Large fluctuations in urine volume were noted.

Apparently, the normal electrolyte concentration was initially maintained at the expense of a loss of 3 l of extracellular fluid. After the 4th day the body sacrificed its osmotic pressure. Probably two regulating mechanisms were opposing each other, one serving the osmo-regulation, the other the volume regulation. At first, the osmo-regulation had priority, but in the face of the considerable haemoconcentration the volume regulation subsequently took precedence. The large fluctuations in urine volume, however, show that the osmo-regulation was not always completely overruled.

In the same year we found high blood chloride levels in patients who had bled from peptic ulcers. To our surprise these patients excreted absolutely no chloride and sodium in their urine. In those days our standard treatment for massive stomach bleeding was to discontinue all oral intake, and dehydration was prevented by parenteral administration of large amounts of saline; several patients even developed oedema. In two patients, a blood transfusion brought about a chloride and sodium diuresis[3], suggesting that the sodium chloride output was related to the circulating blood volume.

Spontaneous resumption of sodium excretion was studied in patients who were operated on because of recurrent haemorrhages. Balance studies were carried out in the post-operative period of 6 patients of whom one died; those who recovered re-

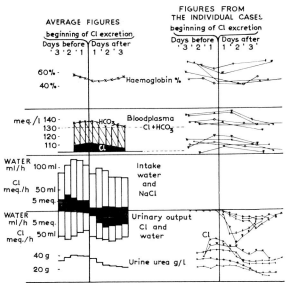

Fig. 2. Five cases of haemorrhage into the intestinal tract, terminated by operation. From BORST[6]. In each case the termination of post-haemorrhagic blood dilution coincides with the fall in urinary urea concentration and the resumption of chloride output (indicated by vertical line). Only in two of the five cases were the sodium concentrations in blood and urine determined (reported by BORST[4]). They ran parallel to those for chloride.

ceived no blood transfusions during this period. In all cases the blood haemoglobin level fell markedly. Since the bleeding ulcer was removed and the general condition improved rapidly, this fall must be attributed to the post-haemorrhagic blood dilution caused by a rise in the blood plasma volume (Fig. 2). At the time that the haemoglobin level ceased to fall the elimination of the excess of (sodium) chloride began. In the following days the blood chloride level fell to normal and oedema disappeared. Concurrently with the (sodium) chloride retention, urea was excreted in the urine at an extremely high concentration, but decreased when (sodium) chloride output was resumed. The high urinary urea concentration indicates a maximal water retention and properly functioning kidneys; the large amount of urea could not have been excreted with less water.

In the patient who died, the blood haemoglobin level rose in the post-operative period. The infusion of 1 l of 6% gum acacia was followed by a temporary haemodilution, the pulse rate declined and the systolic blood pressure rose (Fig. 3). Throughout the post-operative period sodium chloride and water were retained. In the absence of signs and symptoms of severe circulatory failure the sodium retention contrasted with an excessive output of urea and potassium, the urea concentration in the urine being exceptionally high; renal function was apparently unimpaired. Only during the periods of manifest shock did the urea concentration in the urine fall steeply, indicating marked renal failure.

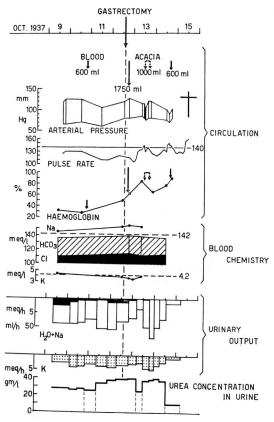

Fig. 3. ♂ 56. Haemorrhage from peptic ulcer terminated by operation. Patient died in post-operative shock. From Borst[4], presentation modified. Selective sodium (and water) retention throughout the post-operative phase. Only during manifest shock also the output of potassium and urea are reduced while the urine urea concentration falls markedly.

These observations clearly showed that:

(a) The output of sodium and chloride was regulated by other factors than their levels in the blood plasma;

(b) Sodium chloride and water, the main components of the extracellular fluid, were retained when the volume of circulating blood was insufficient;

(c) This retention only concerned water, sodium and chloride, was not related to renal failure, and had the character of a compensatory physiological response.

A comparison of our observations with those of McCance shows that in subjects with a markedly reduced blood volume, water is retained in spite of hyponatraemia and sodium chloride is retained despite hypernatraemia. However, the opposition to water retention in the face of hypo-osmolarity is much stronger than that against sodium retention in the presence of hyperosmolarity. It seems that osmo-regulation mainly operates in regulating water excretion.

## II. MAINTENANCE OF THE CIRCULATION BY VOLUME REGULATION

Patients with heart failure, treated by fluid restriction and administration of urea, revealed the same phenomenon as found in the patients suffering from blood loss, *viz.* retention of sodium chloride and high urea concentrations in the urine in the presence of oedema and high blood sodium levels. These patients, however, did not have a low, but rather an excessive, circulating blood volume. Their central venous pressure was found to be high; only the filling of the arterial system could have been insufficient. This led to the concept that volume regulation is not directly related to the circulating blood volume and that only an "insufficient filling of the arterial system"[4, 5] provides a stimulus for the renal retention of water and salt. As a consequence the volumes of the body fluids are not maintained but they are so regulated as to maintain an optimal filling of the arterial system sometimes even at the cost of the development of oedema. The osmo-regulation may also be sacrified since in circulatory emergency water and sodium are retained irrespective of serum osmolarity[6].

In principle this concept was first advanced by STARLING in 1896 and re-emphasized in 1909[7, 8]. Although he had only studied the output of water and had no explanation for the renal factor in nephrotic oedema and for the role of sodium chloride, he was convinced of the relation between circulation and diuresis, of the similarity in renal response to both haemorrhage and cardiac failure and of the compensatory character of the oliguria in both conditions.

The first measurements of sodium and chloride balance in patients with heart failure were made by FUTCHER AND SCHROEDER[9]. They found "an impairment of the ability of the kidney to excrete sodium and chloride (as compared to subjects without heart disease), when the concentration of these ions in the serum was experimentally elevated above normal". WARREN AND STEAD[10] studied the effect of high salt intake in two patients with heart failure who had previously been on a salt-free diet. They found that the ensuing rise in weight and in circulating plasma volume preceded the rise in (antecubital?) venous pressure; values for sodium and chloride in blood and urine were not given. They inferred that the renal retention of extracellular fluid in heart failure is not due to venous engorgement of the kidneys, but to a disturbance of renal function related to a decreased cardiac output.

PETERS[11] suggested that in nephrosis the retention of extracellular fluid was due to a reduction in the circulating blood volume. In discussing the literature on the diuretic effect of acacia infusions he made the oft-quoted statement, "It may well be the fullness of the blood stream that provokes the diuretic response on the part of the kidneys". This supposition was confirmed by LEPORE[12] who demonstrated that the sudden weight loss following acacia injection in patients with nephrosis was preceded by a steep rise in blood volume. PETERS[13, 14] opposed WARREN AND STEAD's "forward failure hypothesis", arguing that in heart failure as in nephrosis reduction in blood plasma volume must precede water and sodium retention. In the former this is attributed to an increased capillary blood pressure, in the latter to a colloid osmotic deficiency. We are of the opinion that in heart failure, according to STARLING's law, a rise in central venous pressure must coincide with forward failure and that forward

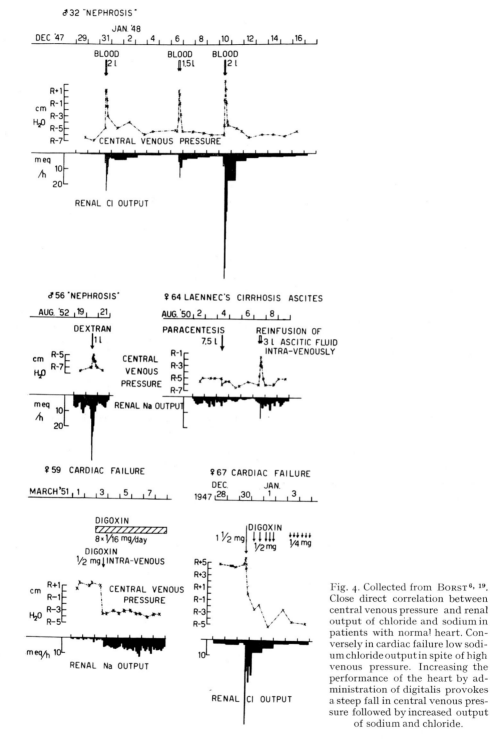

Fig. 4. Collected from Borst[6, 19]. Close direct correlation between central venous pressure and renal output of chloride and sodium in patients with normal heart. Conversely in cardiac failure low sodium chloride output in spite of high venous pressure. Increasing the performance of the heart by administration of digitalis provokes a steep fall in central venous pressure followed by increased output of sodium and chloride.

failure can exist in the presence of an increased blood volume. However, we agree that retention of extracellular fluid is effected by the same mechanism in nephrosis and in heart failure though we reached the conclusion that the total volume of circulating blood (plasma) is a matter of indifference to the kidney[4-6].

Two methods appeared to be of great value for clinical studies concerning the relation between blood volume and the excretion of extracellular fluid:

(a) Utilization of an exact, simple method enabling frequent determinations of the central venous pressure[15, 16, 21].

(b) Strict standardization of diet, posture and activities so that the renal responses can be studied against the background of a regular diurnal excretory rhythm[17, 19, 81].

With these methods it could be demonstrated that in all conditions accompanied by *selective* retention of water and sodium chloride, factors were present which tend to prevent a sufficient filling of the arterial system. They are of two types: some factors primarily concern the heart, whose performance is insufficient in spite of a normal or increased central venous pressure; others primarily tend to depress the central venous pressure by decreasing the amount of blood made available to the heart. When these factors are counteracted and overcompensated, a water and sodium diuresis follows. This is the case both in congestive heart failure treated by digitalis, and in severe haemorrhages treated by blood transfusions. In nephrosis and in cirrhosis of the liver as well as in normal subjects during standing, factors impeding the venous return are active. In nephrosis the blood volume is low, and a large infusion of blood or plasma expander induces a water and sodium diuresis. In liver cirrhosis the circulating blood volume is high but a large part is retained in the portal system. Production of a still larger blood volume by intravenously re-injecting ascitic fluid following paracentesis, elicits a diuretic response (VEENING, quoted by BORST[6]). The same response on the part of the kidneys is seen in subjects who resume the recumbent position after prolonged standing (Figs. 6 and 7).

In "circulatory" oliguria and diuresis only the output of water and sodium and chloride changes markedly; the potassium output is slightly affected and creatinine excretion often remains constant. Usually the diuresis is diphasic, a brisk water diuresis preceding or coinciding with a moderate increase in sodium output[18] (Figs. 6 and 7). The complete diuretic pattern can be sharply distinguished from that following the drinking of water, and the oliguric response from that induced by adrenocortical hormones[19].

In nephrosis and liver cirrhosis treated by blood or plasma expanders there is a close direct correlation between the central venous pressure and the output of sodium and chloride. On the other hand, in heart failure the diuresis induced by digitalis is always preceded by a steep fall in central venous pressure (Fig. 4). Obviously, rises in circulating blood volume and in central venous pressure are not in themselves effective stimuli. They only provoke a diuretic response when the heart functions normally, so that according to STARLING's law of the heart, alterations in central venous pressure are reflected by corresponding changes in the filling of the arterial system*.

---

* According to Starling's law (PATTERSON AND STARLING[20]) the performance of the heart is directly related to the filling of the right atrium. The filling of the arterial system is the result

(footnote continued on p. 42)

*References p. 61–62*

One of the most convincing arguments for this concept is the characteristic "circulatory" type of diuresis accompanying attacks of paroxysmal tachycardia in patients with an otherwise normal heart[6, 19]. Recently, we observed another patient in whom the attacks were accompanied by a marked fall in central venous pressure and a rise in arterial pressure; the circulation time decreased significantly. Fig. 5 illustrates the similarity of the kidney's response to an intravenous infusion of saline and to an attack of tachycardia. In the first instance, however, the central venous pressure did not decrease. If the heart is severely damaged, paroxysmal tachycardia is usually accompanied by oliguria and a rise in central venous pressure[21]. Under

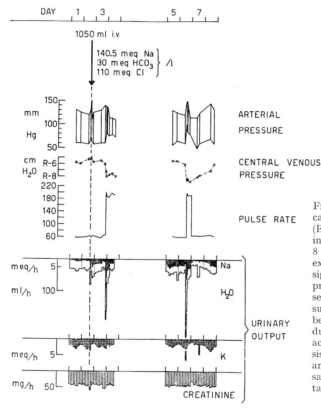

Fig. 5. ♀ 64. Paroxysmal tachycardia, otherwise normal heart (Equal feedings 8 × daily at 3-h intervals and complete bed rest; 8 three-hour urine specimens examined). During the attacks significant fall in central venous pressure and (especially during the second attack) rise in arterial pressure. Circulation time (dye curve) before the second attack 14 sec; during attack 10.5 sec. Attacks are accompanied by polyuria. Diuresis is of the "circulatory" type and similar to that following a saline infusion. After second attack "circulatory" oliguria was evident.

varying conditions of the heart in the same patient, an attack may be followed either by diuresis or oliguria.

These clinical observations almost exclude the possibility that receptors for diuretic stimuli are situated in the venous system or in the right side of the heart, and their presence in the lungs or in the left heart is highly improbable. This conclusion is at variance with that of HENRY AND GAUER[22] who, on the basis of animal experiments, concluded that stretch receptors are located in the heart. Distension of the left heart with a balloon induced diuresis. However, this was accompanied by an

of the performance of the left ventricle and *is determined by the amount of energy transmitted per unit of time with the blood stream into the arterial system.* In some of our papers[6, 17] we erroneously used the term cardiac output when cardiac performance was intended.

extreme tachycardia while the arterial blood pressure and the pressure in the inferior vena cava remained constant. Hence, the diuresis might have resulted from an increased filling of the arterial system. The similarity with paroxysmal tachycardia is striking. Unfortunately no figures are given on the diuresis in the two experiments in which cardiac output was measured and found to be low. Similar objections may be raised against ANDERSON AND FARRELL's experiments[23] on the effect of stretch of the right atrium on aldosterone release.

Of great interest are the observations of EPSTEIN et al.[24] in patients with arteriovenous fistulae. These patients showed high cardiac output and low diastolic arterial pressure. Temporary occlusion of the fistula by compression was accompanied by a fall in cardiac output as well as a rise in diastolic and in (calculated) mean arterial pressure. The kidney responded by a prompt rise in water and sodium output. Both fell to the initial level when the compression was terminated. It is worthy of note that those variations in water and sodium excretion were effected while glomerular filtration rate and renal plasma flow remained constant. The authors end their summary: "The data suggest that renal excretion of sodium may be conditioned by the degree of filling of some portions of the arterial tree".

We must assume that a *single homeostatic mechanism* is responsible for the selective water and sodium retention in all pathological and physiological conditions. The kidney regulates volume in response to stimuli related to flow and pressure. On the other hand, in normal subjects alterations in volume are probably directly reflected in changes in flow and pressure in the arterial system. Circulatory stability is jealously guarded by this homeostatic system. However, if the colloid osmotic pressure is decreased, the venous flow in large regions is impaired, or the heart is unable to respond to a slight rise in central venous pressure with a significant rise in performance, large increases in extracellular fluid are necessary to maintain an optimal filling of the arterial system. In those cases it is especially clear that volume regulation serves no purpose in itself. Therefore, in the following pages the term volume regulation will be placed between quotation marks to indicate that it is ultimately not the volume but the circulation that is regulated.

## Definition of circulatory failure

Circulatory failure or circulatory deficiency can be defined as the condition in which the degree of filling of the arterial system does not meet the demands placed on it by the metabolism. Although every clinician is familiar with the signs and symptoms in manifest cases, it is difficult to diagnose a slight circulatory deficiency.

We must therefore rely on indirect evidence and analogies. When we observe that a normal person, placed on a salt-free diet, loses about 2 l of extracellular fluid and 300 ml of blood plasma, while a fall in central venous pressure is absent or too slight to be demonstrated, it is not clear at first sight that his almost complete renal retention of salt is solely the consequence of an insufficient filling of the arterial system. Only the comparison of this renal response with that found in haemorrhage, in nephrosis and in orthostatic oliguria, makes this concept tenable; but it becomes difficult to reject it after considering that the injection of saline in normal subjects, administration of digitalis in cardiac patients and resumption of recumbency in convalescents, provoke the same characteristic response on the part of the kidneys.

The selective retention of "extracellular fluid" plays a part in the adaptation to the stress of daily life. In a normal young man on a strictly standardized diet the blood plasma volume and the volume of extracellular fluid were found to be significantly higher on a Saturday morning after a busy week than on the following Monday after a 40 h bed rest. During the Sunday an extra amount of water, sodium and chloride corresponding to one l of extracellular fluid was eliminated[25].

Volumes can easily be measured but estimation of the adequacy of the circulation is difficult. It is even doubtful whether measurement of slight circulatory failure is possible at all. It is conceivable that an impending circulatory failure will be prevented by strong compensatory increases in vascular tone, and that this vascular compensatory mechanism also provides the stimulus for the retention of water and sodium. Measurements would then reveal normal values and lead to the erroneous conclusion that sodium output is not regulated by variations in the filling of the arterial system. Hence not even simultaneous measurements of the performance of the heart and the demand on the circulation could give us conclusive information on circulatory deficiency.

We must assume that the kidney receives this information since it responds to an increase in the demand in the same way as to a reduction in the filling of the arterial system. Muscular exercise, hyperthyroidism and fever selectively depress sodium and water output. This is especially true for patients who are on the borderline of heart failure[26-28, 81]. However, in young people with normal hearts, serious febrile diseases are also accompanied by water and sodium chloride retention, sometimes even in the presence of increased pulse pressure and high pulse rate. In these cases too, (relative) circulatory failure can explain the antidiuretic renal response[6, 19].

At the present time no information is available on the type of receptors, though the similarity in response to decreased blood flow and increased metabolism suggests that they must be at least partly chemo-receptors. More has become known in recent years on the location of the receptors and on the mediators which transmit the impulses to diuresis and antidiuresis to the kidney.

### III. PATHWAYS THROUGH WHICH "VOLUME REGULATION" AND OSMO-REGULATION ARE EFFECTED

#### 1. "Volume regulation"

The change in the renal output of water and sodium in response to variations in the filling of the arterial system is probably effected in three ways: purely renal and by mediation of two hormones. The pure renal mechanism concerns itself with both water and salt; aldosterone stimulates the kidney to retain sodium, and ADH regulates water output without influencing the excretion of electrolytes.

*The pure renal mechanism*

The most simple concept is that a reduced arterial filling leads to a reduced glomerular filtration rate, while the tubular reabsorption remains constant. A slight reduction of glomerular filtration rate must then result in an almost complete retention of water and sodium, while the output of other urine constituents is only slightly depressed. Actually, MERRILL[29] found a significant reduction of the glomerular filtration rate in patients with heart failure who retained sodium. The cardiac output of these patients was low.

Many other workers, however, observed that there was no close correlation between sodium retention and glomerular filtration rate. All authors agree that a brief depression of the circulation is followed by a prolonged retention of sodium, though the glomerular filtration rapidly rises to its initial level. It may be noted that our first observations on salt balance during recovery from haemorrhagic shock demonstrated that sodium and chloride could still be completely retained when all other urinary constituents were again normally excreted.

Serious febrile diseases are usually accompanied by water and salt retention. We observed high urea clearances in patients with fever who completely retained sodium and chloride; in a patient with peritonitis the (standard) urea clearance rose to 250% [6]. Other workers found extraordinary high creatinine and inulin clearances in patients with lobar pneumonia, but sodium excretion was not determined in these cases [30]. Studies of the renal excretion pattern under standardized conditions showed that marked reductions in the output of water and salt unaccompanied by changes in creatinine excretion may be found in slight circulatory insufficiency [19]. It is possible that in all these cases the changes in water and sodium output were not purely renal but mainly the result of secondary aldosteronism. However, the similarity of the excretion pattern observed in patients with Addison's disease makes this unlikely (Fig. 6).

The extraordinary selectivity of the pure renal mechanism has been established beyond doubt by the experiments of MARSHALL AND KOLLS, BLAKE, et al. and MUELLER et al. [31–33]. They lightly constricted one renal artery in dogs and compared the renal output of the two kidneys. In some of the animals marked reduction in water and sodium output could be obtained without concomitant changes in the output of other urinary constituents and without changes in the glomerular filtration rate and renal plasma flow. In unilateral perfusion experiments of the kidney, SHIPLEY AND STUDY [34] AND SELKURT [35] found renal plasma flow and glomerular filtration rate almost constant in the face of large fluctuations in arterial pressure, while these fluctuations were accompanied by large percentage variations in sodium and water excretion. Whether slight changes in glomerular filtration rate, too small to be recorded, or whether a more complicated mechanism involving selective alterations in tubular reabsorption are responsible for the large changes in water and sodium has not yet been elucidated.

*The role of the adrenal cortex*

The first evidence of an increased adrenocortical function as a factor in the retention of sodium was found in the renal excretion patterns of our patients with haemorrhage from peptic ulcer; they excreted potassium in excess while sodium was retained. It was already probable that adrenocortical activity was not the sole factor [4, 6], an idea that appears to be confirmed by more recent observations. It was found that adrenalectomized persons and patients with Addison's disease, maintained on constant amounts of adrenocortical hormones, show the normal excretion pattern of circulatory oliguria [19, 36, 37], when they are up and about. This is also clearly demonstrated in Fig. 6. The constancy of the creatinine clearance suggests that the sodium output was also not related to changes in glomerular filtration rate.

*References p. 61–62*

Nevertheless we must accept that an increased aldosterone excretion plays an important part in most cases of more prolonged salt retention. LUETSCHER *et al.*[38, 39] were the first to find an increased urinary aldosterone output in nephrosis, liver cirrhosis and heart failure, as well as in normal people on a restricted dietary salt intake.

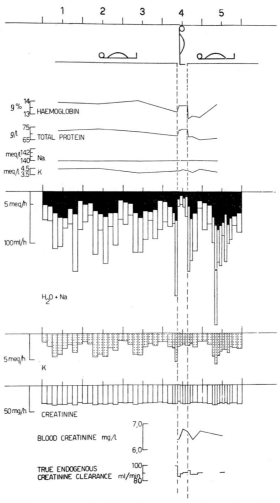

Fig. 6. ♀ 23 year. M. Addison. 75 mg rhetinic acid + 3 mg cortisone (6 × daily). Standard diet and complete bed rest. The typical "circulatory" oliguria and diuresis are not accompanied by corresponding changes in creatinine clearance. (In another study, ACTH administration did not influence the excretion pattern in this patient.)

Temporary pharmacological suppression of the influence of the adrenal cortex on the kidney by amphenon[40] or by the less toxic combination of heparinoid and spirolactone[41] induces a large sodium diuresis in patients with renal sodium retention and high urinary aldosterone accompanying circulatory failure.

In acute circulatory failure aldosterone output is also increased. WOLFF *et al.*[42] and FINE *et al.*[43] found that large blood losses are followed by an increase in urinary aldosterone. A similar response was seen in patients with coronary thrombosis[44]. MULLER et al.[45] demonstrated a rise in the renal excretion of aldosterone during standing. BARTTER's animal experiments[46] showed that a stimulus for increased aldosterone release is derived from the carotid artery, when the pressure in this vessel falls. It is apparent that the release of the mineralocorticoids is related to the "filling of the arterial system" or to what BARTTER[47] calls: "Some function of intravascular volume".

The sodium level of the blood was shown to have no influence on the release of aldosterone (see p. 50).

## The role of the posterior pituitary

Water diuresis and oliguria not accompanied by changes in the electrolyte excretion are usually regarded as part of the osmo-regulation mediated by the hypothalamo-postpituitary mechanism. There is, however, abundant evidence that the circulatory water diuresis and oliguria are also partly regulated by ADH; this will receive further consideration (see next section). On the other hand, the pure renal mechanism also plays an important part in circulatory water excretion. In the experiments of BLAKE et al.[32], MUELLER et al.[33] and SELKURT[35], changes in water and sodium output are always proportional. Excessive circulation can even induce the excretion of hypotonic urine in spite of the administration of ADH[48, 49].

## 2. Osmo-regulation

VERNEY[50, 51] demonstrated that small increments in the sodium concentration of the blood going to the midbrain suffice to elicit an increased output of ADH; a fall in sodium concentration has the opposite effect and results in a massive water diuresis. The reactions are prompt so that the blood sodium levels are maintained within narrow limits and are almost uninfluenced by water intake. It is worthy of note that recent observations demonstrated that the kidney can conserve water by producing hypertonic urine even in the absence of ADH[52].

The postpituitary mechanism also serves in the "volume regulation". The diuresis following the administration of a large volume of water in dogs was interrupted when a large amount of blood was removed; the response was similar to that induced by physiological amounts of ADH[53]. Several workers almost simultaneously discovered that intravenous injection of a large amount of saline elicits a renal response that cannot be distinguished initially from that following the drinking of water. In both instances a brisk water diuresis appears after a delay of approximately 30 min. The increase in sodium output following the administration of saline begins gradually and it often takes more than 24 h before all the administered sodium is excreted (Fig. 7). The initial water diuresis may continue in spite of an increased blood sodium level[18, 54–56]. This diphasic diuresis is one of the many characteristics of the renal excretion pattern associated with "circulatory" diuresis[19].

The effect of alcohol on the circulatory diuresis provides strong evidence that the hypothalamo-postpituitary system takes part in 'volume regulation'. The administration of alcohol blocks the antidiuretic effect of hypertonic saline, but has no influence on the antidiuresis following ADH injection; alcohol probably prevents the release of ADH. It appears that alcohol also minimizes the antidiuretic effect of venous congestion of the legs (KLEEMAN *et al.*[57]) and that of exercise (NEWMAN[28]) without influencing the antinatriuresis. An observation presented in Figs. 11 and 12 leads to the same conclusion.

Water diuresis is poor and delayed in the absence of adrenal glucocorticoids even when the circulation is adequate and the blood sodium level decreased (see also Figs. 11 and 13). The test for adrenocortical deficiency devised by ROBINSON, POWER AND KEPLER is based on this phenomenon (REFORZO-MEMBRIVES *et al.*[58]).

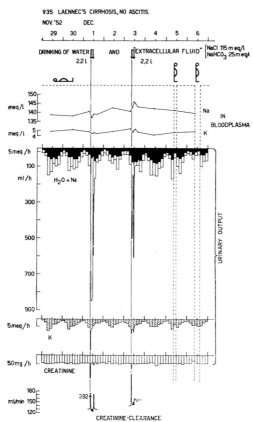

Fig. 7. (Standard diet and complete bed rest). Note similarity of initial responses to drinking water or "extracellular fluid" despite reverse changes in the sodium level of the blood plasma. The additional sodium is slowly excreted. The renal excretion pattern during ambulation contrasts in every respect with the pattern following saline infusion (*cf.* Figs. 5 and 6).

## The effect of thirst

An increased blood sodium level provokes thirst[59]; marked hypernatraemia will, therefore, not develop when the subjects can drink freely. All observations on hypernatraemia have been made in subjects who either had no free access to water or who were unable to drink. It is possible that in exceptional cases of cerebral disease the thirst mechanism itself may be impaired[60].

CIZEK *et al.*[61] observed that dogs which had been subjected to salt depletion initially shunned water. After some days, however, the animals drank much more than they had done previously in spite of a low plasma chloride level. The blood plasma volume was also markedly decreased and according to STARLING [8] circulatory failure is one of the stimuli for the thirst mechanism. PETERS [14] suggested that thirst and release of ADH are responses to the same stimuli. In patients with severe circulatory failure water output is reduced to a minimum, but they are also thirsty and continue to drink in spite of hyponatraemia and even in the presence of massive oedema. This further depresses the sodium level and in cardiac patients it often aggravates the circulatory failure (see Figs. 8 and 10).

*The role of osmotic diuresis*

Our patients with haemorrhages from peptic ulcer excreted large amounts of urea derived from the catabolism of the blood lost into the intestines. This amount of urea could not be excreted with a small amount of water and thereby prevented a sharp reduction in water output. Consequently, the powerful antidiuretic effect resulting from both circulatory failure and hypernatraemia was masked, and only the extraordinarily high urea concentration of the urine testified that antidiuresis was maximal. When the ability of the kidneys to concentrate is impaired the excessive urea concentration in the urine is also lacking. This was the case in two out of the five patients from whom the data are depicted in Fig. 2.

TABLE I

| | | OSMOREGULATION | | 'VOLUME REGULATION' | |
|---|---|---|---|---|---|
| | | BLOOD Na | | FILLING ART. SYSTEM | |
| STIMULUS | | HIGH | LOW | EXCESSIVE | INSUFFICIENT |
| EFFECT | THIRST | increased | | | Increased |
| | RENAL OUTPUT: | | | | |
| | Na | not influenced decreased[1] | not influenced increased[2] | increased increased[2] | decreased decreased[1] |
| | H$_2$O | | | | |
| MEDIATORS | PURE RENAL MECHANISM:[3] | | | | |
| | TUB. REABS. | | | low | high |
| | ALDOSTERONE release | | | low | high |
| | A.D.H. release | high | low | low | high |

1) Minimal (obligatory) water output is determined by the amount of milliosmols excreted and the renal concentrating ability.

2) Delayed response in cortisol deficiency.

3) The regulating function of small variations in glomerular filtration rate is uncertain.
   Severe circulatory insufficiency is accompanied by a marked (non regulatory) fall in glomerular filtration rate and decline in output of all urine constituents.

Table I shows how osmo- and "volume regulation" operate and how occasionally they may reinforce and, at other times, oppose each other's effects. In the presence of serious circulatory failure "volume regulation" almost always takes precedence and hyper- or hyponatraemia may develop when the balance between intake and obligatory water losses is, respectively, markedly negative, or positive.

### 3. The escape phenomena

Since "volume regulation" is effected through three pathways, blocking of one of these does not result in a prolonged retention of sodium and water. A primary retention of either water or sodium results in an increased blood volume and consequently in an increased filling of the arterial system. This provokes a diuresis of both water and sodium along the pathways that have been left open. If only one of the two components of the extracellular fluid is initially retained, osmo-regulation may be disturbed.

### Effect of impaired water excretion

In subjects who receive ADH in amounts exceeding the minimal effective dose, forced water drinking leads ultimately to excretion of hypotonic urine[48, 49]. This escape phenomenon can be readily explained by the fact that "volume regulation" affects water output through two pathways. The rising water volume in the body must increase blood plasma volume and, in subjects with a normal heart, consequently also the filling of the arterial system. This induces the kidney to escape from the inhibitive influence of ADH by means of the pure renal mechanism.

It could be expected that the same stimulus would increase sodium output either directly or indirectly by suppressing the release of aldosterone. Actually, LEAF et al.[62] in similar experiments in man, found a rise in sodium excretion in spite of a pronounced hyponatraemia and a sodium retention when the excess of water was excreted following the cessation of ADH injections. The increased output of sodium in the hyponatraemic phase was found to be accompanied by a decrease in urinary aldosterone excretion rising again after ADH withdrawal[47, 63, 64]. However, in patients with Addison's disease receiving constant amounts of mineralocorticoids at regular intervals, hypotonic expansion of the body fluids is also accompanied by increased sodium output (see Fig. 13).

### Effect of impaired sodium excretion

Balance studies of patients treated with liquorice, a drug with a DOCA-like action, showed an initial retention of sodium and water. Body weight, central venous pressure, arterial pressure and pulse pressure rose markedly; a fall in haemoglobin level indicated a rise in plasma volume. After some time a new equilibrium was reached and the sodium balance even became slightly negative. This was attributed to the effect of the excessive circulation directly on the kidney[65]. It is highly probable that the "escape" during treatment with DOCA and aldosterone, as described by AUGUST et al.[66, 67], must be explained in the same way.

It could be expected that a delayed escape or the absence of any escape at all would be found in patients with severe circulatory failure, since a retention of sodium and water here fails to increase significantly the filling of the arterial system. We do not agree with NELSON AND AUGUST[68] that the "escape" in normal persons and the lack of "escape" in these patients remain unexplained. Unfortunately, these investigators did not provide figures on central venous pressure and blood volume.

The state resembling diabetes insipidus found in subjects who receive excessive amounts of mineralocorticoids is usually explained by the loss of concentrating ability of the potassium-depleted kidney. However, this state must also develop as a part of an escape phenomenon. The retention of sodium induces thirst and renal water retention, but the ensuing excess in extracellular fluid provokes a "circulatory" diuresis, especially during recumbency. Actually, patients with Cushing's disease and normal subjects treated with ACTH or mineralocorticoids often show nycturia[69, 70, 81]. The diuresis accompanying recumbency not only involves water, but also sodium, chloride, and even potassium. In view of observations of DE VRIES et al.[81] on the renal excretion pattern in Cushings disease it is tempting to attribute the hypopotassaemia and the hypochloraemia found in hyperaldosteronism also, if only partly, to an "escape".

## IV. CLINICAL IMPLICATIONS

### I. Hypernatraemia; the dehydration reaction

Prolonged slight to moderate circulatory failure is sufficient to suppress renal sodium output almost completely. Since extrarenal water loss is usually high in comparison to that of salt, the concomitant oliguria is often ineffective to prevent a rise in blood sodium if the intake of water is limited. This rise is more rapid when the ability of the kidneys to concentrate the urine is impaired, or if the effect of an excess of urea to be excreted overrules the stimuli which induce water retention. Only the thirst mechanism affords a sufficient protection against hypernatraemia.

Owing to the fact that a slight circulatory failure may easily be overlooked, the clinician must be aware that patients not able to drink freely are prone to hypernatraemia. This is especially true of patients who have suffered severe cerebral trauma. It is highly probable that the hypernatraemia described in many such cases could have been prevented by administering more water and more blood and plasma[71].

In our bleeding patients, complete sodium retention and hypernatraemia contrasted with a high potassium output despite a normal or even low blood potassium (Fig. 3). In 1944, McCANCE AND BLACK[72, 73] found the same phenomenon in experiments on dehydration which were the reverse of their previous experiments on salt deficiency. This time their subjects received food with salt and the water intake was restricted. The water balance was markedly negative and the sodium level in the blood rose. The high blood sodium level was not accompanied by an increased renal sodium excretion; on the contrary, sodium was retained. As in our bleeding patients, potassium was excreted in excess despite a normal blood potassium level. This paradoxical type of electrolyte metabolism, which had also been found in dehydrated animals[74, 75] and in diabetes insipidus[13], received the name "dehydration reaction" (PETERS[13, 14]). BLOMHERT[76] found that the excretion pattern in this condition exhibited the characteristics of both circulatory failure and excessive release of glucocorticoids. The stimulus for this increased hormone production is possibly derived from the high blood sodium level. It cannot be the result of the dehydration itself, since the excessive potassium output is only found in subjects with hypernatraemia, regardless of whether they are in a dehydrated or oedematous state. Several of our patients demonstrating the "dehydration reaction" had substantial oedema. Therefore, this term is misleading. It is the failure of the circulation, in conjunction with the impossibility of quenching thirst, that maintains the hypernatraemia. Dehydration itself is a cause of circulatory failure in otherwise normal subjects[77], and we may infer that the moderate sodium retention accompanying dehydration must be attributed to this factor.

### 2. Hyponatraemia; the low salt syndrome

Since both water and sodium are retained in circulatory failure, it was to be expected that the usual regimen for oedematous patients, *i.e.* salt-free diet and unrestricted water intake, would often result in hyponatraemia. Actually, a moderate hyponatraemia was found in several cases. Balance studies of a patient with cachectic oedema accompanied by marked hypo-osmolarity were reported by BORST[6] (Fig. 9). Severe hyponatraemia in patients with heart failure and oedema was described by SCHROEDER[78] who introduced the term "low salt syndrome".

However, as long as the circulation is not seriously impaired a significant fall in blood sodium levels is prevented by the hypothalamic-postpituitary mechanism. A relative excess of water will be promptly excreted. Consequently any spontaneous renal salt loss results in an equivalent loss of water. The effect of restricted dietary intake of salt rests on this principle.

Hyponatraemia is only found in serious circulatory failure. In McCance's experiments, salt depletion had resulted in a loss of 3 l of water and a 40% reduction of the plasma volume before the blood sodium decreased. The subjects only then experienced symptoms of severe circulatory failure and the urea clearance was also depressed. Hyponatraemia was the net result of sodium depletion and a slightly less severe water depletion. Similar clinical cases of sodium depletion and dehydration had been published before 1936. Salt loss usually resulted from vomiting or diarrhoea. In the French literature it has been described as "Urémie par manque de sel". These cases are now seldom seen owing to modern parenteral fluid administration.

Paradoxically, nowadays most patients with hyponatraemia have massive oedema; there is an excess of salt and a still larger excess of water. It has been found in cachectic oedema, liver cirrhosis and in heart failure, and is especially prone to develop following treatment with diuretics or with paracentesis. When blood sodium is markedly decreased the patient becomes refractory to all diuretics. The fall in blood sodium is mostly accompanied by a fall in glomerular filtration rate and by a rise in serum potassium and blood urea, the general condition is poor and this "low salt syndrome" has a poor prognosis. An attempt to raise the blood sodium level by the administration of sodium in the oedematous patients usually has a deleterious effect since it further increases the amount of extracellular fluid. The rise in the amount of ascitic fluid and in the volume of circulating blood is especially dangerous in cardiac patients. Only strict limitation of fluid intake and administration of urea to provoke osmotic diuresis can induce a negative water balance and improve the situation (Fig. 8).

A less frequent cause of hyponatraemia is Addison's disease treated with mineralocorticoids only (see Figs. 11 and 13). Experimental hyponatraemia develops when ADH is injected in subjects who are induced to drink normally (see p. 901). It is possible that a similar type of hyponatraemia occurs spontaneously in patients who suffer from a cerebral disease accompanied by excessive production of ADH[60, 79].

However, if these two rare hormonal disturbances and severe renal failure are excluded from our considerations, a low plasma sodium is a sign which warns the clinician of the presence of severe circulatory deficiency.

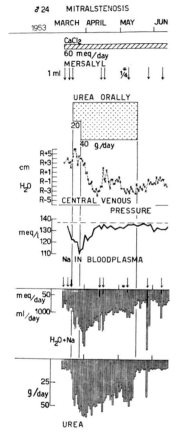

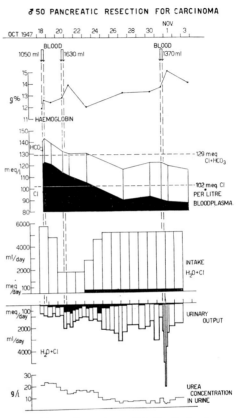

Fig. 8. Low salt syndrome accompanying heart failure; excessive central venous pressure (angle of Louis used as reference point ("R"). Note rapid fall in blood sodium in spite of daily administration of 20 g urea. Strict fluid control and increased dosage of urea result in a rise in blood sodium to a normal level and a fall in central venous pressure. Sodium intake less than 15 mequiv./day during the observation period.

Fig. 9. (From Borst[6]: modified). Cachectic oedema (hypalbuminaemia) accompanied by hyperchloraemia. Resumption of chloride and water diuresis only after second large blood transfusion. Large water intake led to marked hypochloraemia. Third blood transfusion only induced a short lasting water diuresis, insufficient to raise blood chloride level.

V. BALANCE STUDIES IN PATIENTS DEMONSTRATING DOMINATION
OF "VOLUME REGULATION" OVER OSMO-REGULATION

*1. Alternative hypo- and hypernatraemia in circulatory failure*

Fig. 8 shows the data from a case of hyponatraemia in severe heart failure. The central venous pressure was excessive and the pulse rate high. The patient was re-

fractory to mersalyl and very thirsty. The urine volume was small and since fluid
intake was not rigidly restricted, the central venous pressure showed a further rise, the
blood sodium level declined and the patient's condition deteriorated. The condition was
rapidly improved by 40 g of urea daily, combined with controlled water restriction.
Concurrently with the increased water output the central venous pressure fell and the
blood sodium returned to a normal level; responses to mersalyl were again obtained.

In patients who are in severe circulatory failure for a prolonged time, hyper- and
hyponatraemia may alternate. This is illustrated by a patient (Fig. 9) who was
operated on for carcinoma of the pancreas and who had vomited continuously for
several weeks. Since a jejunal tube which had been established did not function
properly, it became necessary to continue with intravenous infusions, initially of saline. The plasma albumin level was very low and the patient was oedematous. The
patient retained the sodium chloride injected and the sum of chloride and bicarbonate
in the blood plasma rose to excessive levels. Two blood transfusions initiated a diuresis of water and, especially, of chloride. After some time it became possible to
administer milk and water through the jejunal tube and the intravenous infusions
were discontinued. The blood chloride rapidly declined to subnormal values. At that
time a blood transfusion initiated a pure water diuresis. Probably the increase in
blood volume was insufficient this time to provoke a (sodium) chloride diuresis also
and to re-establish osmo-regulation definitely.

Another example of alternating hypo- and hypernatraemia is shown in Fig. 10.
The patient had heart failure and massive oedema. At home, in the days before admission, no salt had been taken and the fluid intake had not been restricted. The
blood sodium level was far below normal, the renal function was impaired and the
blood urea increased; mersalyl injections were ineffective. On rigid fluid restriction
the oedema diminished and blood sodium increased to a normal level. Suddenly, the
water diuresis increased and body weight declined more rapidly. The blood sodium
then rose to an abnormally high level. That day the patient had melaena and the blood
haemoglobin fell steeply. The diuresis could be explained by the effect of the urea
derived from the blood lost into the intestines. Thirst became so severe that fluid
restriction could no longer be maintained and this resulted in a rapid fall in blood
sodium and a rise in weight. Nevertheless, the condition had improved and the
responsiveness to mersalyl was restored.

In another patient circulatory failure due to salt depletion was the cause of
water retention (data presented on the left hand side of Fig. 11). Following adrenalectomy, in order to keep his blood pressure low, he was treated with glucocorticoids
only. His sodium balance was slightly negative but the water output was relatively
low in spite of a severe hyponatraemia. His body weight was constant. It is most
probable that water loss was prevented as a result of circulatory failure. However, complete recumbency and the absence of activities during the night were accompanied by
the excretion of larger amounts of hypotonic urine, especially after the patient had been
up and about during the day (Fig. 12). An almost similar diuretic response could
be elicited by a toxic dose (100 ml) of alcohol, demonstrating that the water retention
in the presence of hyponatraemia was at least partly due to the release of ADH.

It should be noted that without mineralocorticoids this patient responded to
the more severe circulatory failure associated with standing by a retention of sodium
while the creatinine output was hardly depressed.

LIPSETT AND PEARSON [80] also treated patients who had been hypophysectomized as well as adrenalectomized, with cortisone only. They attributed the patients' water retention in the presence of hyponatraemia to the marked decrease in glomerular filtration rate (estimated from the creatinine clearance). In our patient the creatinine clearance averaged 70 ml/min; in the hypertensive phase it had been 110 ml/min.

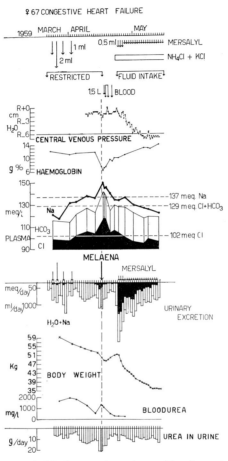

Fig. 10. Hyponatraemia converted to hypernatraemia resulting from strict fluid control and the osmotic diuresis following haemorrhage into the intestinal tract. The loss of 10 l of oedemic fluid induces a blood sodium rise of 30 mequiv./l. Sodium intake less than 15 mequiv./day.

## 2. Hyponatraemia in glycocorticoid deficiency accompanied by excessive circulation

An excessive as well as an insufficient circulation can disturb osmo-regulation. In BLOMHERT's experiments, the initial water diuresis following the administration of a large volume of isotonic saline resulted in a rise in blood sodium to a level definitely above the upper limit of normal (Fig. 7). We found similar but less conspicuous rises of the blood sodium level following the polyuria induced by attacks of paroxysmal tachycardia (see p. 41).

On the other hand, hyponatraemia accompanied by high sodium excretion,

probably as a result of excessive circulation, was found by LEAF *et al.*[62] in subjects
who were injected with ADH and who were required to drink a certain amount of
fluid daily (see p. 50).

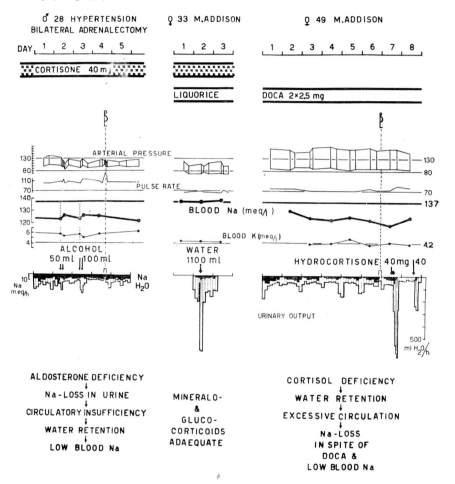

Fig. 11. Data from three patients with adrenocortical deficiency on standard diets and bed rest.
*Centre:* Adequately treated patient; no circulatory insufficiency (low pulse rate), normal blood
sodium and potassium, normal water diuresis. *Left:* Patient with mineralocorticoid deficiency;
circulatory failure, high pulse rate, blood pressure reduced (preoperative level 240–140), negative
sodium balance, high blood potassium. Compensatory water retention leads to low sodium level.
Alcohol diuresis indicates suppression of ADH effect. *Right:* Patient with glucocorticoid deficiency;
no circulatory failure (low pulse rate, high pulse pressure), normal blood potassium. Impaired
water diuresis leads to hyponatraemia and a sodium output slightly in excess of intake.

The same disturbance in water and sodium balance is seen in patients with
Addison's disease maintained in a good circulatory condition with mineralocorticoids
only. Owing to glucocorticoid deficiency, water is poorly excreted even in the presence
of hyponatraemia. As in subjects injected with ADH, the forced intake of fluids induces a negative sodium balance. The data from such a patient can be seen to the right
of Figs. 11 and 13. The diet was strictly standardized as described by DE VRIES[81]: 2800

ml of water and 125 mequiv. of sodium were supplied daily and the patient was kept in bed in complete recumbency. In spite of the injection of more than adequate amounts of DOCA, the sodium balance was negative, the blood sodium level gradually

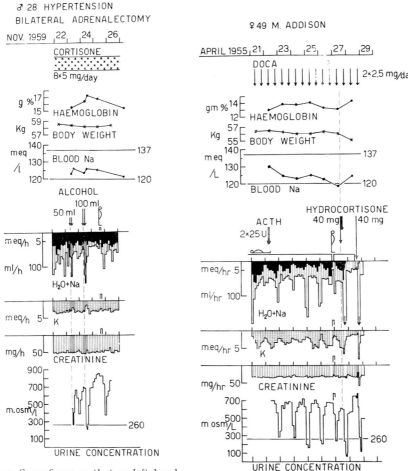

Fig. 12. Same figure as that on left hand side of Fig. 11 with additional data. In the last days of observation water is retained as appears from the rise in body weight and the fall in haemoglobin and blood sodium levels. Both alcohol and night rest induce a water diuresis; in the first instance urine osmolarity falls below serum osmolarity. Orthostatic antinatriuresis unaccompanied by creatinine retention in spite of complete abscence of mineralocorticoids.

Fig. 13. Same figure as that on the right hand side of Fig. 11 with additional data. Almost complete sodium retention during standing and following water diuresis induced by cortisol. Normal diurnal excretory rhythm of electrolytes contrasted by a nightly water diuresis. Fall of urine osmolarity below serum osmolarity during the nights and following hydrocortisone injection. No effect of high dosage ACTH on water and electrolyte excretion.

declined to 119 mequiv./l and the body weight decreased slightly. Injection of 40 mg of cortisol initiated a brisk water diuresis; 2 l of water were eliminated in 6 h. The diuretic effect surpassed that of the drinking of 1100 ml of water in another patient with Addison's disease, who had a normal sodium level and was maintained on both mineralocorticoids and glucocorticoids (data presented in the middle of Fig. 11).

Paradoxically, in the patient who received initially no glucocorticoids the water diuresis provoked by cortisol was followed by a complete sodium retention in the presence of an increasing blood sodium level. Before cortisol treatment, marked sodium retention only occurred in the 3 h that the patient had been up and about (Fig. 13). It is probable that in both instances this retention was caused by circulatory failure. The negative sodium balance on the days preceding cortisol injection can be explained by the excess of water in the body which, as long as the patient remained in bed, maintained the circulation at an adequate and even slightly excessive level.

The renal excretion pattern deserves special consideration. In spite of continuous complete recumbency and avoidance of even slight activities the patient had nycturia. This only involved water; the excretion of sodium and potassium was almost normal with the peak of sodium output in the beginning of the evening. The same type of nycturia was found in a patient with Sheehan's disease [81], [82] and in other patients with Addison's disease maintained on mineralocorticoids only. Fig. 13 shows that during nycturia and especially following hydrocortisone injection the urine osmolarity falls below the plasma osmolarity evidencing an almost complete absence of ADH secretion.

As in the experiment of LEAF [62], the sodium level of the blood was shown to be a factor of no importance in the regulation of the sodium output.

In considering all the information on renal sodium output derived from observations in patients with hypernatraemia and hyponatraemia it may be concluded that sodium excretion is hardly, if at all, related to the sodium concentration in the blood plasma. Whether or not sodium will be excreted is probably almost entirely dependent on the degree to which the metabolic demands of the body are met by the circulation. The slightest deficits and excesses in the circulation are reflected in corresponding changes in sodium output. The influences on water output are no less powerful than those on sodium excretion but they are often neutralized by the osmo-regulation. In the absence of adrenocortical insufficiency and severe renal disease the renal output of sodium may be regarded as the best indicator of the adequacy of the circulation.

### VI. SUMMARY AND CONCLUSIONS

A survey is presented on the factors controlling volume- and osmo-regulation. Data from the literature on experiments in animals and man are interpreted and compared with observations in patients.

The first balance studies on hypo- and hypernatraemia already strongly suggested that the kidney cannot regulate these disturbances by excretion of the relative excess of water, or alternatively of sodium chloride, if the circulating blood volume is markedly lowered. Volume regulation then dominates osmo-regulation.

The same disturbances in the osmo-regulation were observed in heart failure, indicating that the kidney responds identically to a primary cardiac insufficiency and to reduction of the volume of circulating blood.

Two methods have been found to be of special importance for clinical studies of the relationship between the circulation and the renal excretion of water and sodium chloride:

(a) Frequent determinations of the central venous pressure by an exact simple method;

(b) Rigid standardization of diet and complete bed rest resulting in a basic daily excretion pattern so that superimposed renal responses to changes in the patient's condition (e.g., under influence of treatment) can easily be distinguished.

In patients with nephrosis and liver cirrhosis treated with blood volume expanders, a close positive correlation was found between the central venous pressure and the diuresis of water, sodium and chloride. However, in heart failure treated by digitalis and in paroxysmal tachycardia with excessive circulation, the onset of diuresis was preceded by a fall in central venous pressure. The stimuli for volume regulation must, therefore, be linked with the changes in flow or pressure in the arterial system and it is most unlikely that receptors are located in the heart.

Circulatory oliguria and diuresis mainly concern water, sodium and chloride. The creatinine clearance may remain constant. The highly characteristic renal excretion pattern is identical both for primary alterations in the circulating blood volume and for primary changes in cardiac function.

Evidence for the influence of changes in the body's metabolic demands is presented. In fever and during exercise, water and sodium are retained. The excretion of water and sodium chloride is, therefore probably regulated by the deviations from an optimal filling of the arterial system. Owing to this homeostatic mechanism an *optimal circulation is maintained with the aid of variations in the volume of the body fluids.*

Variations in the filling of the arterial system govern the renal excretion of water and sodium chloride through three pathways. One is a pure renal mechanism and the other two depend on variations in the release of aldosterone and ADH respectively. Hence ADH secretion is under control of both osmo- and "volume-regulation". The renal response to graded unilateral narrowing of the renal artery in dogs and observations in patients without functioning adrenocortical tissue demonstrate that circulatory variations in sodium output may be adequately effected by the pure renal mechanism without changes in creatinine clearance. It is therefore probable that the pure renal mechanism mainly operates by varying tubular reabsorption.

The effect of thirst and osmotic diuresis is discussed. The factors controlling "volume"-and osmo-regulation and the pathways through which stimuli are conveyed to the kidneys are presented schematically (p. 49).

Retention of water and/or sodium due to blocking one of the pathways provides the stimulus for an "escape" through alternative routes of both water and sodium.

(a) ADH administration combined with controlled water intake, by causing excess of water in the body (and probably excessive circulation) provokes a sodium diuresis in the presence of hyponatraemia. This diuresis is at least partially conditioned by a decreased aldosterone release. The water diuresis which ultimately occurs must arise *via* the pure renal mechanism. Water diuresis is also impaired in patients with Addison's disease who receive adequate amounts of mineralocorticoids but no glucocorticoids. Also in these patients forced water intake leads to hyponatraemia and a negative sodium balance, showing that the "escape" of sodium is not solely conditioned by reduction in aldosterone secretion.

(*b*) Administration of aldosterone or substances with an aldosterone-like effect leads to an increase in extracellular fluid volume, blood dilution and rises in central venous, arterial and pulse pressures. As a consequence of the excessive circulation sodium is again excreted, presumably *via* the pure renal mechanism. The water diuresis, which occurs in the presence of a slightly elevated blood sodium and results in a condition resembling diabetes insipidus, can also be explained as being a form of escape.

Even in slight (often not directly evident) circulatory insufficiency sodium is retained. When increased protein catabolism coincides with a depressed renal concentrating ability, the renal water output is relatively high even in the presence of dehydration. The normal water output may erroneously suggest that the fluid supply is adequate. If the obligatory water loss exceeds the intake, hypernatraemia appears.

In the prevention of hypernatraemia osmo-regulation operates mainly through the thirst mechanism. Therefore, hyperosmolarity threatens all patients who are not able to drink freely. This is especially true for comatose patients and it is essential that they receive special care in this respect. It has been shown that hypernatraemia can develop in patients with marked oedema. The term "dehydration reaction" is considered to be misleading.

In the prevention of hyponatraemia the mechanism regulating renal water excretion is very effective. Even in moderate circulatory failure small decrements of the blood sodium level result in a depression in the release of ADH. The therapeutic effect of the saltfree diet rests on this principle. However, in severe circulatory failure "volume-regulation" takes precedence over osmo-regulation and water is retained in spite of hyponatraemia.

Owing to the thirst-provoking effect of severe circulatory deficiency the thirst mechanism promotes hyponatraemia in this condition. The low salt syndrome is often found in patients with massive oedema. In these cases large sodium chloride excess is accompanied by a still larger excess of water. Administration of sodium then often has a deleterious effect.

Balance studies demonstrating the favourable results obtained by forced water restriction and the administration of urea in a case of hyponatraemia due to heart failure are presented. It is shown that hypo- and hypernatraemia may alternate in oedematous patients with prolonged circulatory failure.

Cases in which hyper- or hyponatraemia developed, probably as a result of hypercirculation, are described. The electrolyte balance of an adrenalectomized patient receiving only glucocorticoids is compared with the balance of a patient with Addison's disease receiving only mineralocorticoids.

For the interpretation of laboratory data the following practical rules are proposed:

(*a*) Low renal sodium output in patients with normal adrenals and without serious kidney disease indicates the presence of (at least slight) circulatory failure;

(b) In the absence of serious renal failure and of certain rare hormonal disturbances, a markedly lowered blood sodium indicates the presence of severe circulatory failure;

(c) Hypernatraemia indicates the presence of (at least slight) circulatory failure associated with either an insufficient or intentionally restricted water intake. It is not necessarily associated with dehydration and may occur in the presence of oedema.

REFERENCES

1 R. A. McCance, Lancet, 230 (1936) 826.
2 R. A. McCance, Proc. Roy. Soc. (London), 119 (1936) 254.
3 J. G. G. Borst, Z. klin. Med., 130 (1936) 74.
4 J. G. G. Borst, Acta Med. Scand., 97 (1938) 68.
5 J. G. G. Borst, Ned. Tijdschr. Geneesk., 85 (1941) 1523.
6 J. G. G. Borst, Acta Med. Scand., 130 (1948) Suppl. 207.
7 E. H. Starling, Lancet, 150 (1896) 1266.
8 E. H. Starling, The Fluids of the Body, Archibald Constable & Co., London, 1909.
9 P. H. Futcher and H. A. Schroeder, Am. J. Med. Sci., 204 (1942) 52.
10 J. V. Warren and E. Stead, A. M. A. Arch. Internal Med., 73 (1944) 138.
11 J. P. Peters, Body Water. The Exchange of Fluids in Man, Ballière, Tind alland Son, London, 1935, p. 286, 287.
12 M. J. Lepore, Ann. Internal Med., 11 (1937) 285.
13 J. P. Peters, New Engl. J. Med., 239 (1948) 353.
14 J. P. Peters, Am. J. Med., 12 (1952) 66.
15 P. Allen, Can. Med. Assoc. J., 59 (1948) 560.
16 J. G. G. Borst and J. A. Molhuysen, Lancet, 263 (1952) 304.
17 J. G. G. Borst and L. A. de Vries, Lancet, 259 (1950) 1.
18 G. Blomhert, J. A. Molhuysen, J. Gerbrandy, L. A. de Vries and J. G. G. Borst, Lancet, 261 (1951) 1011.
19 J. G. G. Borst, A Ciba Foundation Symposium on the Kidney, edited by A. A. G. Lewis and G. E. W. Wolstenholme, 1954, p. 255.
20 S. W. Patterson and E. H. Starling, J. Physiol. (London), 48 (1914) 357.
21 J. A. Molhuysen, Thesis, Amsterdam, 1953.
22 J. P. Henry, O. H. Gauer and J. L. Reeves, Circulation Research, 4 (1956) 85.
23 C. H. Anderson, M. McCally and G. L. Farrell, Endocrinology, 64 (1959) 202.
24 F. H. Epstein, R. S. Post and M. E. McDowell, J. Clin. Invest., 32 (1953) 233.
25 J. Gerbrandy, Thesis, Amsterdam, 1951.
26 A. A. Kattus, B. Sinclair-Smith, J. Genest and E. V. Newman, Bull. Johns Hopkins Hosp., 84 (1949) 344.
27 B. Sinclair-Smith, A. A. Kattus, J. Genest and E. V. Newman, Bull. Johns Hopkins Hosp., 84 (1949) 369.
28 E. V. Newman, New Engl. J. Med., 250 (1954) 347.
29 A. J. Merrill, J. Clin. Invest., 25 (1946) 389.
30 E. M. Blegen, H. N. Haugen and K. Ørning, Scand. J. Clin. and Lab. Invest., 6 (1954) 8.
31 E. K. Marshall Jr and A. C. Kolls, Am. J. Physiol., 49 (1919) 317.
32 W. D. Blake, R. Wégria, H. P. Ward and Ch. W. Frank, Am. J. Physiol., 163 (1950) 422.
33 C. B. Mueller, A. Surtshin, M. R. Carlin and H. L. White, Am. J. Physiol., 165 (1951) 411.
34 R. E. Shipley and R. S. Study, Am. J. Physiol., 167 (1951) 676.
35 E. E. Selkurt, Circulation, 4 (1952) 541.
36 S. P. ten Holt, L. A. de Vries and J. G. G. Borst, Ned. Tijdschr. Geneesk., 96 (1952) 2244.
37 J. D. Rosenbaum, S. Papper and M. M. Ashley, J. Clin. Endocrinol. and Metabolism, 15 (1955) 1459.
38 J. A. Luetscher Jr., Q. B. Deming and B. B. Johnson, Ciba Foundation Colloquia, edited by G. E. W. Wolstenholme, vol. IV (1952) p. 530.
39 J. A. Luetscher Jr. and B. B. Johnson, J. Clin. Invest., 33 (1954) 1441.
40 G. W. Thorn, E. J. Ross, J. Crabbé and W. Van 't Hoff, Brit. Med. J., (1957 II) 955.
41 V. Cejka, L. A. de Vries, M. E. Smorenberg-Schoorl, J. J. van Daatselaar, J. G. G. Borst and C. L. H. Majoor, Lancet, 278 (1960) 317.
42 H. P. Wolff, K. R. Koczorek and E. Buchborn, An International Symposium on Aldosterone, Churchill, London, 1958, p. 193.
43 D. Fine, L. E. Mv̈selas and T. Auerbach, J. Clin. Invest., 37 (1958) 232.
44 H. P. Wolff, K. R. Koczorek and E. Buchborn, Lancet, 273 (1957) 63.
45 A. F. Muller, E. L. Manning and A. M. Riondel, Lancet, 274 (1958) 711.

⁴⁶ F. C. BARTTER, I. H. MILLS AND D. S. GANN, *J. Clin. Invest.*, 38 (1959) 986 (abstract).
⁴⁷ F. C. BARTTER, G. W. LIDDLE, L. E. DUNCAN JR., J. K. BARBER AND C. DELEA, *J. Clin. Invest.*, 35 (1956) 1306.
⁴⁸ L. G. WESSON JR., W. P. ANSLOW JR., L. G. RAISZ, A. A. BOLOMEY AND M. LADD, *Am. J. Physiol.*, 162 (1950) 677.
⁴⁹ N. G. LEVINSKY, D. G. DAVIDSON AND R. W. BERLINER, *Am. J. Physiol.*, 196 (1959) 451.
⁵⁰ E. B. VERNEY, *Lancet*, 251 (1946) 781.
⁵¹ E. B. VERNEY, *Proc. Roy. Soc., (London) B*, 135 (1947) 25.
⁵² R. W. BERLINER AND D. G. DAVIDSON, *J. Clin. Invest.*, 36 (1957) 1416.
⁵³ H. RYDIN AND E. B. VERNEY, *Quart. J. Exptl. Physiol.*, 27 (1938) 343.
⁵⁴ G. BLOMHERT, *Thesis*, Amsterdam, 1951.
⁵⁵ M. B. STRAUSS, R. K. DAVIS, J. D. ROSENBAUM AND E. C. ROSSMEISL, *J. Clin. Invest.*, 30 (1951) 862.
⁵⁶ R. J. F. MURPHY AND E. A. STEAD JR., *J. Clin. Invest.*, 30 (1951) 1055.
⁵⁷ C. R. KLEEMAN, M. E. RUBINI, E. LAMDIN AND F. H. EPSTEIN, *J. Clin. Invest.*, 34 (1955) 448.
⁵⁸ J. REFORZO-MEMBRIVES, M. H. POWER AND E. J. KEPLER, *J. Clin. Endocrin.*, 5 (1945) 76.
⁵⁹ A. GILMAN, *Am. J. Physiol.*, 120 (1937) 323.
⁶⁰ P. FOURMAN AND P. M. LEESON, *Ciba Foundation Colloquia on Aging*, edited by G. E. W. WOLSTENHOLME AND M. O'CONNOR, J. & A. Churchill, London, vol. IV, 1958.
⁶¹ L. J. CIZEK, R. E. SEMPLE, K. C. HUANS AND M. I. GREGERSEN, *Am. J. Physiol.*, 164 (1951) 415.
⁶² A. LEAF, F. C. BARTTER, R. F. SANTOS AND O. WRONG, *J. Clin. Invest.*, 32 (1953) 868.
⁶³ J. C. BECK, I. DYRENFURTH, C. P. GIROUD AND E. H. VENNING, *A. M. A. Arch. Internal Med.*, 96 (1955) 463.
⁶⁴ A. F. MULLER, A. M. RIONDEL AND R. S. MACH, *Lancet*, 270 (1956) 831.
⁶⁵ J. A. MOLHUYSEN, J. GERBRANDY, L. A. DE VRIES, J. C. DE JONG, J. B. LENSTRA, K. P. TURNER AND J. G. G. BORST, *Lancet*, 259 (1950) 381.
⁶⁶ J. T. AUGUST, D. H. NELSON, G. W. THORN, *J. Clin. Invest.*, 37 (1958) 1549.
⁶⁷ J. T. AUGUST AND D. H. NELSON, *J. Clin. Invest.*, 38 (1959) 1964.
⁶⁸ D. H. NELSON AND J. T. AUGUST, *Lancet*, 277 (1959) 883.
⁶⁹ J. G. G. BORST, *Acta Med. Scand.*, 146 (1953) 33.
⁷⁰ E. J. LENNON, P. P. RUETZ AND W. E. ENGSTROM, *J. Lab. Clin. Med.*, 54 (1959) 918.
⁷¹ J. G. G. BORST, *Lancet*, 261 (1951) 887 (Letter to the Editor).
⁷² R. A. McCANCE, W. F. YOUNG AND D. A. K. BLACK, *J. Physiol. (London)*, 102 (1944) 415.
⁷³ D. A. K. BLACK, R. A. McCANCE AND W. F. YOUNG, *J. Physiol. (London)*, 102 (1944) 406.
⁷⁴ E. KERPEL-FRONIUS, *Z. Kinderheilk.*, 57 (1935) 489.
⁷⁵ J. R. ELKINTON AND M. TAFFEL, *J. Clin. Invest.*, 21 (1942) 787.
⁷⁶ G. BLOMHERT, *Acta Med. Scand.*, 155 (1956) 101.
⁷⁷ J. R. ELKINTON, T. S. DANOWSKI AND A. WINKLER, *J. Clin. Invest.*, 25 (1946) 120.
⁷⁸ H. A. SCHROEDER, *J. Am. Med. Ass.*, 141 (1949) 117.
⁷⁹ W. B. SCHWARTZ, W. BENNET, S. CURELOP AND F. C. BARTTER, *Am. J. Med.*, 23 (1957) 529.
⁸⁰ M. B. LIPSETT AND O. H. PEARSON, *J. Clin. Invest.*, 37 (1938) 1394.
⁸¹ L. A. DE VRIES, S. P. TEN HOLT, J. J. VAN DAATSELAAR, A. MULDER AND J. G. G. BORST, *Clin. Chim. Acta*, 5 (1960) 915.
⁸² J. G. G. BORST, *Livre Jubilaire publié en l'honneur du Professeur Paul Govaerts*, 1955, p. 410.

## DISCUSSION

VINK: What is the extent of the decrease of circulatory blood plasma volume in patients with Addison's disease?

BORST: When a patient with Addison's disease has symptoms of circulatory deficiency there is a diminished blood plasma volume. If we stop the administration of mineralocorticoids and leave the patients for some days on a low salt intake there is always a reduction in blood plasma volume of more than 20% as can be shown by the rise in haemoglobin level.

VINK: How do you explain in these patients the nocturnal water diuresis?

BORST: I have no explanation. The patients who demonstrated a nocturnal water diuresis received a sufficient dose of mineralocorticoids but no glucocorticoids and they had normal blood volumes. It is probable that the nycturia is not related to changes in posture. It is not accompanied by increased sodium output and it is not abolished by keeping the patient flat in bed during the day and night in contrast to what occurs in all types of "circulatory" nycturia.

MULLER: The first point I wish to make is that Addison's disease does not automatically mean absence of adrenal steroids, since varying amounts of hydrocortisone and aldosterone are still secreted as can be shown by injecting the isotopically labeled compounds. Secondly, the quantity of hormones given as substitution-therapy is often excessive and non-physiological.

Thirdly, the fact that variations in the urinary sodium output occur while the patients receive a constant quantity of exogenous hormone, does not imply *ipso facto* that the electrolyte changes are not dependent on the hormone. We may in this connection refer to the concept of "permissive action".

BORST: I must admit that it can't be proven that my patients with Addison's disease were completely devoid of functioning adrenal cortical tissue. These patients, however, showed no reaction to excessive amounts of ACTH (Fig. 13, p. 57). Nevertheless, their renal response to changing from the lying to the standing position was similar to that of normal subjects. The patient with a complete adrenalectomy reacted in the same way. Therefore, I am sure that the sodium-retaining mechanism can operate independently of changes in release of aldosterone by the adrenal cortex.

MULLER: Did you maintain a totally adrenalectomized patient during several days, without any hormone therapy? If so, I would agree, but your first patient received 40 mg of cortisone. I don't know a publication in which such a patient was left without hormone therapy during several days. If you get no reaction on ACTH it means only that your diagnosis of Addison's disease is correct, since this conforms with the definition of this disease. However, nothing is proven about the total output. I have patients who don't react on ACTH but have a daily output of 9–10 mg of hydrocortisone. This is half the amount excreted by a non-stressed normal. The question to be put is, whether 10 mg is a sufficient amount to get the "permissive action" of the adrenal on the kidney.

BORST: If your term "permissive action" implies that the kidney can respond to circulatory stimuli by selectively retaining water, sodium and chloride in the presence of a constant amount of aldosterone, I could agree. On the other hand, I don't think that this renal response is absent in adrenalectomized patients maintained on a constant high sodium intake only. This is, however, of no importance. I only want to stress, that at the moment sodium is retained, there is no increased secretion of aldosterone.

MULLER: In my opinion the only fact which is really important is that you need a certain amount of aldosterone; I can show you a patient who retained sodium like a normal, but with much less aldosterone. There is always a certain degree of wasting by the body. So it produces more hormone than it actually needs and the fact you don't see an increase in output does not mean that the hormone is not needed to retain sodium.

BORST: I don't think there is a great difference in our opinions.

DE GRAEFF: One of the causes of hyponatraemia in cardiac deficiency is ascribed to salt-restriction. About 1 kg of salt is filtered through the glomeruli each day and so the tubular load should be sufficient on a saltfree diet. Is it not the amount of water liberated by catabolism which will determine the degree of hyponatraemia assuming that severe cardiac deficiency is present?

BORST: I don't believe this to be true. I have shown (Fig. 10) that a loss of fluid is accompanied by an equivalent rise in blood sodium. The loss of water by perspiration and in the urine causes the rise of blood sodium.

On the other hand in severe circulatory failure hyponatraemia develops when water intake is not restricted. The kidney retains water. Since severe circulatory failure provokes thirst, the patient drinks eagerly and further depresses his blood sodium. This is seen in all types of circulatory failure (heart disease, nephrosis, liver cirrhosis).

DE GRAEFF: Of course you can influence it by fluid restriction, but some patients need a more severe restriction than others. So I wonder if in these patients who develop a hyponatraemia even after water intake is restricted there is an augmented liberation of endogenous water.

BORST: When fluid was restricted to about ½ l a day, we found without exception a fall in body weight and a rise in blood sodium. If this did not occur, the patient had received water contrary to the regulations. I do not believe that endogenous water can be liberated in sufficient amounts to neutralize the effect of water restriction.

SNELLEN: Some authors claim that thirst is induced by the chloride concentration and not by the sodium concentration.

BORST: I can't answer this question, since sodium and chloride usually rise simultaneously.

SNELLEN: McArdle *et al.* have determined the so-called 4 hour sweating rate by exposing subjects to several combinations of work and heat load. They have found that when sweating more than 4 l per hour an increasing number of subjects show loss of working efficiency. Can you give an explanation for this phenomenon?

BORST: If someone loses 1 l of sweat per hour he has to drink the same amount of water with an amount of salt equal to what has been lost. It may be possible that some people are not able to drink this amount and therefore become dehydrated.

# SOME ASPECTS OF THE HORMONAL CONTROL OF WATER AND ELECTROLYTES

ALEX-F. MULLER

*Therapeutical Clinic of the University, Cantonal Hospital, Geneva (Switzerland)*

Whatever hormonal control mechanisms we try to analyze, three separate points have to be considered: the sites of regulation, the regulating agents and the underlying metabolic events. In the problem which interests us in this review, three principal sites must be distinguished: first, the point of entry, generally the intestines; second, the storehouse, particularly the bones for sodium and the muscles for potassium; third, the point of exit, principally the kidneys. Among the regulating agents the hormones of the adrenal cortex are the most important. However, in recent years interest has been focussed on the sex hormones, particularly progesterone. Concerning the third point to be discussed, the underlying metabolic events, the knowledge accumulated so far is only very fragmentary.

By way of introduction, it might be helpful to review briefly the anatomical distribution in the adult of water and the two electrolytes sodium and potassium. The data are taken from a recent paper by EDELMAN[1]. In a normal young adult male, plasma water represents 7.5%; interstitial lymph water 20%; dense connective tissue and cartilage water 7.5%; bone water 7.5%; intracellular water 55% and transcellular water 2.5%. By transcellular water EDELMAN designates a variety of extracellular fluid collections, which are not simple transudates and which have the common property of being formed by the transport activity of cells. These fluids are formed in the salivary gland, the pancreas, the liver and the biliary tree, the thyroid gland, the gonads, the skin, the mucous membranes of the respiratory and the gastrointestinal tract and the kidney, etc. This scheme emphasizes well the considerable magnitude of those extracellular fluids which are not a direct part of the plasma–interstitial lymph pool. The data on sodium distribution can be summarized in the following manner: plasma sodium 11.2%, interstitial lymph sodium 29.0%, dense connective tissue and cartilage sodium 11.7%, total bone sodium 43.1%, exchangeable bone sodium 13.8%, intracellular sodium 2.4% and transcellular sodium 2.6%. All this sodium is exchangeable, except the total bone sodium minus the exchangeable bone sodium, which makes 70.7% of the total body sodium exchangeable. In edema this fraction may increase by 20–100% and in Addison's disease it may decrease as much as 50%. Finally the data on potassium distribution: plasma potassium 0.4%, interstitial lymph potassium 1.0%, dense connective tissue and cartilage potassium 0.4%, bone potassium 7.6%, intracellular potassium 89.6% and transcellular potassium 1.0%. It is evident that the distribution is quite different from that of sodium, the bulk being this time intracellular. However, the latter is not homogeneous; its concentration varies according to the location and metabolic activity of the cells.

This brief discussion of the anatomical distribution of water, sodium and potassium, leads on to the question of their hormonal control, and for didactic reasons the sites of regulation and the regulating agents will be discussed together. THORN[2], many years ago, pointed out that desoxycorticosterone favours the intestinal reabsorption of sodium and promotes potassium loss. BERGER[3], however, has recently shown in the dog that this hormonal effect is localized exclusively in the mucosal surface of the colon, and that desoxycosterone does not alter the transfer of sodium or potassium across the wall of the small intestines. Normally these electrolyte exchanges across the mucosa of the colon play a very insignificant rôle, yet their importance becomes greatly increased when urine is diverted into the lumen of the colon by the surgical procedure of ureterosygmoidostomy. The prolonged contact of urine with the colonic mucosa favours reabsorption of chloride and sodium and promotes secretion of potassium, thus leading to the clinical and biological picture of hyperchloremic, hypokalemic acidosis.

As the storehouse, the bones play the leading rôle in sodium metabolism, whereas the muscle cells contain most of the body potassium. The sodium ions can penetrate as far as the hydration shell and the surface layer of the bone crystals. They can be concentrated in these structures and they take part in ionic exchange processes. For physico-chemical reasons, only sodium ions can accumulate in bone, whereas potassium and chloride ions do not participate at all in these active surface exchanges and their presence in the outer layer of the hydration shell is the consequence of simple passive diffusion. It is presumed that in normal bone a dynamic equilibrium exists between the sodium ions at the crystal surface and the ions of the hydration shell, and that in turn, the ions of the hydration shell are in equilibrium with the sodium ions of the surrounding fluids. This is an electro-chemical equilibrium and does not imply equality of concentration. Actually, the concentration of sodium at the crystal surface far exceeds its concentration in extracellular fluid. Knowledge of the specific mechanisms involved in these exchanges is lacking. However, in the adrenalectomized animal the bone sodium content diminishes, and after prolonged desoxycorticosterone therapy total bone sodium increases. The fact that bone can act as a donor or acceptor of sodium ions is of importance in many clinical conditions.

Besides bone, muscle sodium and potassium reflect adrenal activity. For instance, chemical analyses of muscle biopsies in patients with CONN's syndrome, have shown an increased sodium content and a decreased potassium content. SWINGLE[4], however, has recently demonstrated that the glucocorticoids must be held responsible for certain intra–extracellular water and electrolyte shifts. This author maintained adrenalectomized rats in a stabilized and apparently normal condition with prednisone alone. However, repeated blood analyses showed a persistently low sodium and high potassium level. For SWINGLE, these data illustrate that the glucocorticoids can guarantee the correct fluid shifts alone, but only in combination with the mineralocorticoids can they maintain the proper extracellular electrolyte concentrations.

As the third site of regulation, the point of exit, the kidney unquestionably plays the principal rôle, but it is worth mentioning the saliva and sweat where it has been repeatedly shown that desoxycorticosterone and more recently also aldosterone can influence the electrolyte composition. The Na/K ratio in saliva is an excellent index of mineralocorticoid hormone activity, and thus in several cases of CONN's syndrome a low Na/K ratio has been found. Concerning the sweat analyses, CONN[5], 10 years ago, noticed consistently a decreased sodium content in sweat in all situations accompanied by general dehydration. He conjectured that the hormones of the adrenal cortex were responsible for this adaptation. To-day, we know that in fact it is aldosterone which plays the principal rôle[6].

In clinical medicine, whenever one analyzes the action of a hormone on the renal handling of sodium and potassium, one thinks in terms of increased or decreased urinary output, forgetting all too often that this represents an end result of a very complex mechanism composed of filtration, reabsorption and secretion. If this triple effect is always kept in mind, certain contradictions can easily be explained. Thus cortisone for instance, will increase urinary sodium when it affects the filtration, whereas it will markedly diminish urinary sodium when its effect on tubular reabsorption of sodium predominates. In this connection it is also important to emphasize that these renal mechanisms are variable, both quantitatively and qualitatively. They further depend on dose, manner and duration of the administered hormone, as well as on salt and water intake, and last but not least on the physiological or pathological state of the organism. Some of these points are particularly well illustrated in one of THORN's[7] experiments: 1 mg of hydrocortisone given by constant intravenous drip increased urinary sodium in an Addisonian patient, whereas 10 mg in the same patient, administered in the same way, markedly diminished urinary sodium.

The overall effect of the great majority of hormones is sodium retention and potassium loss. The burning question, whether a naturally occurring hormone capable of increasing urinary sodium exists, is not yet settled. This point will be considered later in the discussion.

Among the sodium-retaining hormones, those of the adrenal cortex have been studied most extensively. Their classic division into mineralo- and glucocorticosteroids is only justified from the quantitative point of view, in other words when one is dealing with physiological doses. In the pharmacological dose range their activities greatly overlap. From animal work on adrenalectomized rats it seems that aldosterone, expressed on a weight basis, is the most potent naturally occurring sodium-retaining hormone, followed in decreasing order by desoxycorticosterone, 17-hydroxy-desoxycorticosterone (Compound "S"), corticosterone, dehydrocorticosterone, hydrocortisone and cortisone[8].

Besides this continuous spectrum of biological activity for the hormones of natural origin, a similar spectrum for the analogues of synthetic origin can be established. The most active sodium-retaining substance, even surpassing aldosterone, is 2-methyl-9α-fluorohydrocortisone, whereas the "top" glucocorticoid (always expressed on a weight basis) seems to be to-day 16-methyl-9α-fluoro-Δ¹-hydrocortisone. PECHET[9] has compared these synthetic steroids in balance studies on Addisonian and panhypopituitary subjects. He finds that the sodium-retaining properties of the naturally occurring steroids are substantially diminished by 1,2-dehydrogenation, 11β-hydroxylation and 17α-hydroxylation, whereas they are completely negated by 16α- or β-methylation and 16α-hydroxylation. This negation does not mean complete inactivation of the steroid, since 16α- or β-methylation as well as 16α-hydroxylation leaves intact the anti-anabolic and anti-inflammatory properties of 9α-fluoroprednisolone. These studies of PECHET explain why the 16-substituted steroids are such active glucocorticoids, devoid of all sodium-retaining properties.

The sodium-retaining property of aldosterone and DOCA will be considered now in more detail. (The electrolyte effect of cortisone and hydrocortisone is purposely disregarded in this discussion because their action is so highly dependent on various accessory factors.)

When aldosterone became available, it seemed of interest to compare its action with that of desoxycorticosterone or cortexone[10]. For this purpose, a 31 year-old Addisonian subject underwent two metabolic studies (Fig. 1). After an initial period of 10 days of cortexone (5 mg per day), the patient received in addition either 250 and 500 µg of aldosterone for two successive 3-day periods, or 5 and 10 mg of cortexone.

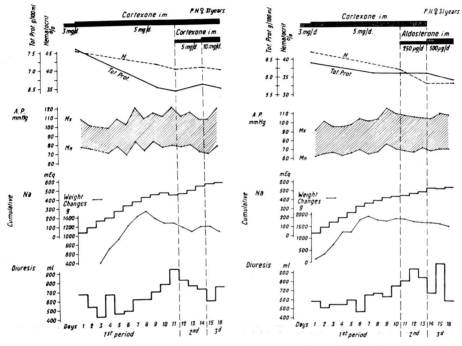

Fig. 1. Comparison between cortexone and aldosterone in an Addisonian subject.

Under these experimental conditions no really significant qualitative difference could be detected between the two hormones in terms of salt and water retention. There was, if anything, an increased diuresis with the supplementary dose of aldosterone. Another point deserves comment in this experiment. On approximately the seventh day, weight increase stopped, diuresis occurred, and less sodium was retained. This escape from sodium retention might be attributed to induced inactivity of the hormone. However, the persistence of a reduced sweat sodium content and a low Na/K ratio in saliva argues against such a possibility. This escape phenomenon with aldosterone or desoxycorticosterone is seen in the Addisonian patient[10,11] as well as in the normal subject[12,13]. It is therefore most unlikely that it is based on a hormonal effect, that is to say on a sodium-diuretic hormone. It is probably the result of other regulatory mechanisms, which override the hormonal effect on the renal tubule. This escape phenomenon has not only a theoretical importance. On the contrary it may be considered as the underlying mechanism responsible for the relative refractoriness of the renal tubules to aldosterone in the CONN syndrome. In fact we find consistently in all cases of pure primary hyperaldosteronism (*i.e.* those not complicated by renal or cardiac disease) a relatively high urinary sodium output in the presence of an elevated aldosterone production, the latter being more or less independent of hemodynamic changes. This is demonstrated in Fig. 2. A 50 year-old hypertensive patient with the classical signs of primary hyperaldosteronism, hypokalaemic, hypochloraemic alkalosis, normal 17-ketosteroids and 17-hydroxy-corticosteroids, normal kidney functions and high urinary potassium excretion, twice received a salt load. Each time he was able to increase his urinary sodium output in spite of an initially high level of aldosterone and, what is more important, a level which did not decrease with increasing sodium intake. This behaviour is almost pathognomic of primary hyperaldosteronism and demonstrates well the renal tubular refractoriness. There is no longer a correlation between urinary aldosterone and sodium output.

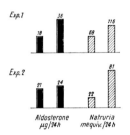

Fig. 2. B. J. ♂ 50 year. Arterial hypertension, hypokalaemia; metabolic alkalosis, isostenuria; satisfactory renal functions; renal biopsy no particularities. 17-ketosteroids 5.8 mg/24 h; 17-hydroxysteroids 4.6 mg/24 h; sodium (urinary) 50–100 mequiv.; potassium (urinary) 30–50 mequiv.; aldosterone 18 μg/24 h, 21 μg/24 h. Impression: Conn syndrome, primary hyperaldosteronism. Diagnostic test: A. Salt load; B. Determination of endogenous secretion of aldosterone, 1160 μg/24 h, sodium (urinary) 120 mequiv. Surgical exploration: left side, small suprarenal (2 g); right side, suprarenal tumour.

The increased production of aldosterone in this case is proved by a high secretion of aldosterone determined by injecting tritiated, randomly labeled aldosterone. After the second surgical intervention, where a tumour was found, the aldosterone production came down to a normal value.

The analysis of potassium excretion in cases of primary hyperaldosteronism as well as after desoxycorticosterone or aldosterone administration, shows, despite considerable variation from case to case, a general trend to a negative balance. This increased potassium elimination is to some extent conditioned by the simultaneous augmentation of renal tubular sodium reabsorption. Thus a salt load during mineralocorticoid excess will regularly increase renal potassium wasting, whereas salt restriction is followed by renal saving of potassium; this fact is particularly well illustrated by the beneficial effect of salt restriction on the hypokalaemia of primary hyperaldosteronism.

Before discussing further the hormonal aspects of natriuresis, the sodium-retaining properties of the sex hormones must be mentioned. Both oestrogens and testosterone induce sodium and water retention. The oestrogen effect on sodium is particularly well illustrated in the premenstrual period, at the time of peak oestrogen excretion in the urine. Another characteristic of the sex hormones, unlike the adrenal cortical hormones, is that they produce sodium retention without potassium loss. It is conceivable that an eventual potassium loss is masked by the anabolic properties of these two sex hormones. The new anabolic synthetic testosterone analogues have similar properties. PRUNTY[14] and others have found that sodium and water retention quite often contribute largely to the initial weight gain.

The next point to be discussed is the natriuresis induced by a hormone or a combination of hormones. Three clinical situations, generally accompanied by normal sodium excretion or definite sodium loss, are considered: pregnancy, hepatitis and the salt-losing form of congenital adrenal hyperplasia.

The conjecture that a sodium-excreting factor may play a rôle in pregnancy is based on the fact that one constantly finds sodium in the urines despite high urinary aldosterone values. Pregnancy is characterized from the hormonal point of view firstly by true hyperproduction of oestrogens and progesterone; secondly by increased plasma glucocorticoid levels, which, however, do not reflect increased secretion of cortisol, as might be expected, but an increased plasma protein-binding of cortisol conditioned by

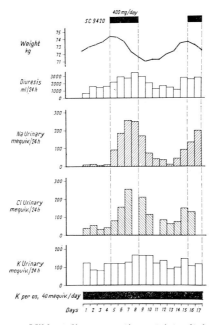

Fig. 3. A. B. ♂ 53 years. Mild cardiac congestion: strict salt-free diet + 4 g NaCl.

high oestrogen levels; and thirdly by high urinary aldosterone excretion. TAIT et al.[15] have investigated the aldosterone metabolism in pregnancy. They studied 6 subjects who, as is the rule, showed markedly increased aldosterone levels in the urine. These high urinary values correspond to the pH-1 fraction of aldosterone which is most likely biologically inactive. This increase in the pH-1 fraction is the result of an altered degradation and detoxication of aldosterone, which is reflected also in the correspondingly decreased glucuronide fraction. Only three women showed a definitely increased secretion of aldosterone, which was also reflected in the high biologically active urinary pH-6 fraction. This pH-6 fraction was normal in the 3 patients with normal secretion rates. Therefore the normal urinary sodium excretion is by no means astonishing in these subjects. However, how can one explain the normal sodium output in those patients with high aldosterone secretion rates? Different factors certainly play a rôle. Among them one seems particularly attractive, namely progesterone, which is known for its sodium diuretic property. In this connection it is of interest that precisely those subjects with a high aldosterone secretion rate also showed a high

70 A.-F. MULLER

urinary excretion of pregnanediol, the main metabolite of progesterone. This sodium diuretic property of progesterone has been studied by LANDAU[16], who thinks that progesterone competes in the kidney tubules with the mineralocorticoids. According to this author, progesterone by itself has no sodium diuretic effect, but it negates completely the sodium retention of aldosterone in an Addisonian patient. This natriuretic property of progesterone has also been used successfully in patients with oedema[14]. This saluretic effect of progesterone certainly deserves further study.

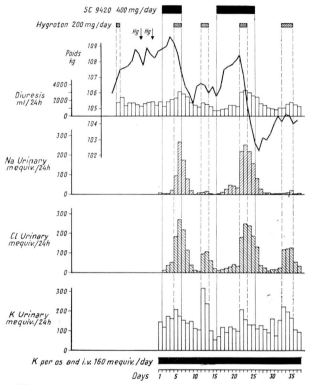

Fig. 4. A. B. ♂ 52 years: Laënnec cirrhosis, salt-free diet.

In conclusion, we can say that in pregnancy the consistently high urinary levels of aldosterone are the result of an increased elimination of the biologically inactive pH-I fraction, the latter corresponding chemically to the 3-oxoconjugate. In addition, certain women show an increased aldosterone production which could be partially the result of an antagonism in the renal tubule to a sodium-diuretic hormone such as progesterone.

It is possible that similar mechanisms are at work in hepatitis, but at the moment the proof is lacking.

A similar antagonism has recently been demonstrated for a series of new synthetic steroids, the spirolactones. According to LIDDLE[17], their sodium excreting property depends on the amount of aldosterone or desoxycorticosterone present in the renal tubule. Similar to progesterone, alone they have no saluretic effect. Fig. 3 shows the clinical application of one of these spirolactones (9420) in a patient with mild congestive failure. Its diuretic property is immediately evident. The spirolactones were also tried in a patient refractory to the usual diuretics (mercurials, sulphon-amides) (Fig. 4). Neither the diuretics nor the spirolactones alone produced a saluretic effect in this 53 year-old patient with severe decompensated cirrhosis and ascites, though both somewhat increased urinary sodium. Only the combination of the two drugs brought about a massive sodium diuresis accompanied by a substantial weight loss. Unfortunately, as was to be expected, this combined therapy sometimes fails.

The third condition where the existence of a salt-excreting factor or an aldoste-rone antagonist might be inferred is the sodium-losing form of congenital adrenal hyperplasia. In view of the difficulties in finding such a sodium-excreting factor, several other theories have been advocated in order to explain the sodium loss. Some workers in the field attribute the sodium wasting to the absence of aldosterone, where-as others mention a deficit in cortisol, the latter being necessary, according to them, for aldosterone to exert its activity in the kidney tubule. Finally some conjecture that among the many abnormal steroids produced by these hyperplastic glands, there might be one with aldosterone-antagonising properties, similar to progesterone and the spirolactones. The problem is far from being solved.

In conclusion one can say that the unquestionable and final proof of the existence of a sodium-excreting factor or hormone in man is still lacking. Yet there definitely exist aldosterone antagonists, like progesterone and the synthetic spirolactones. Whether sodium retention is accomplished by hormones acting upon the renal tubules, by nervous impulses or by intrarenal adjustments of pressure and flow, the nature and sites of action of the different stimuli to sodium retention or excretion constitute one of the most fascinating problems of electrolyte metabolism[18]. It is obvious from the very existence of oedema that the kidneys are not sensitive to the total amount of extracellular fluid, but as PETERS suggested in 1935, they behave in many situations as though they were peculiarly dependent upon some function of the circulating blood volume. It is equally apparent from purely clinical considerations that the total volume of blood is not so important to the kidneys as the way in which it is distributed inside the vascular system.

A normal standing subject is in many ways the paradigm of those clinical states such as congestive heart failure, accompanied by sodium retention. When a man stands erect, venous and capillary pressure in the legs rise, transudation from the blood stream increases, plasma volume falls, blood pools in the large veins and there is compensatory vasoconstriction of arterioles and venules. There is a fall in pressure in the great veins of the thorax, cardiac output usually declines and arterial pulse pressure diminishes, despite the fact that mean arterial blood pressure may not decrease. Renal retention of sodium can be demonstrated within the first 20 minutes after the erect posture is assumed. This occurs even when contraction of the total blood volume (though not its redistribution) is prevented by simultaneously infusing albumin. The renal mechanisms operating in these postural changes are not yet completely understood. It seems likely that while acute alterations in renal water and electrolyte excretion might be attributable to changes in renal hæmodynamics, the occurrence of more prolonged changes might be indicative of hormonally controlled tubular factors. This renal tubular participation is further emphasized by the fact that at least part of the sodium retention caused by standing is attributable to an altered tubular $Na^+ \rightleftharpoons H^+$ exchange. We produced evidence in prolonged experiments that in fact changes in the aldosterone output occurred during postural alterations[19]. GOWENLOCK[20] has confirmed our results. He finds an increase in aldosterone on standing within at most 3 hours. Using the double isotope-derivative method of PETERSON[21], we have been able to demonstrate an even shorter time interval. Fig. 5 shows such an experiment in a normal subject. Whereas changes in sodium excretion take place in the first 30 min, there is a delay of at least 30 min in the urinary aldosterone changes. This interval corresponds well with the one found in the dog by direct assay of aldosterone in the adrenal vein blood. HOLZBAUER AND VOGT[22] as well as BARTTER[23] found

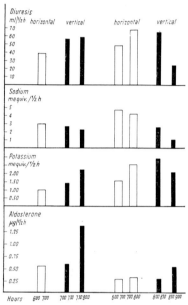

Fig. 5. Influence of position on aldosterone in the normal subject.

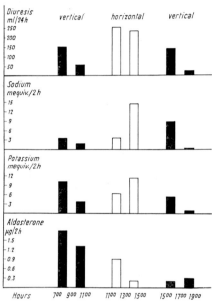

Fig. 6. Influence of position on aldosterone in a hypophyseal dwarf.

intervals of 30 to 60 min. This experiment also illustrates rather well the distinction initially made, *i.e.* between acute and prolonged mechanisms. This dissociation is even better brought out in the next experiment (Fig. 6). This 21 year-old hypophyseal dwarf shows the characteristic electrolyte changes produced by postural alterations, *i.e.* sodium retention on standing and diuresis on lying, yet the aldosterone output does not always vary accordingly, since it does not increase when the subject resumes the erect position. In the recumbent position, however, aldosterone decreases.

What is the defect in the hypophyseal dwarf that prevents him from increasing urinary aldosterone on standing? As is shown in Fig. 7, this very same patient also has difficulty in raising his aldosterone output following salt restriction (15 $\mu$g instead of approx. 40 $\mu$g), though he is perfectly able to adjust his sodium output to his intake after a few days. A superimposable situation can also be encountered in some cases of postural hypotension, as illustrated in the middle diagram. BARTTER[24] has made similar observations. In this connection it might be pertinent to recall that postural hypotension is a frequent symptom in pituitary insufficiency. In both postural hypotension and pituitary insufficiency there is an inability to increase, but not necessarily to decrease, aldosterone. From the circulatory point of view, there exists in both conditions a tendency to inadequate filling of the systemic arterial tree, which is aggravated by the decreased total blood volume after salt restriction. These facts are thus consistent with the hypothesis that renal sodium retention, but not excretion, is conditioned by the degree of filling of some portion of the arterial tree. In this view renal retention of salt would fall into the same category as a variety of vascular reactions (carotid sinus and aortic reflexes) assigned to maintain the integrity of the circulation.

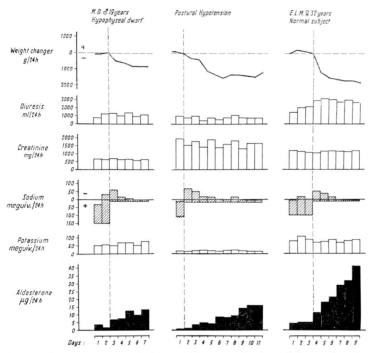

Fig. 7. Influence of salt restriction on aldosterone in three different situations.

This way of reasoning is strengthened by the recent experiments of BARTTER[25] who showed that in the dog the increase of aldosterone is dependent on the fall in arterial pulse pressure in the common carotid artery. According to BARTTER, only the mechanism responsible for the increase of aldosterone is located in the arterial system, whereas the decrease of aldosterone is brought about by an increase in the venous return to the right heart. This might explain why the patient with pituitary insufficiency was perfectly able to lower his aldosterone output while lying down. The concept of a volume receptor is appealing, though undoubtedly there is the danger of oversimplifying the problem. It is difficult "to avoid casting one's lot with that of a neat idea"[26]. "Yet the question of volume regulation is a real one, it cannot be begged by mere descriptions of the filtration and reabsorption of sodium and water by the kidneys"[18].

The final discussion concerns the metabolic events underlying sodium and potassium handling in the kidney. Fig. 8, taken from a paper by MOREL[27], shows the concept of renal tubular handling of these ions. Potassium is entirely reabsorbed in the proximal tubule, whereas sodium is reabsorbed all along the nephron. In the proximal

74     A.-F. MULLER

tubule sodium is retained mainly with an equivalent of chloride and to some extent
by exchanging with H⁺ ions. This sodium reabsorption seems not to be under the
control of aldosterone, although in a recent note NICHOLSON[28] doubts this universally
accepted assumption. In the ascending limb of the loop of Henle and the very first
portion of the distal tubule, sodium is retained by exchanging with H⁺. Most workers
agree that this process is controlled by aldosterone. This segment of the nephron is
also particularly permeable to sodium but not to potassium. (By permeable is meant:
from the interstitial space into the urine). In the remaining part of the distal tubule
this aldosterone-controlled Na⁺⇌H⁺ exchange seems to continue, but in addition
sodium is retained by exchanging with potassium. This mechanism appears to be also
under the control of aldosterone, according to work done by MOREL[27], as well as by
MALVIN et al.[29], using the stop-flow method. NICHOLSON[28], by his technique of damag-

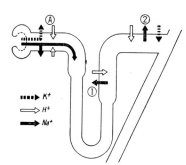

**⋯▶** K⁺  
**⇒** H⁺  
**➡** Na⁺

Fig. 8. Mechanisms of action of mineralocorticoids on
urinary tubule. A: reabsorption (independent of aldosterone) of some of the sodium and all of the potassium filtered
by the glomerulus. 1: Na⁺ ⇌ H⁺ exchange controlled by
aldosterone; 2: Na⁺ ⇌ K⁺ exchange (possibly also Na⁺⇌H⁺)
controlled by aldosterone.

ing selectively portions of the tubular epithelium, confirms these findings. It is interesting to mention that this latter part of the distal tubule is permeable almost exclusively to potassium but not to sodium.

Recently CRAWFORD AND KENNEDY[30], working in Prof. McCANCE's department,
have come to the same conclusion by entirely different experiments.

Concerning the energy requirements, the substrates and the enzymes involved
in this active sodium transport, little is known. LEAF[31] has obtained some data showing that one molecule of oxygen transports 16 mequiv. of sodium and that sodium
transport is activated to the same extent by anaerobic as well as aerobic glycolysis.
But further work is needed to clarify these problems as well as to enrich our knowledge
of the basic concepts, which are essential for the final understanding of the hormonal
control of electrolyte transport.

SUMMARY

The author describes, as far as present information permits, the sites of regulation,
the regulating agents and the underlying metabolic events concerned in the hormonal
control of water and electrolytes. The principal sites of regulation are the following:
the point of entry (generally the intestine), the place of storage (the tissues, particularly the bone), and the site of exit (principally the kidney). Emphasis is laid on the
behaviour of sodium and potassium. The principal agents discussed are the hormones
of the adrenal cortex; the possible effect of testosterone, oestrogen and particularly
progesterone on sodium and potassium excretion is also mentioned. The influence of
these hormones is analyzed in the normal subject as well as under pathological condi-

tions. The diurnal variation of salt and water excretion and its relation to posture is discussed. Special attention is given to the urinary changes of aldosterone. These changes are interpreted as the consequence of volume shifts in the intravascular compartment. Reference is made to the "volume control" of aldosterone secretion. The site and the mode of action of these hormonal agents in the kidney tubules is very briefly discussed.

## REFERENCES

1 J. S. EDELMAN AND J. LEIBMAN, *Am. J. Med.*, 27 (1959) 256.
2 G. W. THORN, *New Engl. J. Med.*, 248 (1953) 232.
3 E. Y. BERGER, *J. Clin. Invest.*, 38 (1959) Abstract.
4 W. W. SWINGLE, *Am. J. Physiol.*, 196 (1959) 283.
5 J. W. CONN, *A.M.A. Arch. Intern. Med.*, 83 (1949) 416.
6 A. FALBRIARD, A. F. MULLER, R. NEHER AND R. S. MACH, *Schweiz. med. Wochschr.*, 85 (1955) 1218.
7 G. W. THORN, J. C. LAIDLAW AND A. GOLDFIEN, *Ciba Foundation Colloq. Endocrinol.*, 8 (1955) 343.
8 R. NEHER, *Clin. Chem.*, 3 (1957) 344.
9 M. M. PECHET AND E. L. CARROLL, *J. Clin. Invest.*, 38 (1959) Abstract.
10 A. F. MULLER, E. ENGEL, A. FALBRIARD AND R. S. MACH, *Metabolism*, 5 (1956) 601.
11 J. T. AUGUST AND D. H. NELSON, *J. Clin. Invest.*, 38 (1959) 1964.
12 A. S. RELMAN AND W. B. SCHWARTZ, *Yale J. Biol. and Med.*, 24 (1952) 540.
13 J. T. AUGUST, D. H. NELSON AND G. W. THORN, *J. Clin. Invest.*, 37 (1958) 1549.
14 F. T. G. PRUNTY AND R. R. McSWINEY, *Scand. J. Clin. Lab. Invest.*, Suppl. 31, 10 (1957) 62.
15 K. M. JONES, R. LLOYD JONES, A. M. RIONDEL, J. F. TAIT, S. A. S. TAIT, R. D. BULBROOK AND F. C. GREENWOOD, *Acta Endocrinol.*, 30 (1959) 321.
16 R. L. LANDAU AND K. LUGIBIHL, *J. Clin. Endocrinol. and Metabolism*, 18 (1958) 1237.
17 G. W. LIDDLE, *Science*, 126 (1957) 1016.
18 F. H. EPSTEIN, *Yale J. Biol. and Med.*, 29 (1956) 282.
19 A. F. MULLER, E. L. MANNING AND A. M. RIONDEL, *International Symposium on Aldosterone*, Churchill, London, 1958, p. 111.
20 A. H. GOWENLOCK, J. N. MILLS AND S. THOMAS, *J. Physiol.*, 146 (1959) 133.
21 B. KLIMAN AND R. E. PETERSON, *Federation Proc.*, 17 (1958) 255.
22 M. HOLZBAUER AND M. VOGT, *J. Physiol.*, 143 (1958) 86 P.
23 I. H. MILLS, A. CASPER AND F. C. BARTTER, *Science*, 128 (1958) 1140.
24 Editorial, *Lancet*, 276 (1959) 925.
25 D. S. GAUN, I. H. MILLS AND F. C. BARTTER, *Endocrine Soc. Abstract*, 1959.
26 A. V. WOLF, *Trans. South-East Sect. Am. Urol. Assoc.*, 1952, p. 162.
27 F. MOREL, *International Symposium on Aldosterone*, Churchill, London, 1958, p. 180.
28 T. F. NICHOLSON, *Federation Proc.*, 18 (1959) 114.
29 A. J. VANDER, W. S. WILDE AND R. L. MALVIN, *Federation Proc.*, 18 (1959) 162.
30 G. C. KENNEDY AND J. D. CRAWFORD, *Nature*, 184 (1959) 1492.
31 A. LEAF, *J. Biol. Chem.*, 234 (1959) 1625.

## DISCUSSION

QUERIDO: I. If I recall correctly you studied the effect of NaCl load in a patient with an aldosterone-producing tumour and did not find a decrease of aldosterone excretion. Was I right in thinking your interpretation to be that the tubule cells had become unresponsive? Is is not, however, more likely that the tumour is functioning independently and the aldosterone output therefore is not controlled by NaCl intake?

II. You showed a slide on which is indicated the large Na$^+$ reservoir in the bones. Do clinical conditions exist where movement of sodium from or to the bones have to be postulated, because of otherwise inexplicable results in the sodium balance?

MULLER: I took the patient with primary aldosteronism to illustrate the escape phenomenon. When you give desoxycorticosterone or aldosterone to a normal person with a relatively normal sodium intake, you will observe during 7–10 days a weight increase and sodium retention. Then, in spite of continued administration of the hormone, sodium is lost in the urine and the weight remains stable or decreases. If you analyze the saliva or sweat, you still see the characteristic pattern of mineralocorticoid excess. So one has to conclude that there is some regulatory mechanism in the kidney which overrides the hormonal effect. I agree with you that in a patient with primary hyperaldosteronism the secretion of the tumour is most probably to a great extent autonomous. As to your second question, I was referring to the work of LUFT who gave desoxycorticosterone over a long time to normal persons, without a weight increase, and still observed a positive sodium balance. When he took these patients off desoxycorticosterone, the loss of sodium was greater than the drop in weight. LUFT presumed that sodium was mobilized from the bones.

PELSER: The conclusions from the studies on which Dr. MULLER gave his lecture are largely based on the assumption that the aldosterone excretion reflects quantitatively the level of aldosterone activity in the body, which is not necessarily true. Is there any evidence available in support of the validity of this assumption?

MULLER: It is correct that excretion of a hormone does not always reflect its secretion. However, in the normal subject, in some cases of congestive heart failure and in nephrosis, this extrapolation is permitted, whereas such a correlation does not necessarily exist in patients with cirrhosis or in pregnant women. The fraction which we determine in the urine corresponds to the biologically inactive pH 1 fraction. Unfortunately, the amounts of biologically active aldosterone contained in the pH 6 fraction are very small and very often it is impossible to determine them. Since we determine a conjugated derivative of aldosterone, it will always be risky to consider it as a true representative of the actual secretion rate in all those cases where the degradation and detoxication of aldosterone is altered.

PELSER: Observations on the prolonged treatment of Addisonian patients with liquorice or glycyrrhetinic acid only (PELSER AND GROEN) showed consistently that the amount of glycyrrhetinic acid required to maintain these patients in electrolyte equilibrium gradually decreased during continued treatment. A remarkable sequence in signs of overdosage was observed in these patients who developed first oedema and later hypertension (mainly systolic). These phenomena were reversible when the dosage of glycyrrhetinic acid was decreased. An explanation of these observations is as yet not available. In view of experiments from the laboratory of Prof. MARRIAN, in which an inhibitory activity of glycyrrhetinic acid on the enzymic breakdown of progesterone in liver homogenates was shown, the suggestion is offered that a similar inhibition of the breakdown of aldosterone in the body could account for the sodium-retaining and potassium-expelling activity of glycyrrhetinic acid in the human organism.

BORST: In my opinion the escape phenomenon is explained by investigations of the Amsterdam group which have been published by MOLHUYZEN (*Lancet*). We studied patients who, in the first period on a high dosage of liquorice, retained sodium and chloride but after two weeks, in spite of continued therapy, lost sodium and chloride. The same phenomenon was observed with ACTH and with DOCA, and others showed that aldosterone has the same effect. The explanation is that there are two mechanisms by which sodium is excreted by the kidney. The first one is regulated by the adrenal, but the second acts independently of the adrenal. When the first fails, the circulatory factor is stimulated. We determined the venous pressure and blood volume in the patient. When both increase and the patient has an adequate heart-function, Na and chloride are lost.

MULLER: I will not deny that proximal tubular sodium retention is probably independent of the mineralocortical hormones. The escape phenomenon certainly reflects a renal mechanism but this is most likely based on glomerular and/or proximal tubular changes, which differ from the distal tubular, $Na^+ \rightarrow H^+$ and $Na^+ \rightarrow K^+$ exchange, which have already been mentioned. In certain situations, *e.g.* standing erect, there exists besides the hormonally controlled distal tubular effect a renal mechanism of sodium retention, which acts very rapidly and which cannot be localized, since one cannot measure minor changes in glomerular filtration rate which certainly could have a very great influence on sodium excretion.

BORST: Besides the adrenal cortical mechanism and the influence of the filtration rate, in our opinion, there is a third mechanism, which is independent of the glomerular filtration. It is a tubular mechanism dependent on changes in the venous-arterial system. A patient with tachycardia, without changes of glomerular filtration, can excrete enormous amounts of sodium without, I am sure, changes in adrenal activity. SELCOURT has found in dogs that when you change the blood pressure in one renal artery, the kidney reacts with an enormous Na diuresis, but only a small increase of blood pressure. These results are comparable and identical with our findings in patients with tachycardia. In fever, on the contrary, we can have an increased glomerular filtration with a complete suppression of sodium output.

# CHARACTERISTIC RENAL EXCRETION PATTERNS IN RESPONSE TO PHYSIOLOGICAL, PATHOLOGICAL AND PHARMACOLOGICAL STIMULI*

L. A. de VRIES, S. P. ten HOLT,

J. J. van DAATSELAAR, A. MULDER and J. G. G. BORST

*Department of Internal Medicine of the University of Amsterdam (Binnengasthuis), Amsterdam (The Netherlands)*

## CONTENTS

## I. INTRODUCTION

The fluids of the body are in a state of dynamic equilibrium. In health the osmotic pressure shows only insignificant fluctuations. Any deviation from the mean is rapidly abolished by a chain of events leading to an appropriate increase or decrease in renal water excretion.

The volume of the body fluids exhibits larger variations; its regulation is a part of circulatory homoeostasis[1-4]. Any factor influencing the circulation, *e.g.* changes in muscular activity or in posture, sets in motion a compensatory chain reaction which leads to an alteration in the renal output of both water and sodium chloride. As a consequence, the volume of the body fluids is shifted in a direction which favours an optimal circulation. The evidence for this concept has been presented in previous papers and will not be discussed in full in the present article.

In view of the key position of the kidneys in several homoeostatic mechanisms, we can attribute changes in the urinary output to a specific cause only if the metabolic and environmental conditions are kept rigidly constant. Fluctuations in the circulation can be minimized by keeping the patients quietly in bed and by preventing significant exogenous changes in the volume of the body fluids: water and electrolytes must be supplied in constant amounts at relatively short and constant intervals;

* This paper has appeared already in *Clin. Chim. Acta*, 5 (1960) 915–937.

large and irregular extrarenal losses must be avoided. In this manner fluctuations in osmolarity of the body fluids are also eliminated. It is, however, virtually impossible to keep mental activity constant.

Associated with the alternation of daily activity and nocturnal sleep, the renal output shows a diurnal rhythm. This rhythm has a certain autonomy. When the subject begins to sleep during the day and is active at night, it requires several days for the excretory rhythm to adjust itself accordingly[5,6]. The diurnal excretory rhythm operates independently of osmo-regulation and "volume" regulation; it not only involves water and sodium chloride, but also potassium and several other urine constituents. Hence, the diurnal excretory rhythm must be regarded as a third type of "natural" diuresis[7].

The diurnal rhythm may counteract osmo-regulation and especially "volume" regulation. In normal subjects water and especially saline administered at the beginning of the night are for a large part retained until the next morning[8,9]. Also the diuretic effect of recumbency and muscular inactivity is mitigated during the night. It is obvious that this is essential for an undisturbed sleep.

Since the diurnal rhythm cannot be eliminated, studying the effect of certain stimuli on the kidney makes it necessary to compare the excretion pattern found on the days the particular agent is administered with the patterns observed during a control period. Our observations were made on subjects who were kept in bed in wards where the light was reduced and no conversation allowed from 8 p.m. till 5 a.m. Every three hours identical amounts of standardized food, *e.g.* biscuits, milk, butter, cheese, were supplied in quantities sufficient to cover caloric requirements and, if indicated, supplemented with water and extra electrolytes. The urine was collected every three hours and, when necessary, at even shorter intervals. All urine specimens were exactly measured and examined for sodium, potassium and creatinine; in special cases other urine constituents were determined. DE VRIES AND VAN DAATSELAAR's[10] method for the selective estimation of creatinine was employed for calculating the endogenous creatinine clearances. Urine osmolarity was calculated from the values for urea, creatinine, $NH_4^+$, $K^+$ and $Na^+$ on the assumption that the partial osmotic pressure exerted by the electrolytes was twice the sum of the osmotic pressures of the three cations. On control days the creatinine output must be almost constant. If patients cannot empty their bladder completely, significant irregularities in this output appear. Patients showing these irregularities were excluded from the experiments. A catheter was never used.

When the excretion pattern and the changes in the composition of the blood, arterial pressure, central venous pressure, pulse rate and body weight are recorded simultaneously, a remarkably comprehensive and detailed insight into the kinetics of body fluids and electrolytes in health and disease can be obtained. The three-hourly urinary excretion pattern is in itself frequently so characteristic that it provides conclusive information about the cause and the degree of fluid and electrolyte imbalance. Some pathological conditions are accompanied by an almost pathognomonic excretion pattern. In other disorders the renal excretory response to the administration of drugs or water and electrolytes may be used as a diagnostic test.

When a selection of the observations on renal excretion patterns made during the past 10 years is considered, two categories can be distinguished, namely, those concerning the types of physiological diureses and their interactions, and those in which non-physiological external forces, *e.g.* hormones administered in pharmacological doses, diuretics etc., act directly on the kidney. In the first instance the response of the kidney is part of a homoeostatic mechanism. In the second the kidney is induced to react in a way that usually disturbs homoeostasis. This disturbance will evoke the compensatory mechanisms and lead to secondary renal responses which oppose the primary effect of the external factor. If the latter continues to exert its influence, an equilibrium will be reached, but at a different level from the original one (see Figs. 24 and 30).

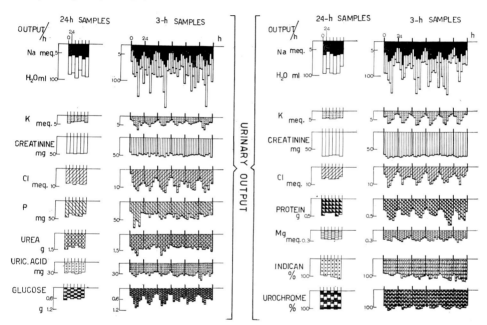

Fig. 1. 43-year old male with renal glucosuria, convalescent after gastrectomy for grossly bleeding peptic ulcer. Note pronounced diurnal rhythm for sodium, chloride, potassium and glucose.

Fig. 2. 34-year old male with massive albuminuria, renal functions normal. Distinct rhythm in the excretion of electrolytes and protein.

## II. THE THREE PRINCIPAL TYPES OF PHYSIOLOGICAL DIURESIS

### A. The diurnal renal excretory rhythm

In most subjects under the described standardized conditions, a rather constant excretion of a large number of substances is found when 24-h urine samples are examined. When the three-hourly specimens are analyzed, the rhythmic excretion pattern first described by SIMPSON [11] becomes evident. The rhythmic fluctuations are very pronounced for water, sodium, potassium and chloride and also for glucose and protein. Other compounds show much smaller variations while the creatinine excretion is almost constant. It must be emphasized that all individuals do not exhibit identical excretory patterns. When basal conditions are maintained, the individual's pattern is repeated daily and does not show considerable variations (Figs. 1 and 2).

The figures demonstrate that the results of short-term experiments cannot be interpreted without knowledge of the subject's individual diurnal rhythm. The excretion pattern of a patient with Addison's disease during a two-day experiment is shown in Fig. 3. The patient remained in bed for the first day and was up and about for 6 h on the second day. No difference in renal excretion could be demonstrated by a study of the 24-h urine samples. However, examination of 3 h and, at crucial points in the experiments even 1½-h specimens, revealed that a marked retention of water, sodium, chloride, phosphate and urea and, to a lesser degree, of potassium had taken place during the period the patient was mobilized. This orthostatic renal retention of water and sodium chloride was completely compensated by the sharp rebound fol-

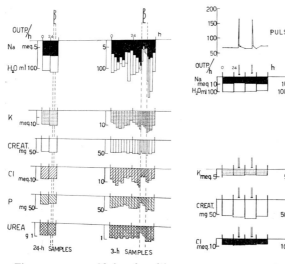

Fig. 3. 23-year old female with Addison's disease, maintained on 8 × 75 mg glycyrrhetinic acid (liquorice derivative) and 3 mg cortisone daily. Ambulation is accompanied, by a depression in the output of all urine constit-

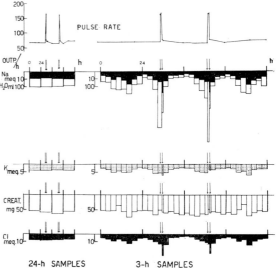

Fig. 4. 55-year old male with attacks of paroxysmal tachycardia; otherwise normal heart. Attacks induce brisk water and sodium diuresis followed by a (compensatory) retention; consequently there is no effect on the 24-h output.

uents (with the exception of creatinine), especially water and sodium. Due to the prompt rebound following recumbency there is no decrease in 24-h output.

lowing the patient's return to bed. The creatinine excretion was virtually unaffected by the change in posture. Fig. 4 shows the excretion pattern of a patient suffering from attacks of paroxysmal tachycardia. No effect of these attacks could be discerned in the 24 h-samples, but, examination of as many urine samples as the patient was able to void, revealed an extremely high and transient water, sodium and chloride diuresis.

The excretion patterns of sodium and chloride and to a greater degree that of water often show slight irregularities. A peak in the water excretion, accompanied by a less marked rise in sodium and chloride output in the first hours of sleep is a common finding (see Figs. 1 and 2). This pattern is found especially in patients recovering from a serious illness or who have hypoalbuminaemia. In a subsequent paragraph evidence will be presented that in these cases circulatory homoeostasis overrules the influence of the diurnal rhythm on the excretion pattern.

The mechanism by which the diurnal rhythm is regulated is still a matter of speculation. The working hypothesis that reciprocal variations in $K^+$ and $H^+$ excretion were conditioned by a rhythmic shift in the reaction of the body fluids produced by a diurnal rhythm of respiratory activity has been abandoned; the available evidence indicates that the $K^+$ changes are probably primary[12]. The qualitatively similar variations in the excretion of so many urine constituents and especially the very close correlations between sodium and potassium output (see Figs. 5 and 6)

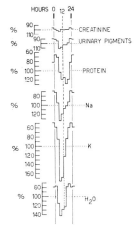

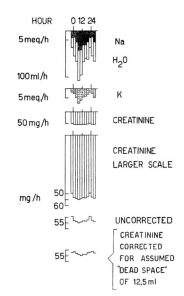

Fig. 5. Massive albuminuria. Same case as shown in Fig. 2. Averages of the excretion curves for 12 days are shown. Excretion rate at different times of the day expressed in percentage of daily mean. Almost complete parallelism in excretion curves of potassium and sodium; peak excretion is before noon. Only protein output is highest in the afternoon. Creatinine excretion shows only insignificant fluctuations.

Fig. 6. 35-year old female with rheumatoid arthritis. Excretion pattern shows average of 17 days. Lowest water output is accompanied by a 10% decline in creatinine output, possibly due in part to the dead space. After correction for dead space, creatinine output still shows a slight depression between 6 p.m. and 3 a.m.

suggest that a single factor is largely responsible for the diurnal variations in the excretion of many different substances. The fact that sodium excretion in some patients reaches its maximum in the afternoon while potassium excretion is always highest before noon, does not necessarily contradict this concept. The nightly retention of water and electrolytes in conjunction with a constant intake results in an increased volume of the body fluids in the early morning. This induces a compensatory water and sodium diuresis. Since the sodium diuresis in response to circulatory factors sometimes reaches its maximum after several hours (see p. 87), the highest sodium output during the day may occur in the afternoon (see Figs. 12 and 13).

Evidence for diurnal variations in hormone production as the cause of the diurnal excretory rhythm is lacking. Hormones inducing large parallel changes in renal sodium and potassium excretion have not been discovered as yet. It is highly improb-

able that the adrenals would be the source of this hypothetical hormone. Adrenalectomized patients may still exhibit pronounced diurnal variations in sodium and potassium output even after cessation of treatment (Fig. 26).

The possibility that the physiological fall in blood pressure during sleep might
induce the diurnal excretory rhythm, must also be considered. A slight decline in
the glomerular filtration rate resulting from the lowered blood pressure could account
for the slight depression of creatinine output and the considerable reduction in the
output of water, sodium, chloride, magnesium, glucose and protein during the night.
An explanation of the fact that the highest loss of protein is sometimes found in the
afternoon (see Fig. 5) requires an additional hypothesis.

The large fluctuations in potassium output, which often exceed those of sodium
(see Fig. 5), are definitely inconsistent with the concept that the diurnal rhythm is
mainly regulated by variations in glomerular filtration rate. A marked fall in blood
pressure, which can be induced in patients with orthostatic hypotension, affects
sodium much more than potassium output[13]. An appreciable fall in creatinine clearance induced by drugs is also accompanied by a considerable reduction in sodium
output while the potassium excretion is only slightly depressed (Fig. 30). In many
patients the nightly reduction in creatinine excretion does not exceed 10% of the
daily average (see Fig. 5), and can be largely explained by the effect of the dead
space[14] (see Fig. 6). If we assume that endogenous creatinine production is constant,
a real depression in creatinine output represents, however, a somewhat larger fall in
creatinine clearance*. In two patients on 5 consecutive days clearance determinations
were made between 9 p.m. and 3 a.m., and between 9 a.m. and 3 p.m. These periods
were so chosen that the effect of the dead space was not significant. In one patient
the clearance during the night and during the day were almost equal while in the
other patient the clearance during the night was, on the average, 12% lower than
during the day. Both patients exhibited pronounced normal diurnal fluctuations in
potassium and protein excretion.

In some patients the fluctuations in creatinine output exceed 20% of the daily
mean; in those cases, however, the variations in potassium and sodium excretion are
not different from those found in patients with an almost constant creatinine output.

In one of our patients who showed a notable diurnal rhythm in creatinine excretion, the lowest nightly water excretion was less than 30% of the peak excretion during
daytime and this difference persisted when, after treatment with mercurial diuretics,
almost no electrolytes were excreted (see Fig. 27). This observation is at variance
with that of STANBURY AND THOMSON[15] who found that electrolyte excretion determined the rate of urine flow.

## B. *Renal excretion patterns associated with osmo-regulation*

The effect of the ingestion of $1\frac{1}{2}$ l of water by a normal subject is shown in Fig. 7.
The water is eliminated in a very short time without any noticeable effect on the

---

* The creatinine output is directly related to the creatinine clearance and the creatinine
level in the blood plasma. If we assume that endogenous creatinine is produced at a constant rate,
a reduction in the creatinine clearance will only initially depress the creatinine output to the same
degree. A 10% reduction in clearance will raise the blood level within 12 h to approximately 110%
of the control level. The output will rise accordingly and again equal the production rate. Hence,
only in observations over a short period does creatinine output provide information on the creatinine clearance.

excretion of sodium, potassium and creatinine. Injection of physiological amounts of antidiuretic hormone (ADH) induces the reverse pattern, causing a retention of water only.

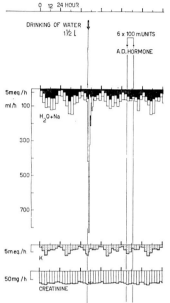

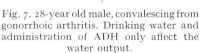

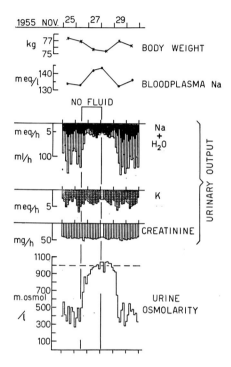

Fig. 7. 28-year old male, convalescing from gonorrhoic arthritis. Drinking water and administration of ADH only affect the water output.

Fig. 8. 43-year old female with Simmonds-Sheehan's disease maintained on 8 × 10 mg cortisone daily. Fluid deprivation had no significant influence on the excretion of sodium, potassium and creatinine. The prompt rise in urine osmolarity indicates maximal renal water retention, probably due to a rise in the endogenous ADH production in response to hypernatraemia. Extrarenal fluid loss resulted in a fall in body weight and a reciprocal rise in blood plasma sodium.

Endogenous ADH apparently does not influence electrolyte excretion either. Fig. 8 shows that fluid deprivation, leading to a sharp rise in the blood plasma sodium level and in the urinary osmolarity, did not affect the rhythmic electrolyte excretion.

*C. Renal excretion patterns associated with circulatory homoeostasis ("volume regulation")*

While osmoregulation is effected by alterations in the output of water only, "volume" regulation, serving circulatory homoeostasis, is connected with water as well as sodium balance. Unless extreme alterations in the circulation take place, the potassium output is only slightly or moderately affected and the changes in creatinine output are often insignificant if corrections are made for the effect of the dead space.

*Changes in posture.* It has already been demonstrated (Fig. 3) that water and sodium chloride are retained when a previously recumbent subject is up and about during a 6-h period. This postural oliguria is especially striking in patients who have remained in bed for a prolonged time. The marked orthostatic depression of the water and sodium output in such a patient is shown in Fig. 9. A slight effect on the potassium excretion can be discerned but the creatinine output remains almost constant. A similar response was obtained at all times of the day. When the patient was up from 6 a.m. till 6 p.m. the sodium and water excretion rhythm was completely reversed. When these patients are mobilized the urinary osmolarity usually shows a prompt rise sometimes to the same level as when ADH was injected. This effect is shown in Fig. 10 which compares the influence of ambulation with that of the administration of ADH.

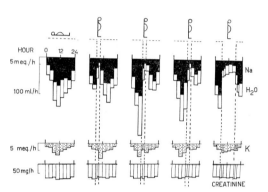

Fig. 9. 20-year old, tall, asthenic male, convalescing from acute glomerulonephritis and requiring several months bedrest. Note distinct orthostatic water and sodium retention followed by a gradual rise in output after resumption of recumbency, irrespective of the time of the day. Only insignificant influence on creatinine and potassium excretion.

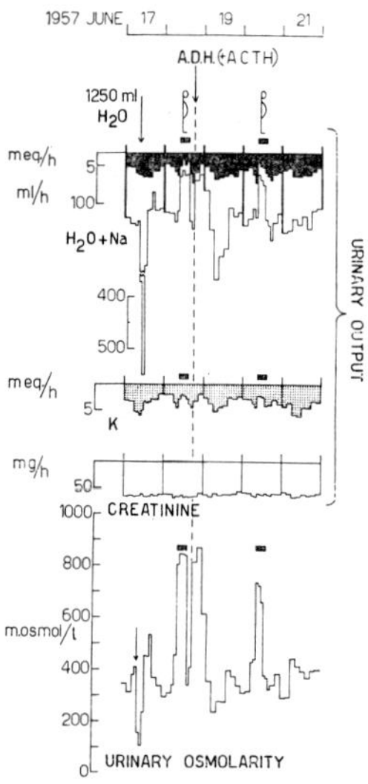

Fig. 10. 25-year old male with Addison's disease maintained on 8 × 5 mg cortisone daily. Similar effect on water excretion and urine osmolarity of standing and of injection of ADH. An unknown amount of ADH was given together with 30 U of ACTH; in other patients it had been demonstrated that this prolonged ACTH preparation was active but contained also large amounts of ADH. No effect of ACTH on electrolyte excretion pattern.

GOWENLOCK, *et al.*[16] suggest that the characteristic excretion pattern during standing is the net result of a slight reduction in glomerular filtration rate in conjunction with a rise in aldosterone secretion. However, in patients in whom no significant fall in creatinine output is found on ambulation, both sodium and potassium output may markedly decline (see Fig. 18). On the other hand, in patients without adrenals and maintained on adrenocorticoids evenly distributed over the 24 h, the sodium output is usually much more depressed than that of potassium when the patients are up and about. This may be found in the presence of an almost constant creatinine output (see Fig. 3).

*Nycturia*. Even in patients who remain constantly in bed, the excretion pattern may be influenced by posture and activities. Occasionally the excretion pattern of water and sodium are completely reversed while the excretion of potassium remains normal. This type of nycturia is frequently found in patients with hypalbuminaemia[31], portal hypertension[17] or heart failure. Complete recumbency during a 24-h period and restriction of muscular activities to a minimum restores the normal excretion pattern (see Fig. 11). Without change in the daily routine the normal diurnal rhythm may return when the serum albumin rises[13] or when the excess in extracellular fluid increases (Fig. 19). Probably, patients who possess factors which tend to depress the circulation are extremely sensitive to the influence of posture and activities.

In patients with glucocorticoid deficiency without mineralocorticoid deficiency the excretion pattern of water is often reversed while sodium and potassium exhibit a normal excretory rhythm with their peaks occurring during daytime[4]. Extra water intake during the day is retained until the evening. If isotonic saline is administered

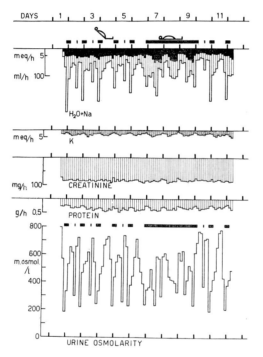

Fig. 11. 23-year old, tall male with albuminuria and slight oedema. Creatinine clearance approximates 100 ml/min. Normal diurnal excretory rhythm of potassium and protein. Conversely sodium excretion is lowest around noon. The effect of posture and activities on water excretion completely overrules the influence of the diurnal rhythm; large volumes of urine with low osmolarity are excreted during the night. Only in case of complete rest from 12.45 till 2 p.m. the corresponding urine specimen is large. On the 4th, 6th and 11th day when the visiting hour is from 1 till 2 p.m. this water diuresis is absent. Constant recumbency and restriction of activities on three consecutive days restore the normal diurnal rhythm in sodium and water excretion.

during the day sodium is excreted within the normal time while water is retained until the evening (see Fig. 12). Complete recumbency and inactivity during a 24-h period do not abolish this type of nycturia. This contrasts with the usual type of nycturia which involves the output of both water and sodium chloride. Cortisone and, in the presence of intact adrenals, ACTH restore the normal rhythm in the water excretion (see Figs. 8 and 23).

*Changes in the volume of the body fluids.* Another stimulus, which affects the

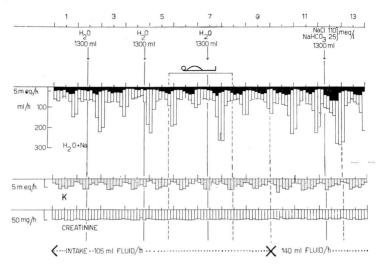

Fig. 12. Simmonds-Sheehan's disease (untreated). Same case as shown in Fig. 8 and Fig. 23. Nycturia was restricted to water; sodium and potassium excretion show a normal diurnal rhythm. Injection of saline during the day was followed by a normal excretion of sodium, but water was retained until the evening. The patient had no signs or symptoms of mineralocorticoid deficiency; blood pressure 130/80, pulse rate 70. Water excretion was normalized by cortisone (see Fig. 8) and by ACTH (Fig. 23).

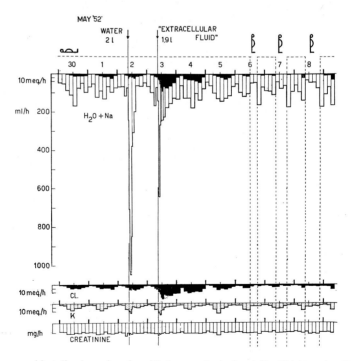

Fig. 13. 21-year old, tall, obese female with hyperostosis frontalis. Brisk water diuresis starts after the same brief delay following the drinking of water or "extracellular fluid". Excretion of the administered extra sodium load requires two days. Complete retention of sodium during standing; resumption of recumbency induces a diphasic diuresis.

urinary output probably by way of the circulation, is the enlargement of the extracellular fluid volume. In Fig. 13 the response to the drinking of water is compared
with that following the drinking of "extracellular" fluid. Both times the patient
responded with a brisk water diuresis; when saline was taken a prolonged sodium
and chloride diuresis lasting more than 48-h followed. The excretory rhythm was not
disturbed. There was no significant change in the potassium and creatinine excretion.
This diphasic diuretic response was described by BLOMHERT et al.[9], as being characteristic for all conditions where the factors present favour a sudden increase in the
circulation. If patients who are accustomed to bed rest have been up and about for a
long time, resumption of recumbency is usually followed by the diphasic diuresis
(Figs. 3 and 13). It is also found during attacks of paroxysmal tachycardia, which are
accompanied by signs of excessive circulation (Fig. 4), and following intravenous
injections of blood, plasma or plasma expanders in patients with hypalbuminaemic
oedema (Fig. 14).

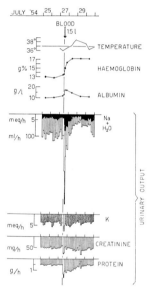

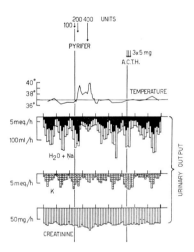

Fig. 14. 50-year old male with chronic
glomerulonephritis, hypalbuminaemia and a
creatinine clearance of 40 ml/min. Water and
sodium diuresis induced by a massive blood
transfusion was interrupted by a temporary
depression coinciding with post-transfusional
fever. Protein output parallels serum albumin
level. Extra protein excretion approximates
the amount of albumin administered with the
transfusion.

Fig. 15. Gonorrhoic arthritis, same case
as shown in Fig. 7. Characteristic response
to fever, viz., initial rise in sodium and
potassium excretion followed by a significant reduction in the excretion of both
electrolytes and a slight rise in creatinine
output. In other cases fever reduced
sodium output more than potassium
output. Second stage is similar to response
to insufficient circulation and differs
essentially from the effect of ACTH.

*The effect of fever.* Following the diphasic diuresis induced by a large blood transfusion, a fall in sodium and water excretion coinciding with a febrile post-transfusion
reaction can be seen in Fig. 14. During fever we always found a marked depression
of sodium and water excretion usually accompanied by a slight to moderate reduction

in potassium output. This depression is sometimes preceded by a brief rise in sodium output coinciding with the rise in temperature. When the temperature has reached its highest level, the excretion pattern is similar to that found in convalescents

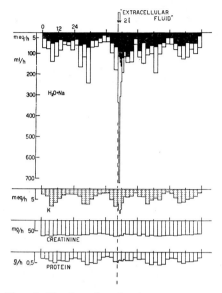

Fig. 16. Massive albuminuria, same case as shown in Figs. 5 and 2. Administration of "extracellular fluid" induces exactly the same type of diuresis as was shown by the patient in Fig. 14. In the present case no increase in protein excretion was observed.

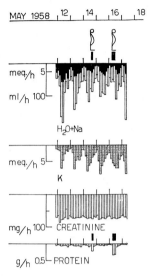

Fig. 17. 26-year old male with orthostatic albuminuria persisting during complete bedrest and only disappearing on lying flat without lordosis (the latter is not shown). Ambulation increases protein loss regardless of the effect on water and sodium excretion.

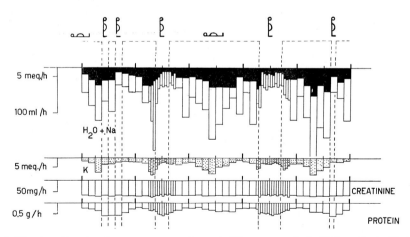

Fig. 18. Massive albuminuria, same case as shown in Figs. 2, 5 and 16. Notice effect of being up and about on excretion pattern. Sharp contrast between considerable reduction in sodium and potassium excretion and unaffected creatinine and protein output.

during standing and is in striking contrast with that induced by ACTH (Fig. 15). This may be regarded as an indication that the renal response is not a result of a stress reaction mediated by adrenocortical hormones, but is possibly related to a relative circulatory insufficiency.

*Albuminuria and circulation.* In patients with albuminuria, a transfusion or an infusion of albumin is followed by a considerable rise in protein excretion leading to a loss of all the albumin administered. In Fig. 14 it can be seen that this loss does not parallel the circulatory diuresis, but is correlated closely with the serum albumin level. A biphasic diuresis following the injection of saline in patients with albuminuria is not accompanied by an increase in protein excretion (see Fig. 16). Moreover, protein excretion is not influenced by posture in most patients with albuminuria. In spite of a marked orthostatic oliguria, the pattern of protein excretion may be an exact duplicate of that on the control days. An illustrative example is presented in Fig. 18. The creatinine excretion remained unaltered. These observations suggest that considerable variations in the output of water, sodium and sometimes of potassium (see Fig. 18) in response to changes in the circulation are promptly executed in the distal part of the nephron while the function of the proximal part is not essentially altered.

On the other hand, in patients with orthostatic albuminuria the protein output rises steeply during standing, irrespective of the effect on creatinine, water and sodium excretion (Fig. 17).

### III. EFFECT OF EXOGENOUS AGENTS ON THE KIDNEY

*A. Hormones and related substances in pharmacological doses; comparison with excretion patterns in endocrine diseases*

WOLTHUIS AND DE VRIES[18] and ROSENBAUM et al.[19] found that treatment with high doses of ACTH or cortisone is accompanied by a loss of the rhythmic variations in potassium excretion; sodium output is depressed but its diurnal excretory rhythm is not influenced. If the excretion patterns were abnormal before, they usually continue to be abnormal during treatment (see Figs. 19 and 24).

Mineralocorticoids reduce sodium output much more than glucocorticoids and initially increase potassium excretion without depressing the diurnal excretory rhythm. However, the retention of extracellular fluid gives rise to compensatory reactions leading to a new but apparently more labile equilibrium. The subjects then appear to be as susceptible to changes in posture as patients who have hypalbuminaemia or another factor which tends to depress the circulation. If glucocorticoids are given concomitantly, the stabilizing effect of the diurnal rhythm on the potassium excretion is also lost and both sodium and potassium excretion are extremely susceptible to changes in posture and muscular activity. This is shown in Fig. 20, which presents the data of a patient treated with ACTH in conjunction with liquorice, a substance with a deoxycortone-like action. Complete recumbency and inactivity prevented the fall in sodium output in the morning hours and the diurnal rhythm in sodium excretion tended to become normal, while potassium output showed no difference during the day and at night. In patients with Cushing's disease the same excretion pattern is often found (Fig. 21). In clear-cut cases it is pathognomonic.

The effect of one injection of ACTH on the excretion pattern may be used as a diagnostic test for adrenocortical insufficiency. We found no response at all in adrenal-ectomized patients (see Fig. 26) and in all patients with Addison's disease. It was also completely lacking in patients who showed signs of Addison's disease but who probably still had some functioning adrenocortical tissue. In the patient mentioned

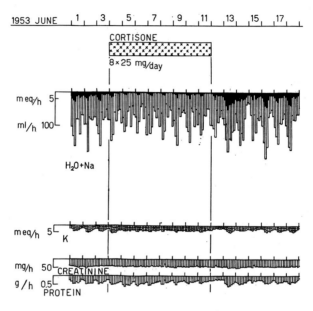

Fig. 19. 20-year old female with hypalbuminaemia due to massive albuminuria, normal renal functions. Relatively high dose of cortisone suppresses the diurnal rhythm of potassium ex-cretion and induces water and sodium retention without influencing their (pathological) ex-cretion pattern. During the rebound period an almost normal rhythmic sodium and water output was observed for three days.

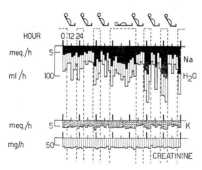

Fig. 20. 51-year old male with rheuma-toid arthritis, treated with ACTH 8 × 7.5 U in conjunction with liquorice 8 × 1 g daily. Nycturia, in spite of bedrest, ex-traordinary effect of posture and muscular activity on sodium- and even on potas-sium excretion. Not only during the night but also in the rest hour after noon when no speaking and no reading were allowed, sodium and potassium output increased.

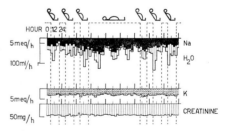

Fig. 21. 30-year old female with Cush-ing's disease. In spite of bedrest there was no regular diurnal rhythm for sodium and potassium excretion. During complete recumbency and inactivity a pronounced rhythmic excretion of sodium appears; no distinct diurnal rhythm in potassium output.

in Fig. 10 the diagnosis was made by a medical officer during a routine examination. The patient showed a typical pigmentation but he had no complaints, the pulse rate was low and the blood pressure normal. He exhibited a normal response to the drink-

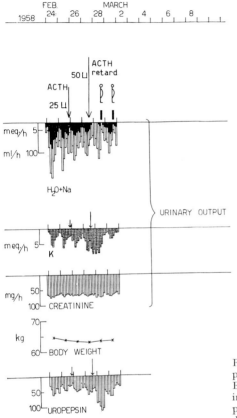

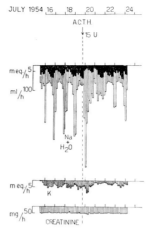

Fig. 23. Simmonds-Sheehan's disease, diurnal rhythm with reversed water excretion. Same case as in Figs. 8 and 12. 15 U of ACTH induce sodium retention and excessive potassium output. Moreover the retained water is excreted and follows a normal diurnal rhythm during a 48-h period.

Fig. 22. 38-year old, asthenic male, with unexplained pigmentation, orthostatic tachycardia. Equivocal response to 25 U of ACTH. Following injection of 50 U of an ACTH preparation with prolonged action, complete suppression of sodium output and excessive potassium excretion. Considerable effect also observed on uropepsin excretion. Unusual strong orthostatic reduction in sodium excretion after bedrest of only one week.

ing of water and to the administration of liquorice. However, injections with ACTH repeatedly failed to influence the electrolyte excretion pattern. In all subjects without signs and symptoms of adrenocortical insufficiency ACTH induced the characteristic change in the electrolyte excretion pattern. If the response was not conclusive, a second injection with a higher dose or with a preparation with a prolonged action always yielded a decisive result (see Fig. 22).

This method can also be used to distinguish between Addison's and Simmonds-Sheeman's disease. In the patient with the latter disease, who presented the characteristic nightly water excretion pattern shown in Fig. 12, ACTH not only induced a potassium and water diuresis with sodium retention, but also restored the normal excretory rhythm (see Fig. 23).

Unexpected results were obtained from a study of the effect of ACTH injections in a patient with albuminuria (see Fig. 24). Aside from complete retention of sodium and the disappearance of the potassium excretory rhythm, water output dropped suddenly. A marked fall of the blood sodium level and a rise in weight ensued. A search for a clarification of this phenomenon revealed that a new batch of ACTH had been used at that time, and after cessation of the injections the water output rose rapidly. Upon injecting the same ACTH preparation again, water retention lasting $4\frac{1}{2}$ h was observed. The ACTH sample apparently contained significant amounts of ADH. It is worthy of note that water excretion was already gradually increasing during the period that 8 ACTH injections were given daily: this can be explained as an escape phenomenon (see ref. [4]).

MOLHUYSEN *et al.*[20] discovered that oral administration of the glycyrrhizic acid fraction of liquorice produces a deoxycortone-like action in normal subjects. Patients who have been suffering from Addison's disease for many years and adrenalectomized persons do not respond to this drug. The response is restored, however, if a dose of cortisone, in itself too small to exert a demonstrable change in the electrolyte

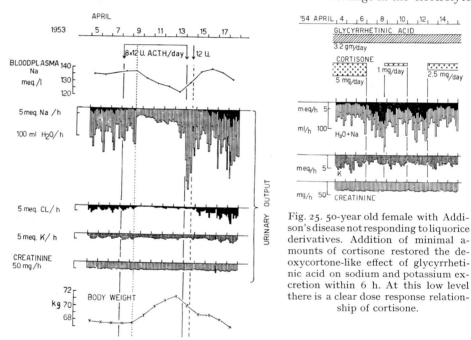

Fig. 25. 50-year old female with Addison's disease not responding to liquorice derivatives. Addition of minimal amounts of cortisone restored the deoxycortone-like effect of glycyrrhetinic acid on sodium and potassium excretion within 6 h. At this low level there is a clear dose response relationship of cortisone.

Fig. 24. Nephrotic syndrome. Same case as in Fig. 19. Treatment with ACTH; the first preparation did not contain any ADH, and apparently very little ACTH. At 9 a.m. on the second day, treatment was begun with another preparation which obviously contained both ACTH and ADH. A single injection with this preparation after treatment had been stopped, again interrupted water diuresis for 3-h. Reciprocal changes in body weight and blood plasma sodium were noted. The rise in water output at the end of ADH treatment indicates the beginning of an "escape phenomenon".

excretion pattern, is given in conjunction with liquorice or its derivatives[21] (see Fig. 25). GROEN AND WILLEBRANDS[22] found that glycyrrhetinic acid prepared from glycyrrhizic acid was more active than its precursor. However, relatively high doses are still necessary to obtain an effect. This is shown in Fig. 26 which presents a balance study of a patient, who underwent adrenalectomy for severe hypertension. 20 mg of cortisone daily appeared to have hardly any effect on electrolyte excretion. On the other hand, when 8 mg of cortisone were daily given in conjunction with 3.2 g glycyrrhetinic acid, a powerful deoxycortone-like response was noted. Aldactone, a spirolactone, which competitively inhibits the effect of aldosterone on the kidney also promptly blocks the effect of the combination of glycyrrhetinic acid and cortisone. The antagonistic effect of this drug gradually disappears in the course of a few days following cessation of its administration.

## B. Diuretics

In Fig. 27 the effect of several diuretics in a patient with severe heart failure is shown. Without treatment sodium was completely retained; potassium and chloride were rhythmically excreted and even the creatinine output showed fluctuations. Mersalyl and chlormerodrin, an orally administered mercurial diuretic caused a marked diuresis of water, sodium, chloride and potassium while acetazolamide (dia-

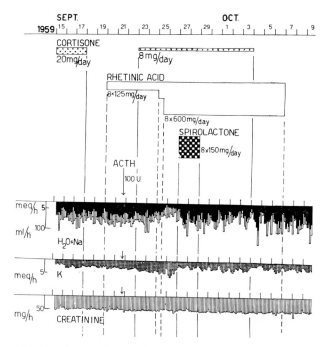

Fig. 26. 29-year old male, after total adrenalectomy for hypertension, intentionally kept in mild circulatory failure by withholding mineralocorticoids. Negligible rebound following cessation of 8 × 2.5 mg cortisone daily. No response to ACTH. Glycyrrhetinic acid in low dosage has no clear effect; the output of both potassium and sodium increases gradually. Addition of 8 × 1 mg cortisone daily induces more marked and reciprocal changes in sodium and potassium excretion. Increasing the dosage of glycyrrhetinic acid has a powerful deoxycortone-like effect. This is promptly blocked by aldactone (spirolactone SC–9420). Aldactone effect declines gradually in 5 days. Rebound is observed following cessation of cortisone administration.

mox) only produced an increase in the output of potassium. When the mercurial diuretics were given for a few days in succession, the water and sodium excretion gradually diminished. Probably the loss of extracellular fluid had given rise to a homoeostatic reaction which partly neutralized the effect of the diuretics.

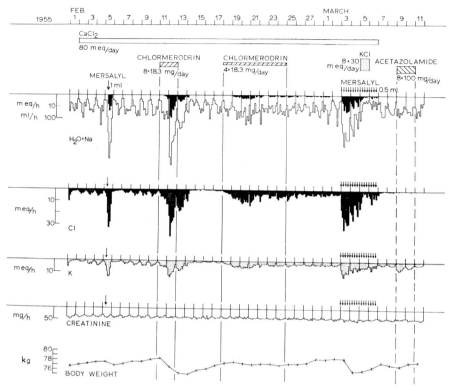

Fig. 27. 24-year old male with mitral stenosis and incompetence and severe heart failure. Excretion patterns of several diuretics modified by hyperaldosteronism. Mercurial diuretics induce sodium, chloride and potassium diuresis. Acetazolamide (diamox) increases potassium output without inducing sodium and chloride diuresis. Mersalyl acts promptly and its effect lasts no longer than 24 h, while that of an orally administered mercurial diuretic (chlormerodrin) starts slowly and continues for at least 5 days after cessation of therapy. Note the distinct diurnal rhythm in creatinine and water output even when almost no electrolytes are excreted.

Striking similarities and differences in the responses to the two mercurial diuretics may be noted. Both induced a considerable increase in chloride excretion which was almost equal to the sum of the excreted sodium and the extra potassium output. However, the effect of the intramuscular injection of mersalyl was prompt and only lasted 24 h while the orally administered drug acted after a delay of 15 h, but the effect continued for several days after the administration had been discontinued. This difference in the duration of the effect was especially striking following prolonged treatment with these drugs. The excretion of small amounts of sodium and significant amounts of chloride for more than a week after cessation of chlormerodrin administration indicates that this drug was slowly eliminated.

In Fig. 28 the effect of mersalyl and hydrochlorothiazide have been compared in the same patient. In the dosages used in this experiment, the effect of hydrochlorothiazide on sodium and water excretion was definitely inferior to that of the mercurial diuretics. However, there was a considerable potassium loss and the plasma potassium fell to the same dangerously low level of 2.5 mequiv./l as had occurred following the injection of 2 ml of mersalyl.

It must be noted that the patient was suffering from very severe heart failure and had been unable to excrete sodium spontaneously for more than six years. He could only be kept in a water and electrolyte equilibrium by means of a salt-free diet, mercurial diuretics, fluid restriction and a daily intake of 30 g of urea. His aldosterone output was extraordinarily high, more than 300 $\mu$g of aldosterone being excreted

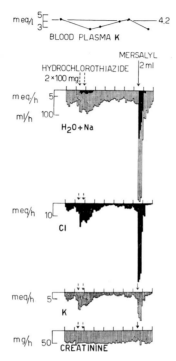

Fig. 28. Severe heart failure. Same case as in Fig. 27. Poor natriuresis and considerable potassium diuresis following hydrochlorothiazide administration. Mersalyl induces high output of sodium chloride and potassium. Both diuretics depress blood potassium to a dangerously low level.

daily. Hence a high potassium output in response to diuretics could be expected, as has been demonstrated by EDWARDS AND WILSON [23].

Quite a different response to acetazolamide and to a mercurial diuretic (thiomerin) was shown by a patient with albuminuria and a moderately reduced creatinine clearance (Fig. 29). Though he had a mild degree of oedema he was kept at a water and sodium equilibrium with a diet providing 160 mequiv. of sodium daily. In spite of heavy protein losses his serum albumin (determined by MAJOOR'S [24] method) was still about 25 g/l (60% or normal). It may be assumed that this patient did not suffer from secondary aldosteronism. In this case, thiomerin gave rise to a sodium diuresis of the same type as that induced by mersalyl in the patient with aldosteronism, but without a concomitant increase in potassium excretion. In the patient with albuminuria acetazolamide induced an appreciable sodium diuresis while the rise in potassium excretion was insignificant.

In this patient the effect of aminophylline, a drug known to increase glomerular filtration rate, deserves special consideration. Following its administration the output

of all urine constituents examined, including creatinine and protein, rose steeply.
The same was found in other patients with albuminuria. It appears that the diuretic
action of this drug is due to theophylline and not to ethylenediamine, the other com-

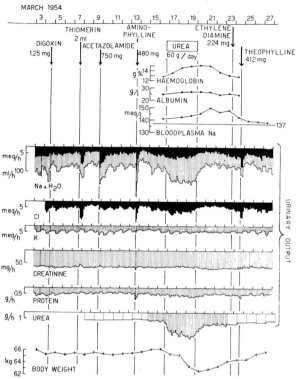

Fig. 29. 28-year old male with albuminuria. Creatinine clearance is approximately 70 ml/min.
Effect of diuretics not modified by hyperaldosteronism. Mercurial diuretic (thiomerin) does not
affect potassium output; acetazolamide induces a much larger increase in sodium than in potassium output. Theophylline and the theophylline-containing compound aminophylline, known to
increase glomerular filtration rate, are the only diuretics which increase protein excretion. Urea
administration induces considerable weight loss, a rise in haemoglobin level and hypernatraemia,
the latter being accompanied by sodium retention and a disappearance of the diurnal potassium
excretory rhythm.

ponent of aminophylline. Theophylline is, however, only slowly reabsorbed after
intramuscular injection and when given alone its effect is delayed and less conspicuous.
In this patient an intravenous injection of digoxin apparently had no effect on the
sodium output. This is the rule in subjects with a normally functioning heart, though
we did find a few striking exceptions.

   The osmotic diuresis induced by an intake of 60 g urea daily had many interesting
features. Initially not only water but also sodium and chloride were excreted in excess;
sodium output declined gradually and after cessation of therapy sodium was retained
in spite of a considerable rise in the blood sodium level. When the patient had reached
his lowest body weight, oedema had not completely disappeared. Probably the reduction in blood plasma volume, evidenced by the rise in haemoglobin, conditioned
the sodium retention. In the presence of a high blood sodium level the potassium
excretion rhythm is lost. This resembles the effect occurring after the administration

of excessive amounts of glucocorticoids (compare with Figs. 19 and 20 and 24). BLOMHERT also found other characteristics of high glucocorticoid activity in subjects with hypernatraemia. The slight rise in protein output can be attributed to the rise in serum albumin.

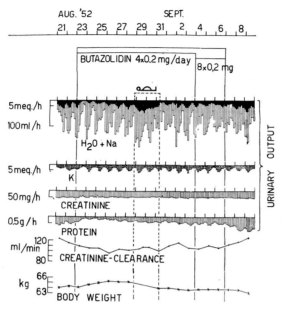

Fig. 30. 56-year old male with chronic arthritis, albuminuria following gold therapy, and hyp-albuminaemia, normal renal functions. Phenylbutazone (butazolidin) depresses the excretion of sodium and to a lesser degree potassium. Retention of extracellular fluid is followed by a rise in sodium output to pre-treatment levels ("escape"). Typical diphasic nycturia. Complete recumbency and inactivity increases sodium output and abolishes the nycturia. Repetition of "escape". Creatinine clearance falls during treatment and rises to pretreatment levels following cessation of therapy. Effect of phenylbutazone starts slowly; rebound is also delayed in accord-ance with the slow excretion rate of phenylbutazone. No close correlation between creatinine clearance and sodium output.

## C. Substances with a depressive action on renal function

Aminopyrine, phenylbutazone, quinidine and several other drugs depress the output of most urinary constituents. In a patient with albuminuria 4 × 0.2 g phenyl-butazone given at 6-h intervals depressed the creatinine clearance by 20% (see Fig. 30). The sodium and protein output declined rapidly and on the second day less than one fifth of the amount excreted on control days was eliminated in the urine. The outputs of potassium and creatinine were only slightly reduced*. After cessation of therapy the creatinine clearance gradually rose to the pretreatment level. The rebound in sodium and protein excretion was also retarded; this retardation was probably due to the slow excretion of phenylbutazone.

This observation is an example of the re-establishment of equilibrium on another level during prolonged treatment with an agent acting directly on the kidney. The retention of sodium and water calls homoeostatic reactions into play which oppose and after some time neutralize the effect of the drug. Complete recumbency and inactivity

---

* See footnote p. 982.

*References p. 99*

establish conditions favouring an increased circulation and lead to a sodium and water diuresis as well as the suppression of nycturia. Subsequently sodium is again temporarily retained. A third depression in sodium output is induced by an increase of the dosage of the drug. It is noteworthy that most changes in sodium output are not accompanied by changes in creatinine clearance. When treatment is discontinued the homoeostatic action is no longer held in balance by the effect of the drug and a rebound occurs. The rise in protein excretion during treatment can be attributed to a rise in the serum albumin concentration consequent to an initial reduction in the urinary albumin loss. The rise in output after cessation of the drug can be explained by a rise in glomerular filtration.

## ACKNOWLEDGEMENTS

We are indebted to head-nurses A. VAN PUTTEN and W. L. E. SIPKES for weighing the patients and supervising the punctual serving of meals and the careful collection of excreta. We wish to thank Mrs. A. A. STUIVER-VAN DAATSELAAR and Mr. H. METZ for the preparation of the graphs.

## SUMMARY

1. The effect of several factors on the renal output of water, sodium, potassium and creatinine, and, in some patients, also of protein and other substances was studied in consecutive 3-h periods under standard conditions. Since the diurnal rhythm cannot be eliminated, the effect of all other factors was evaluated against the background of the large but regular variations of the diurnal excretory rhythm found on control days. It was demonstrated that this elaborate method is indispensable for the study of phenomena of short duration.

2. The three principal types of physiological diuresis and antidiuresis associated with diurnal rhythm, osmoregulation and circulatory homoeostasis ("volume regulation") appeared to be characteristic and could be distinguished from each other and from the effect of external agents.

3. The possible mechanism of the diurnal excretory rhythm is discussed on the basis of differences and similarities in the excretion pattern of several substances. The large parallel variations in sodium and potassium excretion were similarly found in patients with and without significant fluctuations in creatinine output.

4. A tendency to nycturia could be demonstrated in many patients in spite of continuous bedrest. Nycturia could be attributed to an excessive influence of circulatory homoeostasis overruling the diurnal rhythm. Normal excretory rhythm was always re-established by strict recumbency and inactivity. Patients in whom factors were present favouring an insufficient or an excessive circulation appeared to be prone to nycturia.

5. The effect of pharmacological doses of hormones was compared with excretion patterns found in endocrine diseases. The excretion pattern was found to be characteristic in Cushing's disease and in glucocorticoid deficiency unaccompanied by mineralocorticoid deficiency. In the latter condition a non-postural type of nycturia concerning only water output was found.

6. The effect of ACTH on the renal excretion pattern was shown to be a relatively simple and reliable test for adrenocortical insufficiency.

7. The characteristic excretion patterns induced by different diuretics are shown. The influence of hyperaldosteronism on the response to diuretics is demonstrated.

8. Protein excretion varies considerably under the influence of the diurnal rhythm even when the creatinine output shows no appreciable fluctuations. Variations in water and sodium excretion resulting from circulatory homoeostasis or induced by diuretics are only accompanied by changes in protein excretion when creatinine output is appreciably altered. Renal protein output is directly related to variations in the serum albumin concentration.

## REFERENCES

1 E. H. STARLING, *The Fluids of the Body*, Archibald Constable & Co., London, 1909.
2 J. G. G. BORST, *Acta Med. Scand.*, 97 (1938) 68.
3 J. G. G. BORST, *Acta Med. Scand.*, 130 (1948) suppl. 207.
4 J. G. G. BORST, L. A. DE VRIES, A. M. VAN LEEUWEN, G. J. H. DEN OTTOLANDER, V. CEJKA, *Clin. Chim. Acta*, 5 (1960) 887.
5 M. NORN, *Skand. Arch. Physiol.*, 55 (1929) 184.
6 F. GERRITZEN, (1950) quoted by J. G. G. BORST AND L. A. DE VRIES, *Lancet*, 259 (1950) 1.
7 J. G. G. BORST AND L. A. DE VRIES, *Lancet*, 259 (1950) 1.
8 G. BLOMHERT, *Thesis*, Amsterdam, 1951.
9 G. BLOMHERT, J. A. MOLHUYSEN, J. GERBRANDY, L. A. DE VRIES AND J. G. G. BORST, *Lancet*, 261 (1951) 1011.
10 L. A. DE VRIES AND J. J. VAN DAATSELAAR, GORTER AND DE GRAAFF, *Klinische Diagnostiek*, H. E. Stenfert Kroese N.V., Leiden, 1955, p. 278.
11 G. E. SIMPSON, *J. Biol. Chem.*, 59 (1924) 107.
12 J. N. MILLS AND S. W. STANBURY, *Clin. Sci.*, 13 (1954) 177.
13 S. P. TEN HOLT, L. A. DE VRIES AND J. G. G. BORST, *Ned. Tijdschr. Geneesk.*, 96 (1952) 2244.
14 L. A. DE VRIES, S. P. TEN HOLT AND J. G. G. BORST, *Ned. Tijdschr. Geneesk.*, 96 (1952) 2251.
15 S. W. STANBURY AND A. E. THOMSON, *Clin. Sci.*, 10 (1951) 267.
16 A. H. GOWENLOCK, J. N. MILLS AND S. THOMAS, *J. Physiol. (London)*, 146 (1959) 133.
17 J. A. SMITS, *Thesis*, Amsterdam, 1947.
18 F. H. WOLTHUIS AND L. A. DE VRIES, *Acta Physiol. et Pharmacol. Neerl.*, 2 (1951/52) 317.
19 J. D. ROSENBAUM, B. C. FERGUSON, R. K. DAVIS AND E. C. ROSSMEISL, *J. Clin. Invest.*, 31 (1952) 507.
20 J. A. MOLHUYSEN, J. GERBRANDY, L. A. DE VRIES, J. C. DE JONG, J. B. LENSTRA, K. P. TURNER AND J. G. G. BORST, *Lancet*, 259 (1950) 381.
21 J. G. G. BORST, L. A. DE VRIES, S. P. TEN HOLT AND J. A. MOLHUYSEN, *Lancet*, 264 (1953) 657.
22 H. E. PELSER, A. F. WILLEBRANDS, M. FRENKEL, R. M. V. D. HEIDE, J. GROEN, *Ned. Tijdschr. Geneesk.*, 97 (1953) 348.
23 C. J. EDMONDS AND G. M. WILSON, *Lancet*, 278 (1960) 505.
24 C. L. H. MAJOOR, *J. Biol. Chem.*, 169 (1947) 583.

## DISCUSSION

TÁRNOKY: Was liquorice used as such in Addison patients or as a glycyrrhetinic acid preparation?

DE VRIES: We have used both.

TÁRNOKY: Do you think that the effect of liquorice depends on cortisone?

BORST: If we give a large amount of liquorice to a patient, he does not react, but addition of a few mg of cortisone daily suffices to make him respond adequately. On the other hand, a small dose of liquorice has no effect in a patient who receives a large amount of cortisone. The patient, therefore, needs a high dose of liquorice for an adequate mineralocorticoid effect.

TÁRNOKY: On treating rats with glycyrrhetinic acid succinate (a water soluble derivative) we found a salt-water retention which still persisted after 12 weeks. Would Prof. BORST comment on this? His patient developed salt-water retention which proved transient.

BORST: Sodium and water retention terminates in spite of continued treatment in patients whose hearts can react to the rise in blood volume and in central venous pressure with an increased performance. These patients show a rise in pulse pressure and in systolic and diastolic arterial pressure; then the sodium output rises and the balance is re-established or becomes negative. This "escape phenomenon" is not found in patients with heart failure; they continue to retain salt and water and develop massive oedema.

# NEWER CONCEPTS OF RENAL MECHANISM IN RELATION
# TO WATER AND ELECTROLYTE EXCRETION

H. WIRZ

*J. R. Geigy A.G., Basel (Switzerland)*

In man the osmolar clearance* ($UV/P_{osm}$) is roughly about 3 ml/min, which means an excretion of not quite 1 milliosmol/min. This 1 mosm is dissolved in 0.5–15 ml of water, depending on the presence or absence of antidiuretic hormone (ADH). If urine volume and osmolar clearance are the same, the urine is isotonic ($UV/P = V$; $U = P$); this is the case in man at an intermediate state of antidiuresis. In the total absence of ADH (water diuresis), urine is abundant and hypotonic, and in strong anti-diuresis it is hypertonic, the maximum osmolar $U/P$ ratio being about 4 in man, around 8 to 10 in most laboratory animals, and even more in some desert rodents

The frog and most lower vertebrates can also regulate urine concentration to some extent, but their ability is restricted to a range from dilute to isotonic. The capac-ity to concentrate urine beyond isotonicity seems to be limited to those animal clas-ses which contain in at least some of their nephrons a well developed thin segment between the proximal and the distal tubule, *i.e.* the mammals and to some extent the birds. The fact has mostly been overlooked that the mammalian kidney is distinguished by some other features as well. The mammalian kidney alone shows the characteristic "kidney shape" with a clear distinction of cortex and medulla, and only the mammalian nephron forms a loop which involves the thin segment and extends from the cortex to some way down the medulla; its close spatial connection with the collecting duct is another feature of the mammalian kidney.

In 1951[1] we first advanced the hypothesis that urine osmotic pressure might be raised in the mammalian kidney by the action of a countercurrent system, represent-ed by the loops of Henle. The hypothesis was based on considerations of comparative physiology and on experiments involving direct cryoscopy of kidney slices, but chiefly on the mathematical treatment and the model experiments of HARGITAY AND KUHN[2]. It should be emphasized that the credit of first conceiving the countercurrent theory must be given to Dr. WERNER KUHN, professor of Physical Chemistry at the Uni-versity of Basel.

The model of HARGITAY AND KUHN[2] consists of a long tube (Fig. 1) which doubles back on itself (hairpin), the two limbs ($S_1$ and $S_2$) sharing a common semipermeable membrane (M) and being linked to each other by a tube of small diameter (K). If the system is filled with a suitable solution and the free end of the upper limb is connected to a pressure reservoir containing the same solution, two events occur simultaneously. The fluid moves along the tube—from left to right through the upper limb and from right to left through the lower one. At the same time, since the hydrostatic pressure is reduced abruptly at the small connecting tube, some water (but no solutes) is pressed

---

* The volume of plasma which contains the same amount of osmotically active matter as excreted in the urine per minute.

through the semipermeable membrane. This part of the water short-circuits the route, whereas the solutes must run the whole course of the hairpin tube along one limb, round the bend and back along the other limb. As a consequence the solute concentration—the osmotic pressure—increases towards the return point (Fig. 1e). The osmotic pressure difference between the ends of the system may become several times the hydrostatic pressure difference between the two compartments. A relatively small "single effect" is multiplied by countercurrent, hence the term *hairpin countercurrent multiplier*.

The process is better understood if the model is operated in a number of discrete

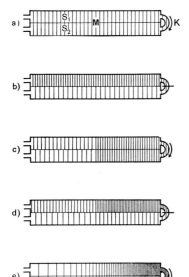

Fig. 1. The model of HARGITAY AND KUHN. $S_1$ and $S_2$: the two limbs of the hairpin tube; M the semipermeable membrane; K the small connecting tube. Description see text.

steps. First the system is filled with a solution which we may call isotonic (Fig. 1a); the connecting tube is then closed entirely (Fig. 1b). An osmotic pressure difference equal to the hydrostatic pressure is set up across the whole of the semipermeable membrane, the contents of the upper compartment being hypertonic by half the hydrostatic pressure and the contents of the lower compartment being hypotonic by the same amount. If the connecting tube is then opened for a moment and reclosed when half the hypertonic content of the upper compartment has drained through the connecting tube to the lower compartment, the right half of both the upper and the lower limb is filled with the same hypertonic solution (Fig. 1c); the hydrostatic pressure immediately starts to operate again. A new osmotic pressure difference is set up between the two limbs; this is of the same magnitude as in the first step, but starts from a higher osmotic level (Fig. 1d). This process may be repeated or, as shown before, the model may be operated continuously. The osmotic single effect (the "Einzeleffekt" of HARGITAY AND KUHN) starts to be multiplied when a hypertonic solution is carried around the bend into the returning limb. In the final steady state (Fig. 1e) the osmotic pressure difference between the two ends of the system may amount to several times the hydrostatic pressure.

During recent years evidence has accumulated that a countercurrent mechanism of a similar kind does in fact operate in the mammalian kidney owing to the loops of Henle. It is irrelevant that the two limbs of one loop are not necessarily in close contact with each other but separated by an interstitial space. It is not even important that each descending limb is in a functional connection only with the ascending limb of the same loop. All the descending limbs cooperate to correspond to the upper compartment ($S_1$), whereas all the ascending limbs correspond to the lower compartment ($S_2$) of the model. It is important, however, that the contents of each descending limb at any one level of the medulla are (slightly) more concentrated than the contents of the ascending limbs at the same level. Furthermore it is significant (and reasonable

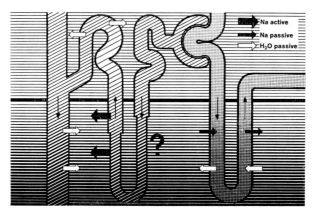

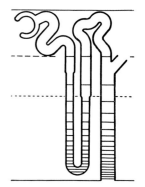

Fig. 2. The concentrating mammalian kidney. The transports involved in the concentrating mechanism are represented by arrows.

Fig. 3. Variation of osmotic pressure in a single nephron and collecting duct (From WIRZ, HARGITAY AND KUHN[1]).

to assume) that by the countercurrent multiplication not only the contents of both limbs of the loops, but also the interstices become more and more concentrated as the tip of the papilla is approached. It is this milieu of increasing hypertonicity which the collecting ducts pass on their way through the medulla. Their function need be nothing more than to allow a passive transfer of water according to the prevailing osmotic conditions: if the milieu is hypertonic, water is drawn out of the collecting ducts and the urine reaches its final hypertonicity (Fig. 2).

One thing must be emphasized at this point (see also below). It is quite certain that in the kidney the single effect is not a hydrostatic pressure difference between the two limbs of the loops, as in the model. Osmotic pressures are measured in terms of atmospheres whereas the hydrostatic pressures available in the loops of Henle amount at most to a few mm Hg. This does not suffice to account for the combination of high urinary osmotic pressure and the still appreciable amount of hypertonic urine produced.

Evidence in favour of the countercurrent hypothesis at first consisted of the demonstration of the osmotic stratification along the axis of the renal medulla.

By direct cryoscopy of kidney slices we showed in 1951 with HARGITAY AND KUHN[1] the rising hypertonicity of tubular and collecting duct content at increasing depths of the rat renal medulla. From these results the course of osmotic pressure along the nephron and collecting duct was outlined as in Fig. 3. It appears that this figure can no longer be accepted as correct. The method failed to disclose the hypotonicity in the early distal convoluted tubule which was found later by micropuncture[3,4]. The results may be influenced by post-mortem diffusion between closely adjacent tubes. Still, we believe that the results were reliable as far as average osmotic pressures at different depths of the medulla are concerned.

A different line of approach was followed by ULLRICH, DRENCKHAHN AND JARAUSCH[5], who investigated the osmotic behaviour of slices taken from various depths of fresh dog kidneys. By interpolation, they computed the osmotic pressure of a saline solution with which the slices would be in osmotic equilibrium. In concentrating kidneys they found a steady increase of osmotic pressure from the cortico-medullary junction to the tip of the papilla. The quantitative significance of these results may be questioned, but their value is of a different kind. Since it is the cells that shrink or swell, the results show that not only the contents of all tubules and the interstitial space but also the intracellular compartment participates in the osmotic stratification of the renal medulla.

The most important part in the rise of osmotic pressure is played by sodium chloride; another very important and intriguing role is played by urea. This was shown by ULLRICH AND JARAUSCH[6], but as early as 1947 LJUNGBERG[7] had found a steady increase in the chloride concentration in slices of the rabbit renal medulla. The results were confirmed by GUINNEBAULT AND MOREL[8], EMERY and coworkers[9], LEVINSKY AND BERLINER[10], SCHMIDT-NIELSEN[11] and others.

The sodium concentration of medullary slices is always high in concentrating kidneys even in those cases where urine sodium is low. There seems to be a correlation between the average papillary sodium concentration and the total molecular concentration of urine; this indicates that sodium is somehow involved in the concentrating mechanism. Urea on the other hand is either evenly distributed throughout the medullary tissue[6] or its concentration is slightly less in tissue water than in urine[10].

All these findings seem to show that there are no steep gradients in the renal medulla concerning the total molecular concentration (osmotic pressure); but that, as in other tissues, there are some very definite barriers with regard to some individual solutes.

Another hairpin countercurrent system is anatomically present in the medulla, namely, that of the blood vessels. The irrigation of the renal medulla with blood is unique in more than one respect. Most of the vasa recta—if not all—originate from juxtamedullary glomeruli. The vas efferens is very short and soon splits up to form a number of small vessels, none of which exceeds the size of a capillary. There are neither arteries nor veins in the entire medulla. The vasa recta retain their small size and large number until very shortly before merging to an arcuate or interlobular vein. Furthermore, in the outer zone of the medulla a large number of arterial and venous vessels are assembled to form the vascular bundles. Here the blood vessels are practically unconnected with any tissue and are in contact only with each other. In some species these vascular bundles closely resemble the rete mirabile of the fish swim-bladder, the countercurrent function of which was recognized many years ago (LONG-LEY, personal communication).

As far as is known, the system of the vasa recta cannot produce an osmotic gradient. Unlike the multiplier system of the loops of Henle it is a passive exchanger, which allows the irrigation of the renal medulla with blood but does not interfere with the osmotic stratification produced by the activity of the loops. The blood proceeding in the descending limbs towards the papilla adapts its osmotic pressure to the surroundings by a passive diffusion of water out of the vessels or by taking up diffusible solutes. The opposite happens in the venous limb; the surplus of osmotically active substances contained in the medullary blood cannot be carried away because they leave the vessels by passive diffusion into the relatively hypotonic surroundings. The solutes are trapped and partly recirculate repeatedly in the medulla.

That the blood of the vasa recta does in fact adapt its osmotic pressure to the surroundings was shown in 1953 by micropuncture. There are a few small rodents, among them the golden hamster, which have a long and slim renal papilla which pro-

Fig. 4. Golden hamster kidney (From WIRZ[12]).

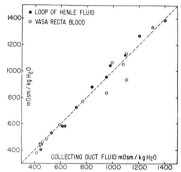

Fig. 5. Relation between the osmolality of collecting duct fluid and fluid from loops of Henle and vasa recta blood. (From GOTTSCHALK AND MYLLE[4]).

trudes beyond the hilus in the ureter (Fig. 4). This papilla can be exposed *in vivo* and lends itself to micropuncture experiments. Using a microcryoscopic method we demonstrated that the vasa recta blood of concentrating hamster kidneys showed the same osmotic pressure as the urine which is simultaneously formed[12].

These results have been brilliantly confirmed in a large series of experiments by GOTTSCHALK AND MYLLE[4] (Fig. 5). Moreover these investigators were able to puncture the loops of Henle near their hairpin bend. The osmotic pressures of blood or loop of Henle fluid were compared with those of the collecting duct fluid of the same medullary level and the values showed close correspondance. This seems to be very conclusive proof in favour of the countercurrent hypothesis.

The system of the vasa recta is usually described as an entirely passive countercurrent exchanger, which is unable to produce an osmotic gradient, but which does not interfere with one already existing. However, some degree of ultrafiltration from the arterial to the venous limb cannot be excluded. This would result in a nearly accurate duplication of the original model of HARGITAY AND KUHN[2], and might account for the high plasma protein concentrations found in the renal papilla by LASSEN, LONGLEY AND LILIENFIELD[13].

As far as the rise in total osmotic pressure is concerned, this effect may be neglected, and in a first approximation (assuming ideal conditions for exchange diffusion) the vasa recta may be treated as non-existent. Assuming some escape from the countercurrent exchange, the blood leaving the medulla of a concentrating kidney would be on the hypertonic rather than on the hypotonic side of isotonicity. Since all fluid entering the medulla is isotonic, and if a hypertonic urine leaves the medulla *via* the collecting ducts, the balance of tonicites requires that a hypotonic solution some-how leaves the medulla. The vasa recta are ruled out as a possible way of escape, and the only open route appears in the ascending limbs of the loops of Henle (LEVINSKY *et al.*[14]).

When the characterization and localization of the mechanism which creates the first osmotic pressure difference and initiates the countercurrent multiplication is considered, we are faced with a number of unsolved problems. It was clear from the start that the hydrostatic pressures which might be found in renal tubules would never suffice to explain the high urine osmotic pressures found in mammals, even if multi-plied by a countercurrent. Some sort of active transport must be postulated to operate in at least one of the membranes of the loop. An active water transport from the descending to the ascending limb was first considered to be the basis of the concen-trating mechanism, but evidence has accumulated that it is due to the transport of an osmotically active solute, most probably sodium with a concomitant anion. Even in the first paper of HARGITAY AND KUHN it was stated that the same multiplication by countercurrent takes place, if the initial osmotic pressure difference is produced not by a water transport but by an active solute transport in the opposite direction. Recently KUHN AND RAMEL[15] have given the mathematical proof that the salt-transporting countercurrent multiplier is theoretically sound.

This statement seems quite satisfactory, for it enables us to understand not only the production of high urinary osmotic pressures without steep osmotic gradients, but also the reabsorption of water to form a hypertonic urine without an active hand-ling of water molecules.

The question of the precise location of the active membrane which provides the sodium pump at once arises. It is safe to say that there are probably no cells that do not pump sodium. Certainly the proximal and distal convoluted tubules, and even the collecting ducts participate in sodium reabsorption. In the proximal convolution about 80% of filtered sodium is estimated to be reabsorbed. Proximal sodium reabsorption, however, does not establish an osmotic pressure difference. The membranes concerned are so readily permeable to water that the proximal tubule content remains isotonic in the diuretic as well as in the antidiuretic state.

The loop of Henle is not accessible for micropuncture except at or near its tip, and this does not give much information about transport activities. But early distal con-voluted tubule fluid is regularly and distinctly hypotonic. This was shown in 1941 by WALKER *et al.*[16], confirmed in 1956[3] (Fig. 6) and again in a thorough experimental study in 1959 by GOTTSCHALK AND MYLLE[4].

The most satisfactory explanation seems to be an active reabsorption of sodium (chloride) through a virtually water-impermeable membrane in the ascending limb of the loop. That the substance actively transported *is* sodium has not been proved experimentally. It is suggested by a number of theoretical considerations and by the findings of GOTTSCHALK AND MYLLE[4] that in saline diuresis much more pronounced hypotonicities are measured than in simple hydropenia or in diureses induced by mannitol or urea.

The fate of this sodium is not entirely known. Apparently it is not removed efficiently from the medulla by the vasa recta which, as discussed earlier, represent a countercurrent exchange system. So the medullary interstitial space is made (slightly) hypertonic. This by itself would not suffice for the operation of the counter-current multiplier. For this, an indispensable prerequisite is the entrance at the hairpin bend of a (slightly) hypertonic solution in the ascending limb. This may be achieved by an osmotic equilibration of the contents of the descending limb with the hypertonic interstitium. Further investigation is needed to decide if sodium is taken up actively or passively in the descending limb, the latter requiring a selective permeability, if a water movement accompanies the sodium transport to the descending limb, or finally, if the equilibration is performed by the water movement alone (Fig. 2).

The final abstraction of water from the collecting ducts to form a hypertonic

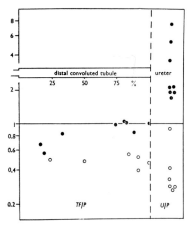

Fig. 6. Distal tubular fluid/plasma ratios (TF/P) and ureteral urine/plasma ratios (U/P) of total molecular concentration in the concentrating ($\bullet$) and the diluting (o) rat kidney. The site of micropuncture is given as percent of the length of the distal convoluted tubule (From WIRZ[3]).

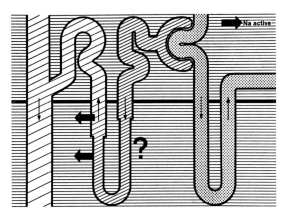

Fig. 7. The diluting mammalian kidney.

urine is conceived as a passive process, the epithelial cells of the collecting ducts serving as semipermeable membranes. This assumption is complicated but not seriously hampered by the findings of HILGER et al.[17] by microcatheterisation that some active ion transport processes occur in the collecting ducts.

Another question which is still open concerns the extent of the combined sodium transport activity and water impermeability of the ascending limb. Is the whole limb including the thin segment of the long loops involved? This seems to follow from the available evidence, which by necessity is derived from post-mortem analyses of medullary tissue[1,5,14]. This assumption implies a change of function of the thin segment at the tip of the loop in spite of the fact that no change of the morphologic appearance is evident. Or is the activity limited to the thick segment of the ascending limb, as ULLRICH proposed? In this case the two limbs of the countercurrent multiplier would be represented by two well-defined and morphologically different structures, but the active part of the concentrating mechanism would be limited to the outer medullary zone. Neither alternative is, at the present time, entirely satisfactory.

So far we have considered only one part of the problem, *i.e.* the production of a hypertonic urine under strong ADH activity. Information on the diluting kidney of mammals is scarce, mostly because it is extremely difficult to obtain a reasonable water diuresis in an anesthetized mammal.

Fig. 6 contains a number of results from two different kinds of experiments. The black dots relate to experiments in the usual antidiuretic state, and the open circles to water diuresis characterized by a hypotonic ureteral urine. In both cases the early distal tubule fluid is definitely hypotonic and independent of ADH activity. The anti-diuretic hormone does not seem to influence to any appreciable degree the sodium reabsorption and water impermeability of the ascending limb. In the absence of ADH (water diuresis) this hypotonicity is guarded throughout the length of the distal convoluted tubule. This means that the walls of the distal convoluted tubules are water-impermeable as well. In the hydropenic animals the osmotically free water is allowed to dissipate and the late distal tubule fluid becomes isotonic. Therefore one of the actions of ADH is to increase the water-permeability of the distal convolution. A similar mode of action of ADH must be postulated for the collecting ducts (Fig. 7). The hypotonicity established in water diuresis at the end of the distal convoluted tubule is undiminished or even enhanced (by sodium reabsorption) when the urine leaves the kidney. We have no accurate information on the osmotic pressure of the interstitial space in water diureses. From the experiments of ULLRICH *et al.*[5] we may guess however, that it is either isotonic or slightly hypertonic. So again a hypotonic solution is carried through a milieu of a higher osmotic pressure requiring a water-impermeable membrane, whereas in hydropenia a passive water transfer is the final step in urine concentration. Whether the countercurrent multiplier system is also affected by the action of ADH is not known, but one might conjecture that the equi-libration of the descending limb of the loop of Henle with the hypertonic medullary interstitial fluid is also influenced by the hormone.

## SUMMARY

During the past few years evidence has accumulated which indicates that in the mammal the process of urine concentration is effected by the action of a countercur-rent multiplier system of the loops of Henle. By means of this a milieu of increasing hypertonicity is created in the medulla; osmotic forces cause water from the collecting ducts to flow into the medulla thus forming a hypertonic urine. The basic active process in the countercurrent mechanism seems to be sodium transport out of the ascending limb and possibly—but not necessarily—into the descending limb of the loops. The function of the antidiuretic hormone seems to be to increase the perme-ability of the distal convoluted tubules and collecting ducts to water. Whether the transport system of the loops of Henle is also affected by ADH cannot, at present, be ascertained.

## REFERENCES

[1] H. WIRZ, B. HARGITAY AND W. KUHN, *Helv. Physiol. et Pharmacol. Acta*, 9 (1951) 196.
[2] B. HARGITAY AND W. KUHN, *Z. Elektrochem.*, 55 (1951) 539.
[3] H. WIRZ, *Helv. Physiol. et Pharmacol. Acta*, 14 (1956) 353.
[4] C. W. GOTTSCHALK AND M. MYLLE, *Am. J. Physiol.*, 196 (1959) 927.

[5] K. J. ULLRICH, F. O. DRENCKHAHN AND K. H. JARAUSCH, *Pflüger's Arch. ges. Physiol.*, 261 (1955) 62.

[6] K. J. ULLRICH AND K. H. JARAUSCH, *Pflüger's Arch. ges. Physiol.*, 262 (1956) 537.

[7] F. LJUNGBERG, *Acta Med. Scand.*, 127 (1947) *Suppl.* 186.

[8] M. GUINNEBAULT AND F. MOREL, *Compt. rend.*, 244 (1957) 2741.

[9] E. W. EMERY, A. H. GOWENLOCK, A. G. RIDDELL AND D. A. K. BLACK, *Clin. Sci.*, 18 (1959) 205.

[10] N. G. LEVINSKY AND R. W. BERLINER, *J. Clin. Invest.*, 38 (1959) 741.

[11] B. SCHMIDT-NIELSEN, *Physiol. Revs.*, 38 (1958) 139.

[12] H. WIRZ, *Helv. Physiol. et Pharmacol. Acta*, 11 (1953) 20.

[13] N. A. LASSEN, J. B. LONGLEY AND L. S. LILIENFIELD, *Science*, 128 (1958) 720.

[14] N. G. LEVINSKY, D. G. DAVIDSON AND R. W. BERLINER, *J. Clin. Invest.*, 38 (1959) 730.

[15] W. KUHN AND A. RAMEL, *Helv. Chim. Acta*, 42 (1959) 628.

[16] A. M. WALKER, P. A. BOTT, J. OLIVER AND M. C. MACDOWELL, *Am. J. Physiol.*, 134 (1941) 580.

[17] H. H. HILGER, J. D. KLÜMPER AND K. J. ULLRICH, *Pflüger's Arch. ges. Physiol.*, 267 (1958) 218.

## DISCUSSION

VINK: Do you think that it would be possible to explain active sodium transport by means of a system of "sodium electrode activity" of the membranes of the different cells of the kidney.

WIRZ: Your suggestion implies an active sodium transport not only in the kidney but everywhere in the body. Therefore you can study the problem more easily in a squid axon or any other simple structure rather than on the complicated system of the renal tubule—especially since the loops of Henle are not accessible.

GLYNN: I wonder whether you need be too worried by the similarity in appearance of the cells of the ascending and descending limbs of Henle's loop. I am thinking of some recent experiments of Dr. VICKERS in Cambridge, which have not yet been published, but which he very kindly said I might mention. He took small fresh-water fish and put them successively in salt solutions of increasing strength, so that after several months they were living, apparently quite happily, in solutions rather stronger than sea water. At the end of this period, examination of the gills showed that the number of 'chloride-secreting' cells had enormously increased—in fact they spread into the adjacent skin. When the fish is in its normal environment these cells take up salt from the water, but presumably in the fish acclimatized to hypertonic surroundings the cells pump the other way—otherwise their great increase in number would make no sense. How cells know which way to pump is a mystery, but the point is that whichever way they pump, they look much the same.

VINK: An important mechanism in your countercurrent system is the sodium transport out of the ascending limb of the loop of Henle. As you need a slightly elevated osmotic concentration in the first part of the descending limb cannot your hypothesis be correlated with the hypothesis of BERLINER[1] that sodium is transported out of the entire loop to the peritubular space.

WIRZ: That sodium is transported out of the ascending limb is no speciality, for any tubule will transport sodium outwards. The speciality is its impermeability to water. What happens in the descending limb is uncertain. It is quite possible that there is no transport of sodium into this limb; it might become equilibrated just by the water permeability letting out water to the hypertonic surrounding. This is the theory BERLINER *et al.* favour in their latest paper[2].

VINK: Only a small percentage of the loops of Henle enter deep into the medulla (papilla). Many of them therefore will scarcely (or not at all) reach the zone of high osmotic concentration. Will the kidney, in your opinion, during hydration and dehydration react with a variation of the quantity of liquid flowing through the "short" and "long" loops, or is the building up of the hypertonic zone dependent on the water and salt need of the body?

WIRZ: If you make a puncture in the cortex of a properly functioning kidney, you will find all nephrons active. I have never seen a sign of an alternating nephron activity. This holds for the diluting as well as for the concentrating kidney. There seems to be some difference in blood flow through the medullary blood vessels according to the Göttingen group[3]. They have shown that the blood flow in the renal medulla is increased in the diuretic state.

A small blood flow through these passive exchangers would favour a good exchange and, therefore, ideal conditions for this countercurrent system. On the other hand, in diuretic states, the large blood flow would tend to disrupt this mechanism.

[1] R. W. BERLINER, *Am. J. Med.*, 24 (1958) 730.

[2] N. G. LEVINSKY, D. G. DAVIDSON AND R. W. BERLINER, *J. Clin. Invest.*, 38 (1959) 730.

[3] K. THURAU, P. DEETJEN AND K. KRAMER, *Pflüger's Arch. ges. Physiol.*, 270 (1960) 270.

# THE INFLUENCE OF ENDOCRINE DISEASE
# ON THE RENAL EXCRETION OF WATER

J. S. ROBSON

*Department of Therapeutics, University of Edinburgh (Great Britain)*

In 1955 WELT[1] discussed the influence of a variety of diseases on the renal excretion of water and it is the purpose of this review to consider the information which has accumulated since this time with special reference to the influence of the endocrine system. In health the urinary solute is excreted at an osmolal concentration usually well within the maximal renal limits of dilution and concentration. The water necessary for the formation of this urine is provided by the operation of a thirst mechanism which supplements the water derived from the oxidation of food.

The process by which water is filtered at the glomerulus, and is reabsorbed or rejected by the renal tubulus has been described by WIRZ in this volume. The proximal tubular reabsorption of water is presumed to occur as a passive consequence to the active and unequal reabsorption of sodium, potassium, chloride, bicarbonate and glucose. Under most conditions 85 to 90% of the volume of the glomerular filtrate is reabsorbed there, leaving a much reduced volume of isotonic fluid to reach the distal concentrating site[2]. Thereafter, depending on the state of water balance, there is a net disproportionate reabsorption of solute or water with the production of urine either more or less dilute than plasma[3]. Factors influencing the volume of isosmotic fluid reabsorbed in the proximal tubule are peculiarly difficult to study in man, for variations in this component would not be expected to reveal themselves in simple changes in urinary osmolality. On the other hand, the ready availability of this simple index renders the distal concentrating and diluting system capable of systematic study.

### THE RENAL POWER TO CONSERVE WATER

In the process of concentrating urine a volume of water is removed from the tubular fluid at the concentrating site and the ratio of the osmolality of urine so that of the plasma ($U/P$ osmolal ratio) rises above 1.0. After at least twenty hours of water and food deprivation, values of this function in health are reported by most authors to lie between 3.5 and 4.5[4]. RAPOPORT *et al.*[5] were the first to publish extensive evidence showing that with increasing rates of solute excretion, induced by intravenous administration of a variety of substances including mannitol, given under conditions of hydropenia, the $U/P$ osmolal ratio falls as the rate of urine flow rises with the osmotic diuresis. The original suggestion[5-7] that this fall is due ultimately to an increased volume of isosmotic fluid delivered to the distal concentrating site in the collecting ducts is still acceptable and is not invalidated by the discovery that even in conditions of water deprivation the fluid in the ascending limb of the loop of Henle and part of the distal tubule is hypotonic[3]. The volume of water reabsorbed by the renal tubules during concentration has been called $T^c{}_{H_2O}$ by WESSON AND ANSLOW[8] and its magnitude is represented by the difference between the osmolal clearance, $(U_{osm}/P_{osm}) \times V$, and the rate of urine flow $V$.

$$T^c{}_{H_2O} = C_{osm} - V \tag{1}$$

As the osmolal clearance rises during increasing osmotic diuresis the value of $T^c{}_{H_2O}$ increases and tends to reach about 5 ml/min/1.73 m², at urine flows above 4–5 ml/min. For some years it has been conventional to express the capacity to conserve water in terms of these two functions and to regard the $U/P$ osmolal ratios obtained at low urine flows and values of $T^c{}_{H_2O}$ at higher rates of solute excretion as representing maximal renal capacities[9]. RAISZ et al.[10] have recently shown in man that during osmotic diuresis, induced in the hydropenic state, a linear relationship exists between $U_{osm}/P_{osm}$ and $V$ and that this is best expressed in the equation

$$\frac{1}{(U_{osm}/P_{osm}) - 1} = aV + b \tag{2}$$

where $a$ and $b$ are constants and $V$ represents the rate of urine flow. From this equation it can be seen that as $V$ approaches zero, $U_{osm}/P_{osm}$ reaches a maximum value which depends on the value of $b$. Dividing eqn. (2) by $V$ and substituting $T^c{}_{H_2O}$ for $(U_{osm}/P_{osm} \times V) - V$ we have

$$\frac{1}{T^c{}_{H_2O}} = a + \frac{b}{V} \tag{3}$$

This equation predicts that as $V$ increases, $T^c{}_{H_2O}$ approaches a maximum represented by the constant $a$. These relationships appear to be independent of whether urea or mannitol is used to induce osmotic diuresis up to a flow of about 20 ml/min.

Although the two parameters, maximum $U/P$ osmolal ratio and $T^c{}_{H_2O}$, are frequently both diminished in pathological states, this is not invariable and they would seem likely to be limited by different physiological and pathological mechanisms. In health in the presence of ADH, passive movements of water due to active sodium reabsorption could be limited by osmotic gradients at low urine flows and by tubular surface area at high urine flows. In disease, the degree of ADH deficiency with the responsiveness of the collecting ducts to its presence and the extent of sodium reabsorption at the critical site in the loop of Henle might be expected to exert an influence of varying degrees upon the two functions at the different rates of solute excretion at which they are measured[11].

### THE RENAL POWER TO ELIMINATE WATER

During sustained water diuresis the urine is rendered dilute by the continued absorption of solute and by the rejection of water in the distal system. This appears possible only in the absence of ADH and an estimate of this capacity can be expressed either as a minimal value of $U_{osm}/P_{osm}$ or as a negative value of the function $T^c{}_{H_2O}$ as determined by eqn. (1). The expression "free water clearance" is frequently used as an alternative to $-T^c{}_{H_2O}$. The limits of the renal power of dilution are not so well defined as those of the power of concentration. SCHOEN[12] found a minimum average value of urine osmolality in 10 normal men to be 59 mosm/l. Further hydration of these individuals appeared merely to extend the duration over which urine of such low osmolality was excreted, and the minimum osmolality remained nearly constant in the same subject. It is possible that this constancy was determined partly by constancy of solute excretion, for it has been shown that minimal urinary osmolality and free water clearance increase with an increased rate of solute excretion during water diuresis[13].

## THIRST

Under normal circumstances these renal mechanisms of dilution and concentration are rarely required to operate at maximum capacity. Thirst replaces water lost from the body before maximum antidiuresis occurs and satiety develops before values for free water clearance reach more than modest proportions. The precise means by which, with free access to water, the natural intake is so nicely balanced as to provide for the inescapable loss of water through the skin and respiratory passages and for the excretion of urinary solute is unknown. Experimental evidence for the existence of a thirst centre in the hypothalamus was first obtained by ANDERSSON[14-16] and GREER[17]. ANDERSSON AND McCANN[18] showed that polydipsia could be induced in goats by the injection of small amounts of hypertonic saline into the sensitive area extending from the dorsal into the ventral hypothalamus. It is not clear at the present time whether these receptors in the hypothalamus are identical with those described by VERNEY[19] as being concerned with ADH release and water conservation[20].

## DIABETES INSIPIDUS

Diabetes insipidus has for long been regarded as the simplest endocrine disorder of water excretion and is characterised by extreme polydipsia and the excretion of a large volume of dilute urine. The renal defect is best explained on the basis of absence or insufficiency of the antidiuretic hormone[21] and in its severest form consists of an inability of the kidneys to establish a urinary/plasma osmolal gradient of 1.0 after an appropriate period of water restriction. During osmotic diuresis induced in a state of hydropenia the osmolality of the urine tends to rise towards that of the plasma and the free water clearance increases[22,23]. Partial degrees of diabetes insipidus occur clinically in which $U/P$ osmolal ratios of above 1.0 can be demonstrated. These abnormalities are rapidly reversed by the administration of pitressin, which also relieves the thirst. Several workers have noted, however, that even with the administration of pitressin in adequate doses the maximum $U/P$ osmolal ratio achieved remains significantly below normal[24,25]. One possible cause of this phenomenon consists of the depression in concentrating power which is known to follow the ingestion of excessive amounts of water by healthy subjects[26,27].

It is the classical view of diabetes insipidus that the polydipsia is a consequence of the polyuria and that the limitation in concentrating power determines the need to excrete the increased volume of water[21]. On this view the volume of water demanded would be determined by the severity of the concentrating defect and would bear a direct relationship to the magnitude of the solute load derived from the diet and catabolism. There is indeed satisfactory evidence to show that the magnitude of the polyuria in experimental diabetes insipidus is directly proportional to the amount of urinary solute[28,29]. LEAF and his associates[30] came to a similar conclusion in extensive investigations on a patient suffering from diabetes insipidus whose thirst and polyuria disappeared following the development of insufficiency of the anterior pituitary.

The amelioration of the polyuria appeared merely to be a result of reduction in solute excretion due to diminution in appetite, and administration of cortisone did not alter water excretion as long as the patient ingested a constant diet. They concluded that cortisone and adrenocortical steroids possessed no specific effect on the polyuria or the renal mechanism responsible for it. In spite of the occurrence of a number of clinical

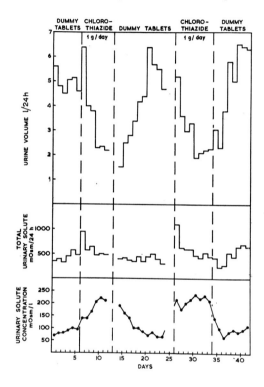

Fig. 1. D.T. ♀ 53 year. Diabetes Insipidus 24 volumes of urine, total urinary solute and osmolal concentration in a patient with diabetes insipidus treated with chlorothiazide and dummy tablets. Maximum $U/P$ osmolal ratios and values of $T^C_{H_2O}$ determined during osmotic diuresis while the patient was receiving chlorothiazide were 0.61 and 0.66 and –4.0 ml/min respectively. These were not significantly different from those obtained with dummy tablets. With i.v. pitressin the $U/P$ ratio rose to 1.7 and $T^C_{H_2O} = +2.6$ ml/min.

cases on the basis of which the classical theory of the primacy of the polyuria has been doubted[31-33], the majority of workers have accepted the classical view even when the syndrome of polyuria and polydipsia have followed damage to the base of the brain as well as to the pituitary stalk and pituitary gland[34,35]. Indeed, in a recent review the presence of a lesion in this area has been used as evidence against the primacy of the polydipsia[25]. In the absence of precise clinico-pathological studies in this syndrome in human subjects, more information on the dominance of a lesion of the thirst mechanism, of the relationship of adrenocortical steroids and of the defect in the power of renal conservation of water to the polyuria could be obtained by studies similar to those reported by ROBSON AND LAMBIE[11]. By controlling the solute load, by the use of dummy and cortisone tablets, and by estimates of maximal $U/P$ osmolal ratios and of $T^C_{H_2O}$ during various phases of the observations in two patients following hypophysectomy, the latter workers were able to show (1) that there was clear evidence of ADH insufficiency, (2) that cortisone administration resulted in considerable increase in polyuria which was not due to an increase in solute load nor to deterioration in the power of the kidneys to conserve water. The conclusion seemed inescapable that in these subjects cortisone induced a primary polydipsia with consequent polyuria and that this polydipsia was relieved by pitressin. These results are in accord with the view that the distinction between the primacy of the polyuria and that of the polydipsia in this syndrome may not be so clear cut as has been thought[36]. There is independent experimental evidence to support the view that the renal defect of diabetes insipidus may be only one component of the polydipsia. LEVKOFF et al.[37] showed in dogs subjected to section of the infundibulum that the spontaneous consumption of water was far in excess of the amount demanded by the concentrating defect and similar views have been expressed by BELLOWS AND VAN WAGENEN[38] and BAKER et al.[39]. The interesting observation has also been made by PASQUALANI AND CODEMELLA[40] that

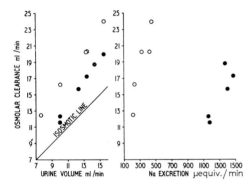

Fig. 2. Normal subject deprived of food and water for 22 h and given 20 units of pitressin. Osmotic diuresis established with mannitol infusion. Two injections of mersalyl (2 ml) given 14 and 3 h before determinations were made 200 mg BAL was then given intramuscularly and determinations made after 30 min. Mersalyl is seen to reduce the value of $T^c_{H_2O}$ and to increase the rate of sodium excretion for any given osmolar clearance. ●, following injection of mersalyl; o, 30 min after 200 mg BAL i.m.i.

the administration of pitressin to patients with diabetes insipidus relieved thirst induced by water deprivation while this was being maintained. The value of this observation, however, would have been greatly increased if control injections of inert solution had been given double blind.

KENNEDY AND CRAWFORD[41,42] have recently reported the effect of chlorothiazide in reducing the urine volume of rats in which diabetes insidipus had been induced experimentally by electrolytic destruction of the connections in the anterior hypothalamus between the supraoptic nucleus and the pituitary stalk. In these animals the osmolality of the urine rose from very low levels in the untreated state to concentrations between 150–250 mosm/l. Fig. 1 shows qualitatively similar results which we have obtained in an adult patient with this disease. Chlorothiazide was given alternately with identical dummy tablets during controlled and constant dietary intake with unrestricted access to water. During chlorothiazide therapy there was a distinct reduction in urinary volume and rise in urinary osmolality. The latter, however, did not rise higher than the value obtained after 16 hours of water deprivation without chlorothiazide and this drug did not alter the maximum $U/P$ osmolal ratio or the value $-T^c_{H_2O}$ determined during osmotic diuresis, which remained at 0.6 and $-4.0$ ml/min respectively. The reduction in urinary volume with therapy in this patient was therefore associated with any improvement in the renal power to conserve water and could be explained by a diminution in water intake due to depression of the thirst centre. Even without chlorothiazide it is clear that the solute load was being excreted at a concentration well below that which the patient was capable of reaching. We have obtained a similar effect in diabetes insipidus with mersalyl given by intramuscular injection. This drug, when given to hydropenic normal subjects, is capable of reducing tubular water reabsorption (Fig. 2)[43,44] though this effect is not invariable[9]

## HYPERPARATHYROIDISM

Polyuria is a frequent complaint in hyperparathyroidism and occurred in a large proportion of HELLSTROM's series of patients[45]. This usually but not invariably subsides following removal of the parathyroid tumour. 68% of a series of 51 patients reported by EDVALL[46] showed increase in concentrating power as assessed by specific gravity shortly after removal of a parathyroid adenoma, and similar findings were reported by COHEN et al. in two patients[47]. In only one of these were estimations of water-conserving power undertaken under exogenous solute loading when an increase in the value of $T^c_{H_2O}$ of from 0.54 to —2.6 ml/min to +1.0 ml/min was observed twelve days after removal of the parathyroid tumour. Table I shows results we have obtained in 4 patients before and after removal of a parathyroid tumour; there was an increase in the $U/P$ osmolal ratio in all patients, and a striking rise in the value obtained for

TABLE I

HYPERPARATHYROIDISM

RENAL POWER TO CONSERVE WATER BEFORE AND AFTER PARATHYROIDECTOMY

| | | Before operation | | | | | After operation | | | |
| | | Calcium | | | | | Calcium | | | |
| Patient | Creatinine clearance ml/min | Serum mg/100 ml | Urine mg/24 h | U/P Osmolal ratio | $T^c_{H_2O}$ ml/min | Serum mg/100 ml | Urine mg/24h | U/P Osmolal ratio | $T^c_{H_2O}$ ml/min | Days post-operati |
|---|---|---|---|---|---|---|---|---|---|---|
| 1 | 19 | 16.8 | 213 | 1.19 | 0 | 9.6 | 176 | 1.52 | 0 | 7 |
| 2 | 65 | 12 | 219 | 1.27 | 1.1 | 7.9 | 81 | 1.65 | 2.6 | 7 |
| 3 | 83 | 15.8 | 630 | 1.64 | 2.4 | 11.1 | 108 | 2.56 | 3.9 | 10 |
| 4 | 84 | 14.5 | 306 | 1.77 | 2.5 | 9.5 | 140 | 2.84 | 5.4 | 7 |

TABLE II

EFFECT OF PARATHYROID EXTRACT ON RENAL POWER TO CONSERVE WATER

| Experimental conditions | U/P osmolal ratio | $T^c_{H_2O}$ ml/min average of 6–9 clearance periods | Serum calcium mg/100 ml | 24 h urinary calcium excretion mg | Creatinine clearance ml/min |
|---|---|---|---|---|---|
| | | Subject A.F. 43 yrs. | | | |
| Control | 3.9 4.0 | 6.7 | 9.1 | 218 | 99 |
| Parathormone 1000 units i.m.i./day, 3½ days | 3.0 2.4 | 5.3 | 12.5 | | 92 |
| Parathormone 1000 units i.m.i./day, 6½ days | 1.5 1.4 | 2.9 | 11.7 | 498 | 98 |
| 5 days after stopping parathormone | 2.2 | 4.5 | 10.0 | 235 | 120 |
| 6 months after stopping parathormone | 3.2 3.3 | 6.2 | 8.9 | 107 | 104 |
| | | Subject B.M. 55 yrs. | | | |
| Control | 3.1 3.3 | 4.7 | 10.7 | 225 | 93 |
| Parathormone 1000 units i.m.i./day, 6½ days | 1.9 2.0 | 3.2 | 11.9 | 490 | 117 |

Parathyroid extract used was Lilly USP Units.

$T^C_{H_2O}$ in three of them, 7–10 days after operation. The creatinine clearance in the patient in whom the response did not occur was only 19 ml/min and on renal biopsy he was found to have severe pyelonephritis. Acute reversible depression in these indices of renal function have also been produced in human subjects by the administration of parathormone, and Table II shows results we have obtained with two human volunteers[48]. These alterations in water conservation were reversed after withdrawal of the hormone and were accompanied by elevation in serum concentration of calcium and by an increase in urinary calcium excretion. They were not attended by significant depression in creatinine clearance. Very similar observations have been reported by EPSTEIN et al. on dogs[49] in some of which hypotonic urine was excreted during moderate mannitol loading. In these animals focal tubular lesions were demonstrated by microdissection to occur in the ascending limbs of the loop of Henle, the distal convolutions and the collecting ducts. These consisted of epithelial cell necrosis and hydropic swelling with calcification of the basement membrane. It seems likely that all of these phenomena are related at least partly either to chronic hypercalcaemia or to hypercalcuria. The effect on $T^C_{H_2O}$ is not seen acutely on intravenous injection of parathormone[43] or of calcium salts[49]. Morphological and functional changes similar to those obtained with parathormone have been found in rats with the administration of large doses of Vitamin D[50] and in a variety of other conditions associated with hypercalcaemia and nephrocalcinosis, including idiopathic hypercalcaemia[51], extensive paralysis[52], and thyrotoxicosis[53].

It seems reasonable to conclude that the polyuria in these conditions is a consequence of a functional defect in water conservation by the kidney and is responsible for all or part of the polydipsia from which these patients suffer. There are, however, individual case records in the literature which suggest the possibility that a primary disturbance of thirst may also contribute to the increase in the rate of water turnover. This aspect has recently been discussed by FOURMAN[54].

## THE EFFECT OF DISEASE OF THE ADRENAL CORTEX AND OF ADRENOCORTICAL HORMONES ON THE CONCENTRATING AND DILUTING MECHANISM

The relationship of adrenocortical hormones to the means by which the kidneys excrete water and to the action of the antidiuretic hormone is extremely complex and has been the subject of several recent reviews[55]. No attempt will be made to deal comprehensively with the various possible interpretations of the large body of data available and mention will be made of only two aspects of this problem.

### (1) The administration of DCA, potassium depletion and polyuria

Persistent polyuria and polydipsia unresponsive to vasopressin were among the early effects noted following long continued administration of DCA (desoxycorticosterone acetate)[56]. In the light of present knowledge it now seems reasonable to believe that part of the effect noted by these workers was the result of potassium depletion induced by the steroid. The original observation of the dependence of the polyuria or its aggravation upon adequate intake of sodium chloride is in accord with what is now known of the dependence of potassium loss induced by DCA upon sodium conservation[57]. There is evidence to show that experimental potassium depletion in rats reduces renal concentrating power and that the magnitude of the defect is proportional to the degree of potassium depletion[58]. This phenomenon is seen in patients suffering from various diseases which lead to potassium depletion[59] and the defect involves water transport both with endogenous solute loads and after mannitol loading. This is seen in Table III, which gives results for $U/P$ osmolal ratio and $Tc_{H_2O}$ before and after repletion with potassium. All these patients complained of thirst and exhibited polyuria. DUSTAN *et al.*[60] have reported very similar data in three patients suffering from aldosteronism and in both groups there is an interesting dissociation in the improvement in water-conserving power following K repletion as revealed by the marked increase in value of $Tc_{H_2O}$ as compared with the more marginal increase in $U/P$ osmolal ratio.

TABLE III

RESULTS OF DETERMINATION OF MAXIMUM $U/P$ OSMOLAR RATIO AND $Tc_{H_2O}$ 22 h AFTER WATER RESTRICTION AND FOLLOWING 20 UNITS PITRESSIN TANNATE IN OIL BEFORE AND AFTER REPLETION WITH POTASSIUM

| Patient and diagnosis | Maximal $U/P$ | | $Tc_{H_2O}$ $ml/min$ | | K |
|---|---|---|---|---|---|
| | K depletion | K repletion | K depletion | K repletion | Retained mequiv. |
| 1. Cushing's syndrome | 1.90 | 2.14 | 0.7 | 2.7 | 1000 |
| 2. Pyloric stenosis | 2.40 | 2.40 | 2.4 | 2.8 | 650 |
| 3. Laxative addict | 1.93 | 2.80 | 0 | 3.2 | 1063 |
| 4. Laxative addict | 1.91 | 2.01 | 0.6 | 2.8 | 1050 |
| | | 2.25 (6 months later) | | 2.5 (6 months later) | |

While it is tempting to explain the polydipsia in all these patients in terms of the polyuria induced by a potassium-linked defect in the capacity to conserve water, there is a considerable body of data which suggests that this is too simple a view. LOEB and his co-workers[61] were unable to prevent the development of polyuria in their DCA-treated animals by feeding potassium, and LEVINSKY *et al.*[62] have demonstrated the development of resistance to pitressin in rats given DCA or fed on low salt diets independent of any potassium depletion. They postulate a direct inhibition of tubular water reabsorption by mineralocorticoids, an idea originally advanced by GAUNT *et al.*[63]. Furthermore, HOLLANDER and his colleagues[58] have shown that rats made deficient in potassium increase their intake of water before any diminution in maximum achievable urinary concentration can be demonstrated. There is some clinical evidence that K depletion in human subjects may also be associated with intense thirst unrelieved by drinking[64], though the absence of a precise estimate of renal concentrating power in these subjects does not permit this conclusion to be reached with certainty.

*(2) Adrenocortical insufficiency and the administration of cortisone*

It has been known for some years that in the presence of adrenocortical insufficiency in man, the capacity to eliminate a water load is reduced and that this is restored by the administration of cortisone[65] though not by DCA or aldosterone[66,67]. Although it appears likely that in adrenocortical insufficiency reduction in the rate of glomerular filtration contributes to this impairment in diluting power, KLEEMAN *et al.*[68] have produced evidence which strongly suggests that the effect of cortisone is the result of an action on the renal tubules consisting either of reduction in the diffusion of water from the diluting segment of the loop of Henle or collecting duct, or of a redistribution of sodium reabsorption in such a way as to enhance the distal tubular component thus liberating "free" water for excretion. This conclusion was based on the demonstration of an improvement in all the parameters of water excretion (flow, osmolality and $-T^C_{H2O}$) without a change in filtration rate and in association with a decrease in solute excretion when cortisone was given to patients with adrenocortical insufficiency. A similar conclusion was reached by RAISZ et al.[69] who gave large doses

### TABLE IV

#### PRIMARY ADRENOCORTICAL INSUFFICIENCY

| Patient | DCA only | | | DCA + 75 mg cortisone/day | | |
|---|---|---|---|---|---|---|
| | Max. U/P ratio | $T^C_{H2O}$ ml/min | Creatinine clearance ml/min | Max. U/P ratio | $T^C_{H2O}$ ml/min | Creatinine clearance ml/min |
| M$^C$K | 2.4 | 2.8 | 78 | 3.2 | 3.8 | 78 |
| GS | 2.8 | 5.1 | 110 | 3.4 | 8.6 | 130 |
| AM$^C$ | 2.8 | 2.7 | 76 | 3.1 | 4.8 | 70 |

Determinations made 22 hours after water and food restriction. DCA had been given by implant. 75 mg Cortisone/day was given orally for 3 days before the determinations.

### TABLE V

#### HYPOPITUITARISM

| Patient | Before cortisone therapy | | | During cortisone therapy | | |
|---|---|---|---|---|---|---|
| | Max. U/P ratio | $T^C_{H2O}$ ml/min | Creatinine clearance ml/min | Max. U/P ratio | $T^C_{H2O}$ ml/min | Creatinine clearance ml/min |
| M | 2.3 | 2.6 | 66 | 2.3 | 3.3 | — |
| C | 1.8 | 1.2 | 53 | 2.1 | 4.3 | 59 |
| W | 1.8 | 1.2 | 73 | 2.4 | 4.8 | 68 |

Cortisone was given by mouth as cortisone acetate 300 mg/day for 3 days. Experimental conditions as under Table IV.

of cortisone to normal subjects during water diuresis. In these individuals there was a regular increase in maximal urine flow and free water clearance. A similar effect has been noted in patients with severe diabetes insipidus [11,70].

While these studies carried out after water loading provide information on the action of adrenocorticosteroids in the absence of ADH, certain older observations in the literature suggest that adrenocorticoids are concerned also with the production of urine more concentrated than plasma. In 1939 WILSON AND SUNDERMAN [71] showed the occurrence of salt retention in patients with Addison's disease given high sodium intakes and subjected to water restriction. They attributed this to limitation in the renal power of concentration. A similar impairment was demonstrated by BURNETT [72] who gave hypertonic saline intravenously to normal subjects and to individuals with adrenocortical insufficiency; in addition, MEMBRIVES, POWER AND KEPLER [73] showed impairment in concentrating ability in patients suffering from Addison's disease following periods of water deprivation. Table IV and V show observations we have obtained in patients with Addison's disease and hypopituitarism after the withdrawal of cortisone for three days and again following its administration. All patients were subjected to a standard period of 20 to 22 hours' food and water deprivation. There is seen to be a marginal increase in maximal $U/P$ osmolal ratio and a very striking rise in the value of $T^c_{H2O}$ in all six patients with the giving of cortisone by mouth. The values of creatinine clearance in the tables are those determined during osmotic diuresis following the infusion of mannitol and are not significantly different with or without cortisone administration. This effect of cortisone on $T^c_{H2O}$ is not seen in normal individuals[11],[69]. These subjects were not given pitressin before or during the observations and the possibility that the stimulus for ADH secretion of comparable periods of

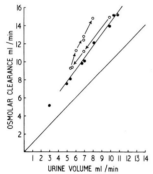

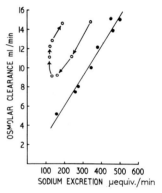

Fig. 3. W.♂, untreated Addison's disease. Relation of minute volume of urine to osmolar clearance during mannitol diuresis. Patient deprived of water and food for 22 h and given pitressin tannate, 20 units i.m.i. (•) control determinations. (o) obtained serially and in the order indicated by arrow, after i.v. injection of 100 mg cortisone hemisuccinate and during sustained infusion of 200 mg hydrocortisone. Clearance periods 10–15 min each.

Fig. 4. W.♂, untreated Addison's disease. Subject as in Fig. 3 and data obtained in course of same experiment. Relation of sodium excretion to osmolar clearance before (•) and after (o) cortisone and hydrocortisone administration given as described (Fig. 3).

hydropenia might differ with or without cortisone must be considered. That this is an unlikely explanation of the results is evidenced in Figs. 3 and 4 in which the relation of osmolar clearance to urine flow and the rate of sodium excretion is shown for an individual suffering from untreated Addison's disease subjected to 20 hours' water deprivation and given 20 units pitressin tannate in oil by intramuscular injection 20 hours before the determinations were made. After the establishment of a vigorous osmotic diuresis during which the urine was collected for nine clearance periods, 100 mg of cortisone hemisuccinate was given intravenously followed by continued mannitol infusion containing 200 mg of hydrocortisone. The open circles show results obtained after the administration of the steroid, when a sharp increase in the value of $T^c_{H2O}$ of up to 2 ml/min occurs. This is accompanied by a reduction in the rate of sodium excretion for comparable rates of osmolar clearance. A similar effect on $T^c_{H2O}$ was seen by ROBSON AND LAMBIE[11] in two patients who paradoxically developed cortisone-dependent polydipsia and polyuria following hypophysectomy. These results raise the interesting possibility that under conditions of osmotic diuresis cortisone, and possibly other adrenocorticoids, act directly on the renal concentrating mechanism increasing the reabsorption of solute-free water. The current view that water reabsorption is dependent upon the establishment of a concentration gradient in the interstitial tissue in the renal medulla might provide a possible explanation of the mechanism of this action. It would seem likely that acute alterations in sodium reabsorption at the critical site in the loop of Henle ought to be accompanied by alterations in urinary osmolality in the presence of ADH. The results are consistent with this view, which receives experimental support from the observations of GUNNEBAULT AND MOREL [74]. These workers showed that in salt-loaded rats the ratio of the concentration of sodium in the papilla of the kidney to that in the plasma is reduced from 1.3 to 0.9 by adrenalectomy. These results confirm WIRZ's demonstration of the existence of a concentration gradient between the papilla and the plasma when the urine is hypertonic and suggest that the establishment of this gradient is dependent upon the presence of adrenocorticoids.

## SUMMARY

In health, the rate of elimination of water by the human kidney is primarily determined by the magnitude of solute load. The thirst mechanism provides a sufficient volume of water available for excretion for this to be accomplished within the limits of the concentrating and diluting power of the renal tubules. Abnormalities in the renal excretion of water occur in a variety of endocrine disorders which include diabetes insipidus, hyperparathyroidism, thyrotoxicosis, hyperadrenocorticalism and aldosteronism, adrenal insufficiency and the post-hypophysectomy syndrome. These disturbances appear to develop both as a consequence of alterations in renal concentrating and diluting power as well as of abnormalities of the thirst mechanism. The influence of these diseases and of the administration of hormones on these parameters of renal function concerned with water excretion and on the thirst centre have been reviewed.

## REFERENCES

[1] L. G. WELT, *Essays in Metabolism*, Little, Brown and Co., Boston, 1955, p. 299.
[2] A. M. WALKER, P. BOTT, J. OLIVER AND M. C. MacDOWELL, *Am. J. Physiol.*, 134 (1941) 580.
[3] H. WIRZ, *The Neurohypophysis*, Butterworth, London, 1957, p. 157.
[4] S. BOYARSKY AND H. W. SMITH, *J. Urol.*, 78 (1957) 511.
[5] S. RAPOPORT, W. A. BRODSKY, C. D. WEST AND B. MACKLER, *Am. J. Physiol.*, 156 (1949) 433.
[6] H. W. SMITH, *The Kidney*, Oxford University Press, London, 1951.
[7] C. D. WEST, S. KAPLAN, S. J. FOMON AND S. RAPOPORT, *Am. J. Physiol.*, 170 (1952) 239.
[8] L. G. WESSON AND W. P. ANSLOW, *Am. J. Physiol.*, 170 (1952) 255.
[9] G. A. ZAK, C. BRUN AND H. W. SMITH, *J. Clin. Invest.*, 35 (1954) 1064.
[10] L. G. RAISZ, W. Y. AU AND R. L. SHEER, *J. Clin. Invest.*, 38 (1959) 1725.
[11] J. S. ROBSON AND A. T. LAMBIE, *Am. J. Med.*, 26 (1959) 769.
[12] E. J. SCHOEN, *J. Appl. Physiol.*, 10 (1957) 267.
[13] C. R. KLEEMAN, F. H. EPSTEIN AND C. WHITE, *J. Clin. Invest.*, 35 (1956) 749.
[14] B. ANDERSSON, *Experientia*, 8 (1952) 157.
[15] B. ANDERSSON, *Acta Physiol. Scand.*, 28 (1953) 188.
[16] B. ANDERSSON, *The Neurohypophysis*, Butterworth, London, 1957, p. 131.
[17] M. A. GREER, *Proc. Soc. Exptl., Biol. Med.*, 89 (1955) 59.
[18] B. ANDERSSON AND S. M. McCANN, *Acta Physiol. Scand.*, 33 (1955) 333.
[19] E. B. VERNEY, *Proc. Roy. Soc., (London) B*, 135 (1947) 25.
[20] A. V. WOLF, *Am. J. Physiol.*, 161 (1950) 75.
[21] C. FISCHER, W. R. INGRAM AND S. W. RANSON, *Diabetes Insipidus*, Edwards, Ann Arbor, 1938.
[22] W. A. BRODSKY AND S. RAPOPORT, *J. Clin. Invest.*, 30 (1951) 282.
[23] H. E. DE WARDENER AND F. DEL GRECO, *Clin. Sci.*, 14 (1955) 715.
[24] C. S. ALEXANDER, D. M. FILBIN AND S. A. FRUCHTMAN, *J. Lab. Clin. Med.*, 54 (1959) 566.
[25] E. D. BARLOW AND H. E. DE WARDENER, *Quart. J. Med.*, 110 (1959) 235.
[26] F. H. EPSTEIN, C. R. KLEEMAN AND A. HENDRIKX, *J. Clin. Invest.*, 36 (1957) 629.
[27] H. E. DE WARDENER AND A. HEXHEIMER, *J. Physiol.*, 42 (1957) 139.
[28] C. A. WINTER, W. R. INGRAM AND R. C. EATON, *Am. J. Physiol.*, 139 (1943) 700.

[29] S. B. BEASER, *Am. J. Med.*, 213 (1947) 441.

[30] A. LEAF, A. R. MAMBY, H. ROSMUSSEN AND J. P. MARASCO, *J. Clin. Invest.*, 31 (1952) 914.

[31] J. F. FULTON AND P. BAILEY, *J. Nervous Mental Disease*, 69 (1929) 1, 145, 261.

[32] R. KOURILOSKY, *Proc. Roy. Soc. Med.*, 43 (1950) 842.

[33] S. H. STRIBLING AND C. L. SPURR, *J. Lab. Clin. Med.*, 44 (1954) 936.

[34] D. IKKOS, R. LUFT AND H. OLIVECRONA, *J. Clin. Endocrinol.*, 15 (1955) 553.

[35] O. H. PEARSON AND B. S. RAY, *Endocrine Aspects of Breast Cancer, Proc. of Conference, Glasgow*, 1957, p. 90.

[36] M. B. LIPSETT, J. P. MACCLEAN, C. D. WEST, M. C. LI AND O. H. PEARSON, *J. Clin. Endocrinol.*, 16 (1956) 183.

[37] A. H. LEVKOFF, T. W. DEMUNBRUN AND A. D. KELLER, *Am. J. Physiol.*, 176 (1954) 25.

[38] R. T. BELLOWS AND W. P. VAN WAGENEN, *J. Nervous Mental Disease*, 88 (1938) 417.

[39] J. P. BAKER, E. F. ADOLPH AND A. D. KELLER, *Am. J. Physiol.*, 173 (1953) 233.

[40] R. Q. PASQUALANI AND A. CODEMELLA, *Acta Endocrinol.*, 30 (1959) 37.

[41] G. C. KENNEDY AND J. D. CRAWFORD, *Lancet*, 276 (1959) 866.

[42] J. D. CRAWFORD AND G. C. KENNEDY, *Nature*, 183 (1959) 891.

[43] J. S. ROBSON AND A. T. LAMBIE, unpublished results.

[44] W. T. AU AND L. G. RAISZ, *Clin. Research Proc.*, 7 (1959) 280.

[45] J. HELLSTROM, *Acta Endocrinol.*, 16 (1954) 30.

[46] C. A. EDVALL, *Acta Clin. Scand., Suppl.*, 229 (1958).

[47] S. I. COHEN, M. F. FITZGERALD, P. FOURMAN, W. J. GRIFFITHS AND H. E. DE WARDENER, *Quart. J. Med.*, 26 (1957) 423.

[48] A. T. LAMBIE AND J. S. ROBSON, *Lancet*, 277 (1959) 328.

[49] F. H. EPSTEIN, D. BECK, F. A. CARONE, H. LEVITIN AND A. MANITIUS, *J. Clin. Invest.*, 38 (1959) 1214.

[50] F. H. EPSTEIN, M. J. RIVERA AND F. A. CARONE, *J. Clin. Invest.*, 37 (1958) 1702.

[51] DORHOUT MEES, *Acta Med. Scand.*, 157 (1957) 199.

[52] C. W. DAESCHNER, J. H. MOYER AND E. M. PFEIFFER, *J. Chronic Diseases*, 7 (1958) 43.

[53] F. H. EPSTEIN, L. F. FREEDMAN AND H. LEVITIN, *New Eng. J. Med.*, 258 (1958) 782.

[54] P. FOURMAN, *Lancet*, 276 (1959) 268.

[55] R. GAUNT, C. W. LLOYD AND J. J. CHART, *The Neurohypophysis*, Butterworth, London, 1957.

[56] C. J. RAGAN, P. FERREBEE, D. W. PHYFE, D. W. AITCHLEY AND R. F. LOEB, *Am. J. Physiol.*, 131 (1940) 71.

[57] A. S. RELMAN AND W. B. SCHWARTZ, *Yale J. Biol. and Med.*, 24 (1952) 540.

[58] R. HOLLANDER, R. W. WINTERS, T. F. WILLIAMS, J. BRADLEY, J. OLIVER AND L. G. WELT, *Am. J. Physiol.*, 189 (1957) 557.

[59] A. S. RELMAN AND W. B. SCHWARTZ, *Am. J. Med.*, 24 (1958) 764.

[60] H. P. DUSTAN, A. C. CORCORAN AND I. H. PAGE, *J. Clin. Invest.*, 35 (1956) 1357.

[61] J. W. FERREBEE, D. PARKER, W. H. CARNES, M. K. GERITY, D. W. AITCHLEY AND R. F. LOEB, *Am. J. Physiol.*, 135 (1941) 230.

[62] N. C. LEVINSKY, D. G. DAVIDSON AND R. W. BERLINER, *Am. J. Physiol.*, 196 (1959) 451.

[63] R. GAUNT, J. H. BIRNIE AND W. S. EVERSOLE, *Physiol. Revs.*, 29 (1949) 281.

[64] P. FOURMAN, *Clin. Sci.*, 13 (1954) 93.

[65] A. SLESSOR, *J. Clin. Endocrinol.*, 11 (1951) 700.

[66] O. GARROD, S. A. DAVIES AND G. CAHILL, *J. Clin. Invest.*, 34 (1935) 761.

[67] A. KECKWICK AND S. L. S. PAWAN, *Lancet*, 267 (1954) 162.

[68] C. R. KLEENMAN, M. H. MAXWELL AND R. E. ROCKNEY, *J. Clin. Invest.*, 37 (1958) 1799.

[69] L. G. RAISZ, W. F. MCNEELY, L. SAXON AND J. D. ROSENBAUM, *J. Clin. Invest.*, 36 (1957) 767.

[70] P. J. SKILLERN, A. C. CORCORAN AND A. L. SCHERBEL, *J. Clin. Endocrinol.*, 16 (1956) 171.

[71] D. M. WILSON AND F. W. SUNDERMAN, *J. Clin. Invest.*, 18 (1939) 35.

[72] C. H. BURNETT, *Renal Function*, Josiah Macey Foundation, New York, 1951.

[73] J. REFORZO-MEMBRIVES, M. H. POWER AND J. KEPLER, *J. Clin. Endocrinol.*, 5 (1945) 76.

[74] M. GUNNEBAULT AND F. MOREL, *Compt. rend.*, 244 (1957) 2741.

## DISCUSSION

WIRZ: The notion of $T^C_{H_2O}$ was conceived at the time when urine concentration was supposed to be made entirely by an active reabsorption of water from the collecting duct. Now you offer two alternative explanations for the occurrence of a $T^C_{H_2O}$. I think that physical chemists would not accept the first one. Limitation of water transport is quite conceivable if it is an active carrier system, which can operate at a limited rate, but a passive transport works on rates depending entirely on surface area, gradients, pore size and so on, and a limitation to any fixed amount is probably not conceivable on the basis of a purely passive transport. Now that does not mean that $T^C_{H_2O}$ do not exist, but probably the explanation is the other one, that the transportation, may be of sodium, in the loop of Henle is the limiting factor, but not the one on the collecting duct.

ROBSON: I would entirely agree with Prof. WIRZ, that the concept of $TC_{H_2O}$ was produced at the time when BRODSKY and others were thinking of primary water movements. It is merely a symbol for the removal of a volume of water which disappears between the glomerular filtrate and the urine in the process of urine concentration and makes no claims as to the mechanism by which this movement occurs. I think that most people, nowadays, are prepared to think in terms of active sodium reabsorption as being one of the main mediators in achieving this movement of water. If that is so, the possibility of partial dependence on surface area and porosity and the other things that you mention would still be acceptable and would be specially marked in osmotic diuresis. Two slides which I showed, seem to show a relationship between sodium excretion and water reabsorption: the cortisone effect and the mersalyl effect. This does show, I think, that in human subjects as you influence sodium reabsorption in either direction so also can you influence maximal capacities to move water at the concentrating side.

# A NEW TREATMENT OF RENAL DIABETES INSIPIDUS

H. REERINK

*Children's Hospital, Rotterdam (The Netherlands)*

At the summer meeting of the Dutch Pediatric Society in 1958, REERINK, BRONGERS AND SCHOUTEN presented the first results of a new treatment of renal diabetes insipidus. This congenital and familial disease represents a form of diabetes insipidus, mostly in boys, in which the kidney is supposed to lack the capacity to concentrate

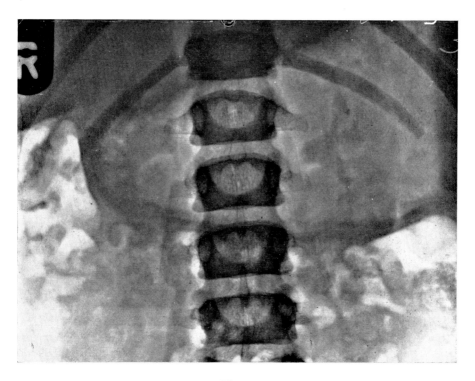

Fig. 1.

because of the inability of the "end organ" to react with the antidiuretic hormone.

The disease has the following characteristic features: abundant urine-flow with low specific gravity; elevated blood levels of sodium, chloride and urea; dehydration; constipation; fever; impaired mental development.

In the Children's Hospital at Rotterdam we treated three boys suffering from this disease of uncontrollable water diuresis paradoxically with the diuretic chlorothiazide (diuril). The effect was a considerable increase in sodium and chloride output, a decrease in aldosterone and consequently a lowering of the plasma levels of these electrolytes to nearly normal values. At the same time we observed that these

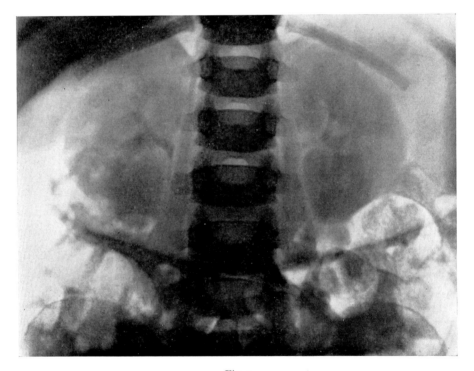

Fig. 2.

children could now be kept on a lower water intake, which before this experiment was not tolerated without signs of serious disturbance, as we proved in one of the patients.

In the discussion following that paper fear was expressed that this form of therapy might lead to circulatory collapse, because the high plasma levels of the electrolytes were considered part of the defense mechanism against loss of body fluid.

Consequently we studied the effect of chlorothiazide upon the extracellular fluid compartment. We did this in a 9-year old boy, a fourth patient, who had not previously been treated with this drug. Using an infusion-apparatus we gave him a constant inulin infusion during 6 to 7 h and calculated the extracellular compartment from inulin blood levels and output. This experiment was done three times under similar conditions except for the treatment with chlorothiazide; the first experiment took place with a sodium plasma level of 175 mequiv./l, and the second and third with a level of 150 mequiv./l. There was *no* difference in the outcome of the three experiments; the extracellular compartment was not reduced. However, we found an improvement of kidney function, indicated by a definite increase in inulin clearance (from $44_6$ to $61_2$) as well as an increase in urea clearance.

Improvement of kidney function could also be shown by using diodrast excretion as a test. Without chlorothiazide there was no visualization of the kidney, while under treatment a clear pyelogram resulted (Fig. 1). As a matter of fact, in a second patient the diodrast experiment gave a remarkable picture (Fig. 2); this is not a normal pyelogram but a "nephrogram", probably due to the impaired excretion of diodrast from the tubule cells into the lumen.

A last example may be given of improved kidney function under treatment with chlorothiazide. A 4-year old boy was first kept without the drug during a week with free allowance for his water intake. Water consumption was stimulated by a perpetual thirst, and the mean volume of the intake was more than 5 l per day. Under treatment, not only was the water intake reduced by more than 30%, but the boy also found time to think and speak of less important things than drinking!

Because the very high levels of the electrolytes are supposed to be the cause of the mental retardation, we think it of primary importance to try to normalize them. For this reason I have thought it appropriate to give this short communication.

# WATER AND ELECTROLYTE CHANGES IN NORMAL
# AND PRE-ECLAMPTIC PREGNANCIES

IAN MACGILLIVRAY

*Midwifery Department, University of Aberdeen and Obstetric Medicine Research Unit (M.R.C.)*
*Aberdeen (Great Britain)*

Although there has been extensive study of total electrolytes and water in non-pregnant subjects little has been done in pregnancy. Yet one of the most baffling problems in obstetrics is pre-eclamptic toxaemia in which an important sign is oedema.

It is known that excessive gain of weight often heralds the onset of pre-eclamptic toxaemia and that at least part of the gain is due to water. The amount of water retained in normal pregnancy is not accurately known nor is the mechanism of the excessive retention in pre-eclampsia known. Furthermore there is disagreement regarding the distribution of the water in pre-eclampsia, some authorities maintaining that all the excess is extracellular while others consider that some of it is retained in the cells. The most popular conception at the moment is that the retention of the extra water is secondary to an excess of salt (sodium chloride) in the tissues.

We have investigated these problems by measuring the various fluid spaces and total electrolytes in normal primigravidae and in primigravidae who developed mild or severe pre-eclampsia near term (after 36 weeks). The results and discussion which follow refer, therefore, to this stage of pregnancy although, to save space and tedious repetition, the limitation is not specifically mentioned. Mild pre-eclamptic toxaemia is defined as a rise in diastolic pressure to 90 mm Hg or more after the 26th week of pregnancy on at least two occasions separated by a day. In severe pre-eclampsia there is, in addition, proteinuria amounting to 0.25 g per l or more. During the investigations the patients received no treatment beyond rest in bed.

## METHODS

A limited number of investigations were carried out in normal non-pregnant females. The investigations and methods employed were:

*(1) Total body water*—calculated from the distribution of deuterium oxide as measured by HYTTEN'S[1] modification of the "falling drop" technique.

*(2) Thiocyanate space*—estimated by BOWLER's method[2].

*(3) Serum volume*—measured by Evans Blue dye.

*(4) Total exchangeable sodium, potassium and bromide, and sodium and bromide spaces*—by the isotope dilution technique. Where simultaneous measurements were made 7.5 $\mu$C $^{24}$Na, 15 $\mu$C $^{42}$K, and 15 $\mu$C $^{82}$Br were administered intravenously, the $^{24}$Na being given on the day prior to the $^{42}$K and $^{82}$Br, and the measurements made according to the methods of ROBINSON *et al.*[3] for Na$^e$ and K$^e$, and BRADLEY *et al.*[4] for Br$^e$. Sodium and potassium concentration in plasma and urine were estimated in a Unicam S.P. 900 flame photometer. Plasma chloride concentration was estimated by Van Slyke's method[5].

It was possible to do all the estimations in only about half of the cases.

TABLE I

TOTAL BODY WATER (T.B.W.) RELATED TO BODY WEIGHT

| | No. of cases | Mean weight in kg | Mean T.B.W. in l | T.B.W. % body weight | Range and S.D. |
|---|---|---|---|---|---|
| Normal pregnancy | 12 | 67.3 | 38.4 | 57.3 | (50.2–63.5) 4.73 |
| Mild P.E.T. | 17 | 70.9 | 41.1 | 58.5 | (48.3–69.3) 4.89 |
| Severe P.E.T. | 13 | 71.6 | 42.4 | 59.4 | (52.2–70.0) 5.24 |
| Non pregnant* | | 60.0 | 31.0 | 51.0 | |

* Composite figures from various authors[6–10].

TABLE II

"EXTRACELLULAR SPACE" RELATED TO TOTAL BODY WATER

| | No. of cases | Mean thiocyanate space (L) | Mean bromide space (L) | Mean sodium space (L) | Thio. sp. % T.B.W. | Br sp. % T.B.W. | Na sp. % T.B.W. |
|---|---|---|---|---|---|---|---|
| Normal pregnancy | 7 | 20.3 | 21.2 | 20.5 | 53.9 | 56.2 | 54.0 |
| Mild P.E.T. | 10 | 20.9 | 21.8 | 22.2 | 47.3 | 49.4 | 50.1 |
| Severe P.E.T. | 7 | 21.0 | 20.3 | 21.9 | 50.8 | 48.6 | 52.5 |
| Non-pregnant* | | 11.5 | 16.1 | 14.5 | 41.0 | 50.3 | 46.5 |

* From various authors[6–9].

TABLE III

THIOCYANATE AND SODIUM SPACES RELATED TO TOTAL BODY WATER

| | No. of cases | Thiocyanate space % T.B.W. | Range and S.D. | Sodium space % T.B.W. | Range and S.D. |
|---|---|---|---|---|---|
| Normal pregnancy | 12 | 53.7 | (42.4–65.7) 7.11 | 54.9 | (46.7–64.7) 5.48 |
| Mild P.E.T. | 17 | 50.8 | (36.3–67.4) 7.41 | 52.1 | (42.4–59.9) 5.14 |
| Severe P.E.T. | 12 | 52.8 | (31.9–65.4) 10.08 | 52.0 | (45.7–56.5) 3.59 |
| Non-pregnant | | 41.0 | | 46.5 | |

TABLE IV

SERUM VOLUME RELATED TO THIOCYANATE SPACE AND TOTAL BODY WATER (T.B.W.)

| | No. of cases | Mean serum vol. | Serum vol. % T.B.W. | Range and S.D. | Serum vol. % thio. space | Range and S.D. |
|---|---|---|---|---|---|---|
| Normal pregnancy | 9 | 4.1 | 10.6 | (8.2–13.5) 1.48 | 20.2 | (17.6–25.3) 2.93 |
| Mild P.E.T. | 15 | 3.5 | 8.7 | (6.4–10.6) 1.13 | 17.5 | (15.2–20.3) 1.61 |
| Severe P.E.T. | 11 | 3.4 | 8.2 | (6.1–11.7) 1.55 | 16.0 | (10.7–27.3) 5.15 |
| Non-pregnant* | | 2.4 | 7.5 | | 20.0 | |

* From various authors[6, 8, 11].

References p. 130

## RESULTS

*Total body water*

In non-pregnant females water accounts for about 51% of body weight according to various authors using deuterium oxide [6-10]. In normal pregnancy at or after the 36th week the percentage of water is increased (Table I). There is a slightly greater, though not statistically significant, increase in severe pre-eclampsia but in mild pre-eclampsia there is little difference from normal pregnancy. However, in the cases of mild pre-eclampsia with clinical oedema the mean total body water percentage of weight was 60.1% while in the non-oedematous it was 57.3%. In normal pregnancy, then, there is a retention of water and in severe pre-eclampsia and mild pre-eclampsia with oedema there is possibly an excessive retention of fluid.

*Extracellular fluid*

There is no exact method for measuring the extracellular fluid but the results from the three methods employed in this investigation show a fairly consistent pattern (Table II). In non-pregnant females the thiocyanate space is less than either the bromide or sodium spaces, but in pregnancy the thiocyanate space is about the same as the bromide and sodium spaces. By all three methods it appears that the extracellular space is greater in normal pregnancy than in the non-pregnant. In pre-eclampsia the extracellular space is the same as in normal pregnancy but as a proportion of total body water it is, if anything, smaller than in normal pregnancy. Using larger numbers of cases (Table III) the thiocyanate and sodium spaces are again relatively larger in normal pregnancy than in non-pregnant females, but again there is little difference between normal pregnancy and pre-eclampsia, the proportion of extracellular water being slightly less in pre-eclampsia than in normal pregnancy.

*Serum volume*

The amount of fluid which is intravascular is shown in Table IV. In normal pregnancy there is an increase in the serum volume both absolutely and as a proportion of the total fluid, but not as a proportion of the thiocyanate space. In pre-eclamptic toxaemia there is a reduction in the serum volume compared with normal pregnancy. This reduction occurs in the absolute amount as well as in terms of percentage of total water or "extracellular fluid".

*Exchangeable sodium*

The total amount of exchangeable sodium and the amount per kg body weight are increased in pregnancy (Table V). The amount per l of total body water remains about the same as in non-pregnant females. In both mild and severe pre-eclampsia there is the same total amount of sodium as in normal pregnancy but the amount per kg body weight and per l of body water is less. This indicates that in pre-eclampsia there is a retention of water without a proportionate retention of sodium.

*Exchangeable chloride*

The results with chloride are very similar to those for sodium. There is an increase in the total chloride and in the amount per kg, but the amount per l of body water remains the same as in the non-pregnant female (Table VI). In pre-eclampsia the total amount of chloride is the same as in normal pregnancy but the amount per kg of body weight and per l of body water is less.

## TABLE V
### EXCHANGEABLE SODIUM (Naᵉ) RELATED TO WEIGHT AND TOTAL BODY WATER

|  | No. of cases | Mean $Na^e$ | $Na^e/kg$ | Range and S.D. | $Na^e/$ L.T.B.W. | Range and S.D. |
|---|---|---|---|---|---|---|
| Normal pregnancy | 12 | 2993 | 44.6 | (38.2–49.6) 3.65 | 78.1 | (70.5–90.8) 5.74 |
| Mild P.E.T. | 17 | 2976 | 42.1 | (35.9–49.7) 4.30 | 72.8 | (61.5–83.1) 6.53 |
| Severe P.E.T. | 13 | 3067 | 43.1 | (36.8–49.7) 4.16 | 72.7 | (61.5–79.0) 5.95 |
| Non-pregnant* |  | 2250 | 39.5 |  | 77.6 |  |

\* EDELMAN et al.[7].

## TABLE VI
### EXCHANGEABLE CHLORIDE (Clᵉ) RELATED TO WEIGHT AND TOTAL BODY WATER

|  | No. of cases | Mean $Cl^e$ | $Cl^e/kg$ | Range and S.D. | $Cl^e/$ L.T.B.W. | Range and S.D. |
|---|---|---|---|---|---|---|
| Normal pregnancy | 7 | 2179 | 33.1 | (24.9–38.8) 5.57 | 57.6 | (46.1–68.3) 7.82 |
| Mild P.E.T. | 10 | 2254 | 30.8 | (26.5–34.7) 3.04 | 50.9 | (40.3–59.0) 7.00 |
| Severe P.E.T. | 8 | 2171 | 29.1 | (22.3–36.0) 4.54 | 51.0 | (35.8–65.2) 10.86 |
| Non-pregnant* |  | 1700 | 28.5 |  | 57.0 |  |

\* From various authors[9, 10].

## TABLE VII
### EXCHANGEABLE POTASSIUM (Kᵉ) RELATED TO WEIGHT AND HEIGHT

|  | No. of cases | Mean $K^e$ | $K^e/kg$ | Range and S.D. | $K^e/cm$ | Range and S.D. |
|---|---|---|---|---|---|---|
| Normal pregnancy | 21 | 2540 | 40.6 | (32.0–53.4) 4.62 | 16.5 | (13.4–19.1) 1.66 |
| Mild P.E.T. | 24 | 2620 | 36.2 | (27.2–42.4) 3.63 | 16.5 | (11.2–20.4) 2.34 |
| Severe P.E.T. | 25 | 2586 | 35.9 | (31.4–43.7) 3.10 | 16.5 | (14.0–21.6) 1.73 |
| Non-pregnant (aged 16–37) | 26 | 2376 | 43.6 | (35.6–53.9) 5.58 | 15.4 | (11.7–19.4) 1.67 |

## TABLE VIII
### SODIUM : POTASSIUM RATIO

|  | No. of cases | $Na^e/K^e$ | Range and S.D. |
|---|---|---|---|
| Normal pregnancy | 21 | 1.18 | (1.000–1.400) 0.113 |
| Mild P.E.T. | 24 | 1.21 | (0.920–1.508) 0.160 |
| Severe P.E.T. | 25 | 1.20 | (0.969–1.441) 0.135 |
| Non-pregnant (aged 16–37) | 26 | 0.97 | (0.787–1.300) 0.122 |

## Exchangeable potassium

The total amount of exchangeable potassium and the amount per cm of height is increased in normal pregnancy but the amount per kg body weight is less than in non-pregnant females (Table VII). In pre-eclamptic toxaemia the total amount of potassium is about the same as in normal pregnancy, but the amount per kg is less. The amount per cm of height is the same in pre-eclampsia and normal pregnancy.

## Na:K ratio

There is a slight increase in the Na:K ratio in pregnancy compared to the non-pregnant (Table VIII) indicating a relatively greater retention of sodium. The difference between normal pregnancy and pre-eclampsia is, however, insignificant.

TABLE IX

CALCULATED SODIUM AND WATER STORAGE IN NORMAL PREGNANCY

|  | Amount of fluid (litres) | Na level (mequiv.) | Total Na (mequiv.) |
|---|---|---|---|
| Mother[12] |  |  |  |
| Intravascular | 1.2 | 140 | 168 |
| Extravascular | 2.2 | 140 | 308 |
| Infant |  |  |  |
| Weighing 7 lb. and with sodium space of 43%[13] | 1.4 | 120 | 168 |
| Placenta |  |  |  |
| Assuming all extracellular fluid to be foetal blood | 0.1 | 120 | 12 |
| Liquor Amnii |  |  |  |
| Average volume 788 ml[14] | 0.79 | 125 | 99 |
| Total | 5.69 |  | 755 |

In normal pregnancy, therefore, there is proportionate retention of sodium and water.

The present findings confirm that there is storage of sodium and water in normal pregnancy. Moreover the amount of sodium which is stored is equal to that required to retain the extra water which accumulates in pregnancy (Table IX).

### DISCUSSION

The average of the values for total body water as a percentage of body weight in normal pregnancy found by other workers[15-20] is about 57%, which agrees with our findings of 57.3%. This is significantly greater than the non-pregnant value of 51% showing that pregnant women retain water.

The difference in the percentage of the total body water between normal pregnancy and pre-eclampsia is not marked but it indicates that in pre-eclampsia there is relatively more water than in normal pregnancy. To express the total body water as a percentage of body weight is somewhat fallacious, however, as it is not known whether the proportion of body weight which is fat changes in pre-eclampsia compared to normal pregnancy. At the moment no reliable information is available about the fat content of the body in pregnancy. MCCARTNEY and co-workers[20] used the formula of SIRI[21] to measure the proportion of body fat but this formula is applicable only to the non-pregnant state.

PLENTL AND GRAY[22] found that the total body water as a percentage of body weight was the same in normal pregnancy as in pre-eclampsia. This difference from our finding may be explained by differing amounts of fat in their patients, but as pre-eclampsia is a condition associated with oedema it seems probable that there is relatively more water in pre-eclamptic toxaemia than in normal pregnancy. The true answer to this problem will not be obtained until the fat content of women with normal pregnancies and with pre-eclamptic toxaemia is measured accurately.

The extracellular space is impossible to measure with accuracy but with the methods we have employed there is an increase in the proportion of total water which is extracellular in normal pregnancy compared to the non-pregnant. There is, however, little difference in this proportion in normal pregnancy and pre-eclamptic toxaemia indicating that there is as much water retained in the cells as there is in the extra-cellular space in pre-eclampsia.

This general increase in fluid in normal pregnancy is also shown in the serum volume, which increases significantly. Contrary to the behaviour of the other fluid spaces in pre-eclampsia, however, the serum volume is decreased both absolutely and as a proportion of the total body water. This fall in serum volume is probably related to the generalised vasoconstriction occurring in pre-eclampsia.

In normal pregnancy the increase in fluid is paralleled by an increase in total exchangeable sodium, so that the amount of sodium per l of total body fluid remains the same as in the non-pregnant state. PLENTL AND GRAY[22] have stated, however, that there is no increase in total exchangeable sodium per kg body weight in normal pregnancy. Unfortunately, it is not possible to calculate from their published data the amount of sodium per l of body water.

In pre-eclampsia, although the total exchangeable sodium remains about the same as in normal pregnancy, the amount per kg body weight and per l of body water falls, suggesting that water is retained without sodium. On the other hand, PLENTL AND GRAY[22] find that, although there is no difference in the total body water as a percentage of body weight between normals and pre-eclamptics, there is a marked increase in the exchangeable sodium per kg in pre-eclampsia. Their findings thus suggest that sodium is retained without water.

Further support for our findings that water is retained without sodium is afforded by the results for exchangeable chloride. These are remarkably similar to the sodium findings.

Potassium increases by about 150 mequiv. in normal pregnancy which can be accounted for by the gestation products and growth of uterus and breasts. In pre-eclampsia there is a fall per kg body weight which is probably due to the retention of water but may be due to increase in fat.

The sodium:potassium ratio increases in normal pregnancy compared with the non-pregnant state, indicating that relatively more fluid than lean tissue constitutes the weight gain in pregnancy. There is no difference in the ratio between normal pregnancy and pre-eclampsia which suggests that there is no greater retention of sodium in pre-eclampsia than in normal pregnancy.

### SUMMARY

Total body water, measured with deuterium oxide, is increased in normal preg-nancy compared with normal non-pregnant females and is further increased in pre-eclampsia. The fluid retention occurs partly in the extracellular space as measured with thiocyanate, bromide and sodium and partly in the intracellular space. The serum volume measured with Evans Blue is increased in normal pregnancy, but in pre-eclamptic toxaemia the serum volume is smaller, both absolutely and as a proportion of total body water than in normal pregnancy. Exchangeable sodium and chloride are increased in normal pregnancy, but the amount per l of the total body water remains about the same as in non-pregnant females. In pre-eclamptic toxaemia, however, the amount per l of the total body water is less even though the total amount is the same as in normal pregnancy. The amount of exchangeable potassium is slightly increased in normal and pre-eclamptic pregnancies but the amount per kg is decreased in both. The pre-eclamptic patients have less potassium per kg body weight than the normal patients but the amount per cm of stature is the same. It is concluded that some of the water retained in pre-eclampsia is retained without sodium chloride.

## REFERENCES

[1]  F. E. HYTTEN, in preparation (1960).
[2]  R. G. BOWLER, Biochem. J., 38 (1944) 385.
[3]  C. V. ROBINSON, W. L. ARONS AND A. K. SOLOMON, J. Clin. Invest., 34 (1955) 134.
[4]  J. E. S. BRADLEY, D. DAVIDSON, I. MACINTYRE AND A. RAPOPORT, Biochem. J., 62 (1956) 33.
[5]  D. D. VAN SLYKE, J. Biol. Chem., 58 (1923–24) 523.
[6]  P. R. SCHLOERB, B. J. FRIJS-HANSEN, I. S. EDELMAN, A. SOLOMON AND F. D. MOORE, J. Clin.
[7]  Invest., 29 (1950) 1296.
[8]  I. S. EDELMAN, H. B. HALEY, P. R. SCHLOERB, D. B. SHELDON, B. J. FRIJS-HANSEN, G. STOLL
[9]  AND F. D. MOORE, Surg. Gynecol. Obstet., 95 (1952) 1.
[10]  H. GILDER, S. F. REDO, D. BARR AND C. G. CHILD, J. Clin. Invest., 33 (1954) 555.
[11]  D. IKKOS, H. LJUNGGREN, R. LUFT AND B. SJÖGREN, Metabolism, 4 (1955) 231.
[12]  J. D. MCMURRAY, E. A. BOLING, J. M. DAVIS, H. V. PARKER, I. C. MAGNUS, M. BALL AND
[13]  F. D. MOORE, Metabolism, 7 (1958) 651.
[14]  G. A. ZAK AND D. P. EARLE, J. Lab. Clin. Med., 49 (1957) 504.
[15]  L. LEITCH, in D. BAIRD, Combined Textbook of Obstetrics and Gynaecology, Livingstone, Edin-
[16]  burgh, 1957.
[17]  F. X. FELLERS, H. L. BARNETT, K. HARE AND H. MCNAMARA, Pediatrics, 3 (1949) 622.
[18]  D. L. HUTCHISON, C. B. HUNTER, E. D. NESLER AND A. A. PLENTL, Surg. Gynecol. Obstet., 100
[19]  (1955) 391.
[20]  C. LAMBIOTTE-ESCOFFIER, D. B. MOORE AND H. C. TAYLOR, Am. J. Obstet. Gynecol., 66 (1953) 18.
[21]  D. HUTCHISON, A. A. PLENTL AND H. C. TAYLOR, J. Clin. Invest., 33 (1954) 235.
[22]  J. SEITCHIK AND C. ALPER, Am. J. Obstet. Gynecol., 68 (1954) 1540.
[23]  J. SEITCHIK AND C. ALPER, Am. J. Obstet. Gynecol., 71 (1956) 1165.
[24]  H. B. HALEY AND J. W. WOODBURY, Surg. Gynecol. Obstet., 103 (1956) 227.
[25]  C. P. MCCARTNEY, R. E. POTTINGER AND J. P. HARROD, Am. J. Obstet. Gynecol., 77 (1959) 1038.
[26]  W. E. SIRI, U.C.R.L. 3349, University of California, Berkeley, Calif., 1956.
[27]  A. A. PLENTL AND M. J. GRAY, Am. J. Obstet. Gynecol., 78 (1959) 472.

## DISCUSSION

BORST: Did you also investigate the plasma proteins in pre-eclamptic patients? If there is a loss of fluid from the vascular system to the tissue spaces, there are two possible reasons, an increased central venous pressure or a lowering of the plasma protein concentration.

MCGILLIVRAY: I have done some electrophoretic studies in pre-eclampsia and there is lowering of the plasma proteins.

BORST: Especially of the albumin.

MCGILLIVRAY: Yes, I have also studied the tissue fluid proteins compared to the serum proteins in these patients. I have not sufficient cases as yet to say definitely, but the preliminary findings show that there is a reduced amount of protein, a very much reduced amount in the tissue fluid compared to the serum, and that the percentage of albumin in the tissue fluid is much greater than in the serum.

# MECHANISMS OF POTASSIUM LOSS BY THE KIDNEY

ANNE T. LAMBIE

*Department of Therapeutics, University of Edinburgh, Clinical Laboratory, Royal Infirmary, Edinburgh (Great Britain)*

Even today in clinical practice potassium depletion seems liable to be overlooked until it has reached an advanced stage. When it occurs, as it frequently does, in association with water depletion and sodium depletion the consequences of the loss of potassium tend to be overshadowed by these more dramatic disturbances of the extracellular fluid. Indeed it is a historical fact that the effects of potassium depletion were recognised only after clinical workers had learned to correct the more obvious deficiencies of sodium and of water.

It is sometimes said that the advent of the flame photometer, which has made the estimation of the concentration of potassium in the extracellular fluid such a simple matter, has contributed largely to the increase in our knowledge of the physiology of this ion and to the ease with which potassium depletion can be diagnosed. Although this is in part true, the flame photometer has also revealed how poor is the relationship between the concentration of potassium in the extracellular fluid and the body stores of this substance[1]. There are few situations in which this discrepancy is so well illustrated as during the treatment of diabetic ketosis[2]. Here, within a few hours and in the absence of any significant alteration in the external balance of potassium, the serum level of the ion may fall from values high enough to exert a deleterious effect upon the heart muscle to values sufficiently low to produce death from respiratory paralysis. The reverse effect is seen in acute renal failure with oliguria or anuria, in which a very striking increase in the level of potassium in the serum may occur as a result of the transfer of this ion from the cells, despite the fact that the patient is usually receiving nothing but glucose and water and the net external potassium balance is very slightly negative. The rate at which these alterations can occur is not always fully appreciated and we have seen fatal increases develop over a period of a few hours.

The reason for the discrepancy between total body potassium and the serum levels of this ion lies in the fact that the great bulk of the potassium is within the cells. The concentration of potassium in the extracellular water is of the order of 3.5–5.0 mequiv./l while the intracellular concentrations are between 25 and 35 times greater. The forces responsible for maintaining this gradient are, as yet, by no means clear, but they appear to be dependent upon the metabolic activities of the cell and to be influenced by a wide range of chemical agents including cardiac glycosides[3] and certain steroids, by the oxygen saturation of the blood[4], by the metabolic changes which occur in uraemia[5], by disturbances of acid–base balance[6] or of carbohydrate metabolism[7] and by many other factors. This disparity between the concentration of potassium in the serum and the body stores of the ion obviously tends to make the diagnosis of potassium depletion more difficult. The view has, therefore, gradually gained ground that the most important single factor in making a diagnosis of potas-

sium depletion is an awareness of the clinical conditions which are inevitably associated with abnormal losses of potassium.

It is the aim of this paper to review the renal causes of potassium depletion and
to discuss them in the light of what is known about the mechanisms whereby potassium is excreted by the kidney.

### THE RENAL EXCRETION OF POTASSIUM

The normal individual in metabolic balance with respect to potassium excretes
in the urine some 50–100 mequiv. of this ion daily—this being approximately the net
quantity absorbed from his diet. In a person with normal renal function this amounts

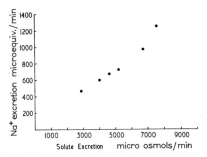

Fig. 1. Relationship of Na+ excretion to
total solute excretion during mannitol
diuresis. Normal subject. 20 h food and
water deprivation. 20 units pitressin tannate in oil i.m.i.

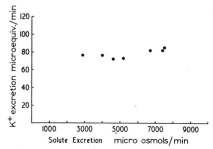

Fig. 2. Relationship of K+ excretion to
total solute excretion during mannitol
diuresis. Normal subject. 20 h food and
water deprivation. 20 units pitressin tannate in oil i.m.i.

to about 10% of the potassium filtered by the glomeruli and its appearance in the urine
would be most simply explained by the assumption that 90% of the filtered load of
potassium is reabsorbed by the renal tubules, the remainder being excreted. The
observations of McCANCE AND WIDDOWSON[8] made in 1937 cast some doubt upon this
simple view. In a single patient suffering from alkalosis and chronic renal disease,
McCANCE demonstrated that the clearance of potassium (11.5 ml/min) exceeded that
of inulin (9.3 ml/min) by about 25%. These findings suggested the possibility that
potassium might be secreted by the renal tubules but, because of the inherent difficulty of measuring the rate of glomerular filtration accurately, particularly when it
is very low, their validity was questioned, though, as BERLINER has pointed out[9]
it is difficult to understand why the backdiffusion of inulin should exceed that of
potassium. Net tubular secretion of potassium, however, can be demonstrated under
conditions which are normally associated with an increased excretion of this ion.
Thus, it has been shown by BERLINER et al.[10,11] to occur both in man and in dogs
during the infusion of potassium salts and in dogs following the administration of
acetazolamide. MUDGE[12] has demonstrated the same phenomenon in dogs during
urea diuresis and during the infusion of potassium chloride and sodium bicarbonate, while FRANGLEN et al.[13] showed that net secretion of potassium occurred in
dogs during acute alkalosis of metabolic origin and in man during acute respiratory
alkalosis induced after potassium loading. The number of studies in which net
secretion of potassium has been demonstrated in the normal human subject is comparatively small. Moreover, the majority of the experiments quoted were carried out
under the somewhat special and artificial circumstances of potassium loading and

marked alkalosis. However, numerous observations have been made in man which tend to support the idea that in more ordinary circumstances, when net secretion of potassium is not demonstrable, the filtered potassium is still largely reabsorbed and the urinary potassium is normally derived by a process of secretion. Among these are the observations made during the course of an osmotic diuresis induced by the infusion of mannitol. In these circumstances the rate of urinary sodium excretion can be shown to increase as the total amount of excreted solute rises (Fig. 1). Since no significant alteration of glomerular filtration rate occurs this is best inter-

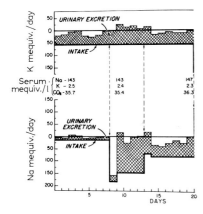

Fig. 3. Balance study carried out upon a case of primary aldosteronism on low and high intake of sodium. Intake is plotted downwards from the base line and urinary excretion upwards from the lowest point. A clear area below the base line represents positive balance, a shaded area above the base line negative balance.

preted as evidence that mannitol reduces the reabsorption of sodium in the proximal tubule, as well as interfering with the proximal tubular reabsorption of water, although the exact way in which it exerts this effect is not clearly understood. When, on the other hand, potassium excretion is plotted against solute excretion (Fig. 2) little if any dependence can normally be demonstrated. Our findings with regard to this are in agreement with those reported by others[14-16]. These observations suggest that potassium and sodium are handled by the kidney in different ways. If the potassium filtered at the glomerulus were entirely reabsorbed in the proximal tubule and the secretory process, demonstrated by BERLINER et al.[10] under conditions of potassium loading were, in fact, the normal means whereby this ion is added to the urine, then the results obtained during osmotic diuresis could be readily explained. Such a secretory process would not be affected by the presence in the tubular fluid of an osmotically active substance and consequently potassium excretion might be expected to remain independent of the solute load during mannitol diuresis. This view is also supported by the observations of BLACK et al.[17], using $^{42}$K. These workers showed that the specific activity of the urinary potassium was close to that of the potassium in the renal venous plasma and appreciably different from that of the K in the plasma entering the kidney by the renal artery, suggesting that it had been derived mainly from the tubular cells.

More recently in a series of experiments carried out upon dogs in which the glomerular filtration rate in one kidney was reduced by means of an inflatable cuff placed around the renal artery, DAVIDSON et al.[18] demonstrated that the rate of potassium excretion could be maintained despite reductions of up to 40% in the glomerular filtration rate, provided that the amount of sodium reaching the distal tubule was maintained at a high level by means of the administration of mersalyl, acetazolamide or sodium sulphate. These studies, which demonstrate that the excretion of potassium is not dependent upon the filtered load of the ion, provide support not only for the idea that the reabsorption of the filtered potassium is virtually complete but also for the theory advanced by BERLINER *et al.* that potassium is secreted by the cells of the distal tubule in exchange for sodium.

In the light of this hypothesis it might be anticipated that both the amount of sodium reaching the site of exchange in the distal tubule and the capacity of the distal tubular cells to reabsorb sodium would exert a profound influence upon the rate of potassium excretion.

### THE AMOUNT OF SODIUM AT THE SITE OF EXCHANGE

Fig. 3 shows the effect of a large intake of sodium upon the excretion of potassium. The observations recorded here were made upon a case of primary aldosteronism, one of those reported by RELMAN AND SCHWARTZ[19]. During the first eight days of the study the sodium intake was kept very low (12 mequiv./day) and on an average intake of potassium the patient (whose serum potassium concentration was at that time 2.5 mequiv./l) was in positive balance with respect to this ion. From the 9th to the 13th day the patient was given large amounts of sodium chloride in her diet, the average daily sodium intake being about 170 mequiv., and during this period her potassium excretion rose and she went into negative potassium balance. Reduction of the sodium intake to more normal proportions on the 14th day resulted, after 24 h, in a fall in the urinary excretion of potassium and the achievement of a small positive potassium balance. This study demonstrated the fact that patients suffering from aldosteronism are not necessarily in negative balance with respect to potassium all the time, and shows moreover that the urinary potassium loss in such patients is at least partially governed by the sodium intake. During the period of sodium loading the urinary aldosterone fell slightly and the increased potassium excretion cannot therefore be attributed to hormonal factors. It seems much more likely that the amount of sodium reaching the site of exchange in the distal tubule is the determining factor. When the sodium intake was low or moderately low the amount reaching the site of exchange was too small to permit a large tubular secretion of potassium, and the patient, consequently, was able to maintain herself in potassium balance. Sodium loading, by providing more sodium for exchange with potassium, resulted in the loss of potassium in the urine. In view of these results it would seem rational to restrict the intake of sodium in cases of aldosteronism or of Cushing's syndrome in which difficulty is experienced in replenishing the body stores of potassium by the administration of potassium salts, even although the patient is not oedematous, and MUDGE[20] quotes a case in which this therapeutic measure was applied successfully. It is fairly generally appreciated that the administration of excessive amounts of sodium chloride to patients receiving intravenous fluids can exacerbate previously existing deficits of potassium. In this connection the recent work of ELKINGTON's group[21] is of interest. These workers have published data which suggest that in normal individuals receiving a very low intake of potassium, the conservation of this ion is facilitated by the simultaneous restriction of sodium.

The amount of sodium reaching the distal tubule can also be increased by the use of diuretics which interfere with the reabsorption of this ion in the proximal part of the nephron. While this extra sodium delivered to the site of exchange, is only one of several factors affecting potassium excretion, it may well be of importance in those circumstances which tend to increase the capacity of the distal tubular cells to reabsorb sodium or to secrete potassium.

## SODIUM REABSORPTION AT THE SITE OF EXCHANGE

The capacity of the cells of the renal tubule to reabsorb sodium is known to be increased by a number of naturally occurring and synthetic steroids including aldosterone, DCA, cortisone, hydrocortisone and many of the new synthetic derivatives. DCA was the first synthetic hormone to be employed in a therapeutic capacity and shortly after its introduction it became clear that its administration resulted not only in sodium retention but also in potassium depletion[22,23]. That these two effects are merely different facets of the same physiological process has been shown by RELMAN AND SCHWARTZ[24]. These workers showed that normal subjects given large doses of DCA (up to 40 mg daily) did not excrete excessive amounts of potassium provided that their sodium intake was restricted (14 mequiv./day) and they were consequently excreting very little sodium in their urine. Similar results have been reported by others[25,26]. Cortisone, hydrocortisone and many of the newer steroid derivatives appear to share with DCA this property of promoting sodium retention and potassium excretion by the renal tubular cells, and patients receiving large doses of these steroids for therapeutic purposes should be given potassium supplements. It may also be desirable to limit the intake of sodium in order to restrict the loss of potassium in the urine. The renal capacity to reabsorb sodium is also known to be increased in individuals who have been subjected to a period of sodium depletion—probably, though by no means certainly, as a result of an increased production of endogenous aldosterone[27]. SCHWARTZ et al.[28] infused neutral sodium sulphate into sodium-depleted subjects and showed that by comparison with normal controls they excreted a smaller proportion of the administered sodium, much of which had been reabsorbed in exchange for potassium and for hydrion which appeared in the urine. We have obtained similar results.

The metabolic situation which exists in these experiments is probably very similar to that found in oedematous patients given diuretics. Such patients have, in the first place, an increased stimulus to reabsorb sodium, the exact nature of which is not, at present, fully understood, and this tendency may well have been exacerbated by a low sodium diet. The administration of diuretics results in the delivery to the site of exchange in the distal tubule of a large amount of sodium, some of which is reabsorbed in exchange for hydrion[29] or for potassium. When circumstances are such as to favour sodium-potassium exchange rather than sodium-hydrion exchange, the loss of potassium in the urine will be proportionately greater.

## THE RATIO OF AVAILABLE POTASSIUM TO AVAILABLE HYDRION

The mechanism proposed by BERLINER et al.[10] to account for the secretion of potassium by the renal tubular cells is very similar to that advanced by PITTS et al.[30,31] to account for the acidification of the urine. A great deal of evidence exists which supports the theory that potassium and hydrogen ions can be regarded as competing for exchange with sodium, the issue being determined in all probability by the ratio of available potassium to available hydrion in the renal tubular cells[32,33]. Alteration of this ratio in favour of potassium may occur during the administration of carbonic anhydrase inhibitors such as acetazolamide and chlorothiazide which interfere with the intracellular production of hydrogen ion, and it is well known[34],[35] that the administration of these substances leads to a reduction in hydrogen ion excretion and an increased excretion of potassium. BERLINER *et al.*[10] showed that this kaliuresis could be inhibited by the simultaneous administration of mercurials and concluded therefore that it was the result of increased tubular secretion of potassium. Substances such as lithium chloride[36] and sodium maleate[37] which interfere with hydrogen ion secretion by some means other than by the inhibition of carbonic anhydrase activity, have also been shown to increase the excretion of potassium. When acetazolamide is

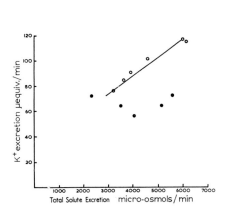

Fig. 4. Effect of acetazolamide upon K+ excretion during mannitol diuresis. o after 500 mg acetazolamide i.v.i.; • before acetazolamide.

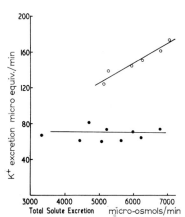

Fig. 5. Effect of chlorothiazide upon K+ excretion during mannitol diuresis. • before chlorothiazide; o after chlorothiazide 500 mg i.v.i.

administered during the course of a mannitol-induced osmotic diuresis (Fig. 4) the rate of excretion of potassium not only increases but also becomes dependent upon the solute load. Exactly similar results have been obtained following chlorothiazide administration during osmotic diuresis[14] (Fig. 5). These changes were associated with the expected diuresis of bicarbonate and increase in the pH of the urine and it would seem likely that this relationship between the rate of excretion of potassium and the total quantity of solute excreted holds good in circumstances which favour potassium–sodium exchange rather than sodium–hydrion exchange. Under these conditions the factor limiting the rate of potassium excretion appears to be the amount of sodium reaching the site of exchange in the distal tube.

It has been reported that the administration of Parathormone results in a diuresis of sodium, potassium and bicarbonate[38],[39] and it is of some interest that we have shown that following the administration of parathyroid extract (Para-thormone Lilly) given during mannitol diuresis, potassium excretion also becomes dependent upon the solute load[14] (Fig. 6). This alteration in potassium excretion is accompanied by an increase in the rate of bicarbonate excretion. The results are best explained on the basis of an inhibition of hydrion secretion in the distal tubule by exogenous "Para-thormone". The suggestion has been made that patients suffering from hyperparathyroidism *per se* suffer from a defect in hydrion excretion and may on occasion become potassium depleted[40–42]. The evidence for this at the moment is not convincing as such patients usually suffer from considerable structural renal disease, and in a single patient free from serious renal disease and having proven hyperparathyroidism the response to an infusion of neutral sodium sulphate given after sodium depletion[28] was normal, the urinary pH falling in 80 min to 4.0[14].

During potassium loading hydrion is transferred from the cells to the extracellular fluid as potassium is taken up by the cells[43]. In these circumstances it seems likely that the intracellular ratio is altered in favour of potassium and this would provide an explanation for the old observation that the administration of the neutral salt potassium chloride is associated with the formation of an alkaline urine containing increased amounts of potassium and diminished amounts of hydrion[44]. In acute alkalosis, whether metabolic[45] or respiratory[46] in origin, hydrion is transferred from the

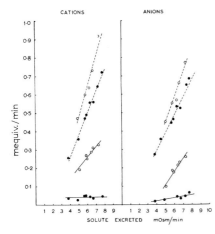

Fig. 6. Effect of parathormone upon potassium and bicarbonate excretion during mannitol diuresis in a normal subject after 22 h of food and water deprivation and 20 units of pitressin tannate i.m.i. 150 USP units parathormone (Lilly) given by intravenous injection followed by an infusion of parathormone of 450 USP units/h thereafter. Cations: • before parathormone; o after parathormone; ———— potassium; – – – – sodium. Anions: • before parathormone; o after parathormone; ———— bicarbonate; – – – – chloride.

intracellular to the extracellular fluid in exchange for sodium, or alternatively sodium is taken up by the cells accompanied by bicarbonate ions. This might be expected to reduce the amount of available intracellular hydrion and, assuming that the renal tubular cells share in this process, to result in the increased excretion of potassium which has been observed to accompany the bicarbonate diuresis of acute alkalosis[43, 47]. The movements of potassium, in these circumstances, are less clearly defined but the amounts involved appear to be very small and may well be of little importance in determining changes in the intracellular ratio of available potassium to available hydrion.

Pyloric stenosis is the most commonly encountered clinical condition which is associated with a metabolic alkalosis. It is well known that patients suffering from this condition are frequently depleted of potassium and it has also been realised for some time that much of the potassium is lost, not in the vomitus but in the urine. A number of suggestions have been put forward to explain this continued loss of potassium in the urine which occurs in the face of progressive potassium depletion. BLACK[48] originally proposed that it is the result of accelerated tissue breakdown and increased adreno-cortical activity. Other workers, while admitting that these factors may contribute to the kaliuresis, take the view that in the early stages of the disorder, before the effects of an increase in $pCO_2$[49] and of cellular potassium depletion[50] become predominant, the metabolic alkalosis which results from loss of gastric hydrochloric acid must be an important cause of increased loss of potassium in the urine. The administration of absorbable alkalis to such patients might be expected to result in an exacerbation of the metabolic alkalosis and, consequently, to an increased loss of potassium in the urine.

### CLASSIFICATION OF POTASSIUM-LOSING RENAL CONDITIONS

From the above discussion the three factors which lead to an increase in potassium excretion in the urine would appear to be as follows:

(1) An increase in the amount of sodium reaching the site of exchange in the distal tubule. *
(2) An increase in the capacity of the distal tubular cells to reabsorb sodium.
(3) An increase in the ratio of available potassium to available hydrion present in the distal tubular cells.

The various clinical conditions associated with an excessive loss of potassium in the urine can be classified under these three headings (Table I). This classification is obviously over-simplified but it is helpful in enabling one to understand the mechanism of abnormal potassium loss in these clinical situations. The place of the mercurial

TABLE I

| *Increased Na+ reaching site of exchange* | *Increased K+/H+ ratio in distal tubular cells* |
|---|---|
| Administration of large amounts of sodium | Alkalosis—pyloric stenosis, administration of |
| Mercurial diuretics, chlorothiazide, | alkali, mercurials? |
| acetazolamide | Acetazolamide |
| | Chlorothiazide |
| *Increased Na+ reabsorption* | Fanconi syndrome |
| Administration of steroids | Renal tubular acidosis |
| Cushings syndrome | Chronic pyelonephritis |
| Aldosteronism—primary | |
| secondary (C.C.F. hepatic cirrhosis, nephrosis) | |

diuretics in such a classification is somewhat difficult to assign. The administration of mersalyl by two injections given a few hours apart to a normal volunteer, results, not in an increased output of potassium, but rather in a diminution of potassium excretion[18] (Fig. 7). Similar results have been reported in dogs[11,51] and have been attributed to the fact that mercurials inhibit the tubular secretion of potassium. On the other hand numerous references are to be found in the literature which show that the administration of these drugs to oedematous patients may result in a less marked augmentation ot sodium excretion and a very definite increase in the rate of excretion of potassium[52,53]. This may be partly due to the fact, mentioned previously, that such patients have an increased tendency to reabsorb sodium in the distal tubule in exchange for potassium or hydrogen ions. Moreover the continued administration of mercurials leads to the development of a metabolic alkalosis and it is possible that this further facilitates loss of potassium in the urine.

Most of the other conditions listed fall into one or other of the three categories. In the case of the carbonic anhydrase inhibitor, acetazolamide, the most important effect, as far as increasing the urinary potassium is concerned, is the inhibition of hydrogen ion secretion in the distal tubule but since this substance inhibits sodium–hydrogen exchange in the proximal as well as the distal tubule[11] it has, in addition, the effect of increasing the amount of sodium reaching the site of exchange. Chlorothiazide not only acts as an inhibitor of hydrogen ion secretion but also interferes with proximal tubular reabsorption of sodium and of chloride, thereby increasing the delivery of sodium to the distal tubule.

An increased capacity to reabsorb sodium leading to loss of potassium in the urine is seen during the administration of exogenous corticoids and in those clinical conditions which are associated with overproduction of endogenous adrenocorticoids.

The effect of acute alkalosis upon the relative concentrations of available potassium and available hydrion in the distal tubular cells and upon the excretion of potassium has already been discussed, and although it is somewhat dangerous to assume that information derived from acute experiments is necessarily applicable to chronic

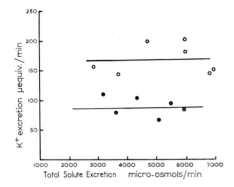

Fig. 7. Effect of mersalyl upon K$^+$ excretion during mannitol diuresis. Normal subject. 20 h food and water depletion. 20 units pitressin tannate in oil i.m.i. Mersalyl 2 ml i.m.i. 14 h and 3 h before start of experiment. B.A.L. 200 mg i.m.i. given 30 min before collections represented by open circles. • mersalyl; o B.A.L.

clinical conditions, it would still seem reasonable to include pyloric stenosis and the metabolic alkalosis which arises as a result of the administration of absorbable alkalis in the third category. Into this category fall the conditions associated with an inborn defect which limits the capacity of the renal tubular cells to transport hydrogen ions, namely the Fanconi syndrome and renal tubular acidosis[54,55].

In the conditions so far discussed the loss of potassium in the urine has been the result of a functional rather than a structural change in the kidney. Within recent years, however, there has been considerable controversy as to whether chronic renal disease can, by itself, ever result in potassium depletion. Several patients originally reported as having potassium-losing nephritis have proved to be suffering from aldosteronism[56,57]. Nevertheless there seems good reason to believe that in certain instances chronic pyelonephritis can produce loss of potassium in the urine by damaging the renal tubules and producing what is, in effect, an acquired form of renal tubular acidosis by destroying the ability to secrete hydrogen ion normally. We have recently studied a case of this sort, a middle aged woman who gave a history of tiredness and muscular weakness of twelve months' duration and a rather longer history of thirst and polyuria. These symptoms were extremely suggestive of potassium deficiency and, in fact, her serum potassium concentration was found to be 2.7 mequiv./l. There was no reason to suspect loss of potassium from the gastro-intestinal tract and the low blood pressure and the presence of a mild degree of acidosis (serum bicarbonate 22.0 mequiv./l) made a diagnosis of aldosteronism unlikely. The blood urea was within normal limits, the creatinine clearance 75 ml/min and the urine was sterile on culture and contained no protein. Nevertheless renal biopsy revealed the presence of a severe degree of chronic pyelonephritis. When given a diet containing only 15 mequiv. of potassium daily the patient continued to excrete appreciably larger amounts of this ion in her urine during a period of observation which lasted for 15 days (Fig. 8). The administration of 6 g of ammonium chloride per day over a 3-day period resulted in the production of a severe degree of metabolic acidosis (serum bicarbonate 10 mequiv./l). Despite this the pH of the urine had fallen, at the end of this period, only as far as 6.1 and the rate of urinary excretion of bicarbonate remained high at from 8 to 12 μequiv./min. This patient had, in effect, an acquired renal tubular acidosis and

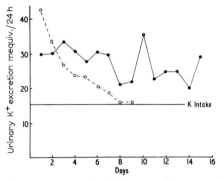

Fig. 8. K+ excretion in a case of acquired renal tubular acidosis during administration of a low K diet (15 mequiv./day). •——• R.T.A.; o---o control.

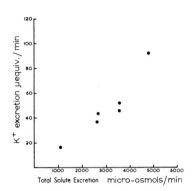

Fig. 9. K+ excretion during mannitol diuresis–chronic pyelonephritis with acquired R.T.A.

it seems likely that as a result of her limited ability to secrete hydrogen ion, potassium was being lost in her urine. During the course of a mannitol diuresis, the minute excretion of potassium showed the same dependence upon the magnitude of the solute excretion that we have observed in patients receiving carbonic anhydrase inhibitors (Fig. 9). This patient has since died and at autopsy the presence of severe bilateral chronic pyelonephritis was confirmed. The adrenal cortices were entirely normal. MAHLER AND STANBURY[58] recently described a very similar case and are of the opinion that this defect in hydrogen ion secretion with the attendant tendency to the loss of potassium in the urine is by no means uncommon. It seems reasonable to include this syndrome in the third category of the classification.

## SUMMARY

In the light of our present knowledge of the means whereby potassium is excreted by the kidney it would appear that the three most important factors influencing the rate of potassium excretion are (1) the amount of sodium reaching the site of the sodium/potassium exchange in the distal tubule, (2) the capacity of the distal tubular cells to reabsorb sodium and (3) the relative amounts of potassium and hydrogen available for exchange with sodium. The evidence for this and some of its clinical implications have been discussed.

## REFERENCES

[1] F. D. MOORE, I. S. EDELMAN, J. M. OLNEY, A. H. JAMES, L. BROOKS AND G. M. WILSON, Metabolism Clin. & Exptl., 3 (1954) 334.
[2] H. E. MARTIN AND M. WERTMAN, J. Clin. Invest., 26 (1947) 217.
[3] I. M. GLYNN, J. Physiol., 136 (1957) 148.

[4] E. CALKINS, I. M. TAYLOR AND A. B. HASTINGS, *Am. J. Physiol.*, 177 (1954) 211.

[5] E. F. GROLLMAN AND A. GROLLMAN, *J. Clin. Invest.*, 38 (1959) 749.

[6] J. M. BURNELL, M. F. VILLAMIL, B. T. UYENO AND B. H. SCRIBNER, *J. Clin. Invest.*, 35 (1956) 935.

[7] W. O. FENN, *J. Biol. Chem.*, 128 (1939) 297.

[8] R. A. MCCANCE AND E. M. WIDDOWSON, *Lancet*, 233 (1937) 247.

[9] R. W. BERLINER, *First Conference on Renal Function*, Josiah Macy Jr. Foundation, New York, 1950, p. 102.

[10] R. W. BERLINER, T. J. KENNEDY JR. AND J. G. HILTON, *Am. J. Physiol.*, 162 (1950) 348.

[11] R. W. BERLINER AND T. J. KENNEDY JR., *Am. J, Med.*, 11 (1951) 274.

[12] G. H. MUDGE, J. FOULKS AND A. GILMAN, *Proc. Soc. Exptl. Biol. Med.*, 67 (1948) 545.

[13] G. T. FRANGLEN, E. MCGARRY AND A. G. SPENCER, *J. Physiol.*, 121 (1953) 35.

[14] J. S. ROBSON AND A. T. LAMBIE, unpublished observation.

[15] S. RAPOPORT, C. D. WEST AND W. BRODSKY, *Am. J. Physiol.*, 157 (1949) 363.

[16] G. M. BULL, *Modern Views on the Secretion of the Urine*, Churchill, London, 1956, p. 256.

[17] D. A. K. BLACK AND E. W. EMERY, *Brit. Med. Bull.*, 13 (1957) 7.

[18] D. G. DAVIDSON, N. G. LEVINSKY AND R. W. BERLINER, *J. Clin. Invest.*, 37 (1958) 548.

[19] A. S. RELMAN AND W. B. SCHWARTZ, *J. Clin. Invest.*, 36 (1957) 923.

[20] G. H. MUDGE, *Bull. N.Y. Acad. Med.*, 34 (1958) 152.

[21] R. D. SQUIRES AND E. J. HUTH, *J. Clin. Invest.*, 38 (1959) 1134.

[22] R. F. LOEB, D. W. ATCHLEY, J. W. FERREBEE AND C. RAGAN, *Trans. Assoc. Am. Physicians*, 54 (1939) 285.

[23] G. W. THORN, R. P. HOWARD AND K. EMERSON, *J. Clin. Invest.*, 18 (1939) 449.

[24] A. S. RELMAN AND W. B. SCHWARTZ, *Yale J. Biol. and Med.*, 24 (1952) 540.

[25] D. W. SELDIN, L. G. WELT AND J. H. CORT, *Yale J. Biol. and Med.*, 29 (1956) 229.

[26] D. S. HOWELL AND J. O. DAVIS, *Am. J. Physiol.*, 179 (1954) 359.

[27] F. C. BARTTER, G. W. LIDDLE, L. E. DUNCAN JR., J. K. BARBER AND C. DELEA, *J. Clin. Invest.*, 34 (1956) 1306.

[28] W. B. SCHWARTZ, R. L. JENSON AND A. S. RELMAN, *J. Clin. Invest.*, 34 (1955) 673.

[29] R. E. WESTON, J. GROSSMAN AND L. LEITER, *J. Clin. Invest.*, 30 (1951) 1262.

[30] R. F. PITTS AND R. S. ALEXANDER, *Am. J. Physiol.*, 144 (1945) 239.

[31] R. F. PITTS, W. D. LOTSPEICH, W. A. SCHEISS AND J. L. AYER, *J. Clin. Invest.*, 27 (1948) 48.

[32] H. M. ANDERSON AND G. H. MUDGE, *J. Clin. Invest.*, 34 (1955) 1691.

[33] J. ORLOFF AND D. G. DAVIDSON, *J. Clin. Invest.*, 38 (1959) 21.

[34] T. B. COUNIHAN, B. M. EVANS AND M. D. MILNE, *Clin. Sci.*, 13 (1954) 583.

[35] A. LEAF, W. B. SCHWARTZ AND A. S. RELMAN, *New Engl. J. Med.*, 250 (1954) 759.

[36] J. FOULKS, G. H. MUDGE AND A. GILMAN, *Am. J. Physiol.*, 168 (1952) 642.

[37] R. W. BERLINER, T. J. KENNEDY JR. AND J. G. HILTON, *Proc. Soc. Exptl. Biol. Med.*, 75 (1950) 791.

[38] R. ELLSWORTH AND W. NICHOLSON, *J. Clin. Invest.*, 14 (1935) 823.

[39] B. E. C. NORDIN, *Scot. Med. J.*, 3 (1958) 466.

[40] S. I. COHEN, M. G. FITZGERALD, P. FOURMAN, W. J. GRIFFITHS AND H. E. DE WARDENER, *Quart. J. Med.*, 25 (1957) 423.

[41] O. WRONG AND H. E. F. DAVIES, *Quart. J. Med.*, 28 (1959) 259.

[42] L. E. BOTTINGER, *Acta Med. Scand.*, 148 (1954) 51.

[43] K. E. ROBERTS, M. G. MAGIDA AND R. F. PITTS, *Am. J. Physiol.*, 172 (1953) 47.

[44] R. F. LOEB, D. W. ATCHLEY, D. W. RICHARDS, E. M. BENEDICT AND M. E. DRISCOLL, *J. Clin. Invest.*, 11 (1932) 621.

[45] R. B. SINGER, J. K. CLARK, E. S. BARKER, A. P. CROSSLEY JR. AND J. R. ELKINGTON, *Medicine*, 34 (1955) 51.

[46] J. H. ELKINGTON, R. B. SINGER, E. S. BARKER AND J. K. CLARK, *J. Clin. Invest.*, 34 (1955) 1671.

[47] S. W. STANBURY AND A. E. THOMPSON, *Clin. Sci.*, 11 (1952) 357.

[48] D. A. K. BLACK AND R. P. JEPSON, *Quart. J. Med.*, 23 (1954) 367.

[49] A. S. RELMAN, B. ETSEN AND W. B. SCHWARTZ, *J. Clin. Invest.*, 32 (1953) 972.

[50] B. M. EVANS, N. C. HUGHES, M. D. MILNE AND S. STEINER, *Clin. Sci.*, 13 (1954) 305.

[51] G. H. MUDGE, A. AMES III, J. FOULKS AND A. GILMAN, *Am. J. Physiol.*, 161 (1950) 151.

[52] H. L. BLUMGART, D. R. GILLIGAN AND M. C. VOLK, *Medical papers dedicated to Henry Asbury Christian*, Waverley Press, Baltimore, 1936, p. 191.

[53] G. T. LESSER, M. F. DUNNING, F. H. EPSTEIN AND E. Y. BERGER, *Circulation*, 5 (1952) 85.

[54] J. H. SIROTA AND D. HAMERMAN, *Am. J. Med.*, 16 (1954) 138.

[55] F. ALLBRIGHT AND E. C. REIFENSTEIN JR., *Parathyroid Glands and Metabolic Bone Disease* Williams and Wilkins, Baltimore, 1948.

[56] G. F. M. RUSSELL, J. MARSHALL AND J. B. STANTON, *Scot. Med. J.*, 1 (1956) 122.

[57] M. D. MILNE, R. C. MUEHRCKE AND I. AIRD, *Quart. J. Med.*, 26 (1957) 317.

[58] R. F. MAHLER AND S. W. STANBURY, *Quart. J. Med.*, 25 (1956) 21.

## DISCUSSION

Borst: We frequently see patients who have lost great amounts of fluids by vomiting and they are alkalotic. They have a very low glomerular filtration rate. They are shocked and we must expect the amount of sodium reaching the distal tubules to have been reduced. How do you explain that often there is an excessive potassium excretion, while you must expect that there is no sodium in the distal tubule available for exchange against potassium.

Lambie: If we accept Berliner's views about the mechanism for secretion of potassium, we have to assume that when potassium is secreted, sodium is present for reabsorption in exchange for potassium. I think that one of the factors which contributes to the diminished excretion of potassium in urine, which I believe occurs in the latter stages of pyloric-stenosis, may be the fact that in severely dehydrated patients, less sodium is reaching the distal tubules. Have you any information about the amount of sodium in the urine? Presumably as long as any sodium is present in the urine, some must be reaching the distal tubules and must be available for exchange.

Borst: There was no sodium in the urine for many days and even after the situation had improved there was no sodium in the urine for many days.

Lambie: I can only get over that difficulty by suggesting the stimulus for reabsorption of sodium was so great, that one of the reasons for there being no sodium in the urine was that it was all being exchanged for potassium.

Borst: That is a good explanation but we have another concept. We think that the body was obliged to defend itself against the alkalosis and had to excrete alkali. There was no sodium available because there was a secretion-insufficiency in which sodium had to be retained. Therefore the only substance that could be excreted was potassium. But the explanation could be a too simple one.

Lambie: Well, I think this is just two sides of the same question. Two factors are operating. The alkalosis may increase the amount of available potassium, or rather diminish the amount of available hydrogen ions for exchange. And again if you have sodium depletion you have an increase in the capacity of the distal tubular cells to reabsorb sodium.

# ELECTROLYTE CHANGES IN HYPOTHERMIA

ERIC NEIL

*John Astor Professor of Physiology, University of London, Middlesex Hospital Medical School. London (Great Britain)*

Hypothermia is used as an adjunct to cardiac and cerebral surgery. The lowering of the metabolic rate produced by cooling allows the surgeon to arrest the circulation, either of the body as a whole or of the brain, for a period adequate for him to effect some necessary repair. Introduced by BIGELOW *et al.*[1] for cardiac surgery, hypothermia has been pioneered also by BOEREMA and his group[2] in Holland.

The name "artificial hibernation" should not be applied to the state of therapeutic hypothermia in the homoiotherm, for the homoiotherm does not hibernate either naturally or artificially. Animals that are true hibernants—such as the hedgehog, the marmot and the thirteenlined squirrel—can continue their winter sleep undisturbed by this review, delivered in Holland on a cold January day.

There is insufficient time available to consider the effect of hypothermia on other than the hydrogen and bicarbonate ion concentrations, sodium and potassium ion concentrations and the blood volume. Those interested in the wider aspects of the physiology of hypothermia may consult reviews by NEIL[3] and COOPER[4].

## HYDROGEN ION CONCENTRATION OF THE BLOOD

$[H^+]$ in blood varies from $10 \cdot 10^{-8}$ to $1.6 \cdot 10^{-8}$ or to put it in convenient if oft ill understood terminology, pH varies from 7.0–7.8 in conditions compatible with life in the homoiotherm. As metabolism constantly supplies $H^+$ to the body fluids, the mechanism of its "suppression" and eventual removal is of fundamental importance. Suppression of $H^+$ added to the blood from the tissue cells is achieved by the provision of hydrogen ion acceptors, such as the histidine ions in the haemoglobin molecule, the proteinic anions of the plasma protein and the bicarbonate anions. Each of these anions accepts $H^+$ and is thereby converted into a feebly dissociated acid (in the case of Hb⁻ and Pr⁻) or into carbonic acid, which thanks to the presence of carbonic anhydrase is in turn converted into $CO_2$ which is evolved by the lungs.

This special position of the anions Pr⁻, Hb⁻ and $HCO_3^-$ has led to their being described as buffer anions: anions whose concentration is dependent on the $[H^+]$ of the blood. The total concentration of buffer anions in the blood is normally of the order of 50 mequiv. but this can be considerably altered by the addition of untoward quantities of $H^+$, such as occurs in metabolic acidosis, or by the loss of excessive amounts of $H^+$, such as occurs in vomiting. Unlike the buffer anions the blood contains some 100 mequiv. of anions (such as Cl⁻) whose charge is unaffected by changes of the blood pH; it is reasonable to refer to such anions as "fixed anions".

The blood also contains metallic cations (approximately 150 mequiv./l) whose total concentration is electrochemically equivalent to that of the total anions. Unfortunately, despite the fact that the cations which electrochemically balance the "fixed anions" are in no way different from those which balance the "buffer anions", it has become customary to refer to "fixed base" and to "buffer base". Fixed base is that concentration of cations which is electrochemically equivalent to the "fixed anions" and "buffer base" is similarly equivalent to the "buffer anion" concentration.

As the total cationic and fixed anionic concentrations remain invariant for a given blood over the biological range of pH produced by increasing the $pCO_2$ to which such blood is exposed, it follows that the buffer anion concentration (and hence the buffer base concentration) remains constant. However, although the buffer anion concentration remains at say 50 mequiv./l, in these conditions the parcellation of buffer anions is considerably altered. To take a simple example, using experimental data:

Normal human blood has a bicarbonate ion concentration of 35 mequiv./l and a pH of 7.00 after equilibration with $CO_2$ at a tension of 170 mm Hg. The haemoglobinic and plasma protein ion concentrations together equal 15 mequiv./l in these conditions. The total buffer anionic concentration is $15 + 35 = 50$ mequiv./l. When another sample of the same blood is equilibrated with $CO_2$ at a tension of 15 mm Hg, the pH is 7.70, $[HCO_3^-]$ is 15 mequiv./l and the combined $[Pr^-] + [Hb^-]$ is 35 mequiv./l. Thus the total buffer anion concentration is again 50 mequiv./l but its parcellation is entirely different: indeed it is this "ebb and flow" between the proteinic anion concentration and the bicarbonate ion concentration which permits the transfer of $CO_2$ in the body with such minimal changes of pH.

The ionization of the strong electrolytes is almost independent of temperature over the range which we have to consider; correspondingly, the total cation and the fixed anion concentrations are almost unaffected by change of temperature. It follows that the buffer anion concentration is unaffected by temperature, but again the parcellation of the buffer anions is profoundly changed by alterations of temperature. As the temperature falls, the ionization of the proteins is progressively reduced[5-11]. As less proteinic anions are formed, more bicarbonate ions take their place and thus the ability of the blood to carry $CO_2$ at any given carbon dioxide tension is improved; as a result the $[HCO_3^-]$ is increased.

The pH of the true plasma is given by the equation

$$pH = pK + \log \frac{[HCO_3^-]}{[H_2CO_3]}$$

All the factors in the right hand side of this equation are altered by changes in the temperature of equilibration of the blood:

1. $[H_2CO_3] = \alpha pCO_2$ where $\alpha$ is the coefficient of solubility of $CO_2$. At $37°$, $\alpha = 0.0313$ mmoles $CO_2$ per l per mm partial pressure of $CO_2$. Thus at $pCO_2 = 40$ mm Hg, $[H_2CO_3] = 40 \times 0.0313 = 1.252$ mmoles/l at $37°$. At $26°$, $\alpha = 0.0411$ and at $pCO_2$ of 40 mm Hg, $[H_2CO_3] = 40 \times 0.0411 = 1.644$ mmoles/l.

2. $[HCO_3^-]$ is increased for any given $pCO_2$ as the temperature falls owing to the simultaneous reduction in protein dissociation.

3. $pK'$ which is the negative logarithm of the apparent first dissociation constant of carbonic acid, is 6.11 at $37°$ and shows a temperature variation $(dK'/dT)$ of $-0.005$. Hence at $26°$ $pK' = 6.165$. It should be clear from the discussion above that this alteration of $pK'$ is due to the changes in $[H_2CO_3]$ and $[HCO_3^-]$.

It should not be forgotten moreover, that the pH of "neutrality" varies with temperature. The dissociation constant of water at $25° = 10^{-14}$. At this temperature pH = pOH = 7.00. At $38°$, $pK_w = 13.6$ and pH = pOH = 6.80. At $0°$, $pK_w = 15.0$ and pH = pOH = 7.50. Hence blood with a true plasma pH of 7.40 at $38°$ is 0.6 pH above that of neutrality but at $25°$ a blood with a pH of 7.40 is only 0.4 pH above that of neutrality. It could thus be argued that if the pH values of blood samples equilibrated at these two temperatures were identical then the blood equilibrated at the lower temperature is more acidaemic. As AUSTIN AND CULLEN[12] remarked, with alteration of temperature there occurs a large associated alteration of hydroxyl ion concentration and the theoretical significance of this remains obscure.

Such theoretical points as have been presented above serve to show that one cannot lightly interpret the changes in [H+] which occur in blood during the course

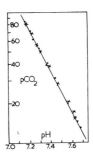

Fig. 1A. Dissociation lines of human blood at $37°$ and $26°$. The $CO_2$ content (vol.%) is plotted against the $CO_2$ tension each on a logarithmic scale. Note that the carrying power of the blood for $CO_2$ is increased at the lower temperature. — • — $37°$; —×— $26°$.

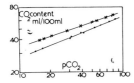

Fig. 1B. Log $pCO_2$/pH graph of human blood. The points obtained by equilibration at $37°$ lie on the same line as those obtained by equilibration at $26°$. —•— $37°$; —×— $26°$.

of experimental hypothermia. However, experimental findings from *in vitro* experiments with blood have served to clarify the situation, and were indeed used by BREWIN *et al.*[9,10] specifically for the purpose of interpreting *in vivo* changes in hypothermic animals and patients.

*In vitro experiments*

Samples of a given blood are equilibrated in tonometers with a series of $CO_2$/air mixtures at $37°$. After equilibration the $pCO_2$, the total content of $CO_2$ in the blood, and the pH measured at $37°$ are determined. It is found that the dissociation "curve" of $CO_2$ plotted as log content of $CO_2$ against log $pCO_2$ is a straight line, (Fig. 1A) confirming PETERS[13]. When the log $pCO_2$ values are plotted against the corresponding pH values, the relationship is linear (Fig. 1B).

On repeating the equilibrations at a temperature of $26°$ and on measuring the pH values at the temperature of equilibration, the $pCO_2$/pH points lie on the same line as that yielded by the results of the equilibrations at $37°$ (Fig. 1B). The log $CO_2$ dissociation line, however, occupies a higher position than that at $37°$, confirming MARTIN AND LEPPER[7] and ADAIR *et al.*[8]. As previously stated, this greater $CO_2$-carrying power at the lower temperature is due to the diminution in proteinic ion concentration in these circumstances.

If separated plasma is equilibrated at temperatures of $37°$ and $26°$ in this manner, then the log $pCO_2$/pH line of plasma at $26°$ lies to the left of that at $37°$ (Fig. 2B) indicating that at the lower temperature, separated plasma is more "acid" at any given $pCO_2$. The log $CO_2$ content/log $pCO_2$ dissociation line of plasma at $26°$ is only slightly above that at $37°$ (Fig. 2A). This gives the clue for the "acidosis" which equilibrated plasma reveals at 26°: the decrease in protein ionization and hence the potential increase in $[HCO_3^-]$ is insufficient to offset the greater $[H_2CO_3]$ consequent upon the increased solubility of $CO_2$ at the lower temperature.

One can, therefore, predict that a solution of haemoglobin submitted to equilibra-

Fig. 2A. Logarithmic $CO_2$ dissociation lines of separated ox plasma equilibrated at 37° and 26° respectively. Note that the $CO_2$ combining power of the plasma is increased at the lower temperature. Upper line—equilibrations at 26°. Lower line—equilibrations at 37°.

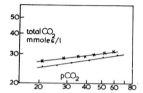

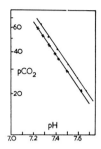

Fig. 2B. Log $pCO_2$/pH graphs of separated ox plasma obtained by equilibrations at 37° and 26° respectively. Note that the points obtained from equilibrations at 26° lie to the left of those obtained at 37°. —·— 37°; —×— 26°.

tions with $CO_2$ at the two different temperatures would yield a log $pCO_2$/pH line at 26° which lay to the right (*i.e.* "alkaline" side) of that at 37° and that the difference in the log $CO_2$ content/log $pCO_2$ dissociation lines would be of a degree dependent upon the concentration of haemoglobin. Both these predictions have been verified by experiment[11], as shown by Figs. 3A and 3B. Determination of the buffer value of horse haemoglobin at 37° and 26° respectively gave the following values:

$$\text{At } 37° \ [HbO_2^-] = 2.85 \ [HbO_2] \ (\text{pH} = 6.64)$$
$$\text{At } 26° \ [HbO_2^-] = 2.73 \ [HbO_2] \ (\text{pH} = 6.80)$$

where $[HbO_2^-]$ is the concentration of haemoglobin ions and $[HbO_2]$ is the molar concentration of haemoglobin per litre. The values 6.64 and 6.80 are those of p$I$—a

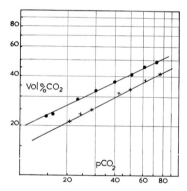

Fig. 3A. Log dissociation lines of a solution of haemoglobin crystals (horse). Note that $CO_2$ carrying power at 26° (circles) is greater than that at 37° (crosses).

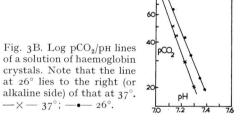

Fig. 3B. Log $pCO_2$/pH lines of a solution of haemoglobin crystals. Note that the line at 26° lies to the right (or alkaline side) of that at 37°. —×— 37°; —•— 26°.

constant similar to, but not necessarily identical with that of the isoelectric point at the prescribed temperature[14,15]. The titration curve of oxyhaemoglobin determined in our experiments at 26° (Fig. 4) is very similar in position to that published by GERMAN AND WYMAN[16] from determinations over a temperature range between 23° and 25°. These more refined analyses reveal that the coincidence of the log $pCO_2$/pH lines of blood samples equilibrated at different temperatures (the pH determinations being made at the temperature of equilibration) is fortuitous and is essentially dependent upon the blood containing haemoglobin. Further experiments[9] show, as indeed might be expected, that the slope of the line steepens as the concentration of haemoglobin is increased, for the slope is in essence a measure of the buffering power of the blood. Moreover, the haemoglobin concentration must exceed 7 mmoles/l for the coincidence of the log $pCO_2$/pH lines to be maintained at different temperatures[9,17]. Lastly it should be evident that the position of the log $pCO_2$/pH line is profoundly affected by the "buffer anion" content of the blood as shown by Fig. 5. An increase in buffer anion concentration shifts the line to the right—as would occur in metabolic alkalosis—and conversely a reduction in buffer anion concentration shifts the log $pCO_2$/pH line to the left—metabolic acidosis. In each case, however, the coincidence

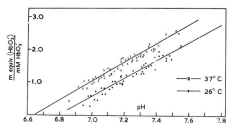

Fig. 4. Graph shows mean results obtained from 10 solutions of horse haemoglobin crystals. Note that the ionisation of haemoglobin $\left(\dfrac{[HbO_2^-]}{[HbO_2]}\right)$ is greater at $37°$ than at $26°$. The slope of the line gives the value of $\beta_0$. The table shows the results obtained on each of the haemoglobin solutions $(G_1-G_6, N_4-N_6)$[11]. —×— $37°$; —•— $26°$.

$$HbO'_2 = \beta_0 [HbO_2][pH - pI]$$

| | $G_1$ | $G_2$ | $G_3$ | $G_4$ | $G_5$ | $G_6$ | $G_8$ | $N_4$ | $N_5$ | $N_6$ | Mean |
|---|---|---|---|---|---|---|---|---|---|---|---|
| $\beta_0$ 37 | 2.84 | 2.66 | 2.98 | 2.84 | 3.10 | 3.01 | — | 2.66 | 2.60 | 2.92 | 2.85 |
| $\beta_0$ 26 | — | 2.40 | 3.00 | 2.75 | 2.96 | 2.87 | 2.75 | 2.40 | 2.60 | 2.87 | 2.73 |
| $pI$ 37 | 6.84 | 6.60 | 6.70 | 6.62 | 6.70 | 6.70 | — | 6.66 | 6.55 | 6.67 | 6.64 |
| $pI$ 26 | — | 6.75 | 6.87 | 6.79 | 6.84 | 6.85 | 6.80 | 6.80 | 6.70 | 6.84 | 6.80 |

of the log $pCO_2$/pH plot for a given blood is unaffected by its temperature of equilibration.

*In vivo experiments*

The identity of the log $pCO_2$/pH graph derived from equilibrations of samples of a given blood at different temperatures dispels the notion that a gaseous acidosis occurs in hypothermic conditions *in vivo* due to the altered solubility of $CO_2$ *per se*. Unless the tension of $CO_2$ in the blood rises in the blood during cooling of the animal—as indeed it usually does in spontaneously breathing animals due to the gradual failure of the respiratory centre—there can be no gaseous acidosis. Naturally, when the alveolar $pCO_2$ rises in these conditions, gaseous acidosis is present just as it would be in normothermic animals.

The pathway of "acid–base" balance can be simply followed during hypothermia *in vivo* by removing blood samples of 10–15 ml and subjecting them to equilibration with a series of $CO_2$/air mixtures at *one* temperature—that of $26°$ being the most convenient. The $CO_2$ contents are determined and the pH values are read at a glass electrode temperature identical with that of the equilibrating tonometer bath. Log

$CO_2$ content/log $pCO_2$ dissociation lines and log $pCO_2$/pH graphs are constructed from the results of each series of equilibrations and these dissociation lines and pH plots of the several blood samples obtained at various intervals during the experimental procedure are immediately comparable with one another because they have all been obtained by equilibrations with $CO_2$ at one and the same temperature.

Such *in vivo* experiments have yielded the following results:

*a. Animals spontaneously breathing subjected to cooling to 26° and then rewarmed.* Using blood stream cooling of lightly anaesthetized (thiopentone) dogs in which shivering was prevented, BREWIN et al.[9] found that as the body temperature was lowered below 30°, the respiration became progressively inadequate and there developed gaseous acidosis in which arterial $pCO_2$ values of over 100 mm Hg not uncommonly occurred. Unless the arterial $pCO_2$ rose above 100 mm Hg, there was only slight evi-

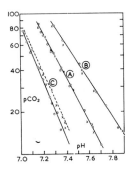

Fig. 5. Log $pCO_2$/pH graphs of human blood. The buffer base content of the blood, normally 49.0 mmoles/l was altered to 65.0 mmoles/l by suitable addition of sodium bicarbonate, and to 35.0 mmoles/l by addition of lactic acid. Note that the points obtained by equilibration at 37° and 26° are unaffected by temperature in the case of blood with a normal or raised buffer base content. In the case of blood with a lowered buffer base content there is a slight discrepancy. —•— 37°; —×— 26°. A, 49.0 mmoles Bb+/l; B, 65.0 mmoles Bb+/l; C, 35.0 mmoles Bb+/l.

dence of metabolic acidaemia after cooling and this disappeared when the animal was rewarmed. When the gaseous acidosis was severe, however, even though the arterial blood was satisfactorily oxygenated by filling the lungs with an oxygen-rich gas mixture, metabolic acidaemia became more marked as evinced by the shift to the left of the log $pCO_2$/pH graph of the blood removed and by the lowering of the level of the log $CO_2$ content/log $pCO_2$ dissociation line. Such a state of affairs is similar to that seen in hypercarbia which develops during apnoeic diffusion oxygenation in normothermic animals, in which very high arterial $CO_2$ tensions are commonly developed[18]. This metabolic acidaemia, which is associated with a rise in the lactate concentration in the blood is not satisfactorily explained yet, but may represent the results of a metabolic blockade exerted on the cells by the high $CO_2$ tension resulting in the formation of an excess of $H^+$. These findings occur despite the known effect of hypercarbia on the liberation of sodium ions from the cells of the body tissues[19].

The constant finding of metabolic acidaemia usually of mild but occasionally of more severe degree, using the technique described above, is not in agreement with the results of FLEMING[20], CRANSTON, PEPPER AND ROSS[21] and McMILLAN et al.[22]. All these authors, (on the basis of inadequate data) have denied that cooling *per se* induces metabolic acidaemia. As BREWIN et al. showed however, the results of CRANSTON et al.[21], when correctly interpreted, clearly reveal that metabolic acidaemia occurred in their experimental animals. DETERLING et al.[23] have shown that metabolic acidaemia results from cooling.

Such results are somewhat of academic interest for the surgeon uses hypothermia as a means to an end. In cardiac surgery the patient is artificially ventilated, the chest is opened and the heart is shut off from the rest of the cardiovascular system to permit cardiotomy and repair of congenital defects. Thanks to the reduction in metabolism, a period of ten minutes circulatory arrest is permissible at a body temperature of 26° without causing irreversible anoxic damage to the brain. On closing the heart, the circulation is restored, the chest is closed and the patient is rewarmed.

BREWIN et al.[9] deliberately mimicked the whole of this procedure with the exception of cardiotomy in a series of 26 dogs. The combined results of such experiments are shown in Figs. 6A and 6B. It can be seen that the equilibrations performed on blood samples removed following cooling and 10 min circulatory arrest, soon after the satisfactory restoration of the circulation, revealed metabolic acidaemia. This is hardly surprising, for lactate levels of 40–50 mg/100 ml (or 4.5–5.5 mequiv./l) in the

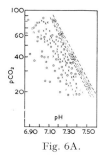
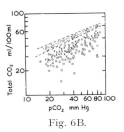

Fig. 6A.                                            Fig. 6B.

Fig. 6. Shows composite results of 26 experiments on dogs cooled, subjected to 9–10 min circulatory arrest and rewarmed to 37–38°. All animals were cooled to a body temperature of about 26°. Equilibration of all blood samples was performed at 26°. (A) Log $CO_2$ dissociation graph. (B) Log $pCO_2$/pH graph. Both graphs show that fixed acidosis evident in the post-clamp samples becomes more severe as rewarming is completed. In each graph the broken lines show the limits of the "pre-cooling" points. —•— pre-cool; —×— post-clamp; —o— re-warm.

"post-clamp" samples revealed that there was a considerable formation of anaerobic metabolites during circulatory arrest. However, on rewarming these animals after closing the chest and re-establishing adequate spontaneous respiration the metabolic acidaemia, often if not invariably, became even more serious as shown in Figs. 6A and 6B. This indicated that there was some degree of failure of the ordinary mechanisms of disposal of the excess of $H^+$ions, a large proportion of which could be traced to the excessive concentrations of lactate which blood samples, removed after rewarming, revealed. Histological examination of the liver revealed a serious residuum of congestive damage. BREWIN et al. showed that the central venous pressure rose during occlusion of the circulation to a height of 25–30 cm $H_2O$ due to vis a tergo and to venoconstriction. They argued that this central venous congestion coupled with hepatic anoxia was responsible for the histological pictures which they obtained. Galactose and bromsulphalein clearances were measured before cooling, after cooling and after rewarming without there being any circulatory arrest. The results obtained were compared with those derived from similar studies in which galactose clearances were measured in dogs before cooling, after cooling with circulatory arrest and, on release of the circulation, after rewarming. The clearance values in the cooled animals fell to about one-third of those in the normothermic animal, but whereas the clearance values of the animals which had simply been cooled were satisfactorily restored to almost normal on rewarming, those obtained on animals subjected to cooling and circulatory arrest showed little if any improvement on rewarming the animals. Consequently, evidence of both structural damage and functional impairment of the liver was quite clear. BREWIN et al.[9], thereupon examined the effect of preventing the rise of central venous pressure during circulatory occlusion in the cooled animal by siphoning off some 300–400 ml of venous blood into a siliconed reservoir wherein it was stored until, on release of the clamps on the venae cavae, it was readmitted to the circulation. This simple technique proved startingly effective in preventing structural damage of the liver and in promoting a satisfactory restoration of galactose clearance on rewarming the animals. Correspondingly the metabolic acidaemia, which was manifest immediately after circulatory occlusion was released, was barely discernible when the animals were rewarmed.

To summarize, [H+] changes in hypothermia require careful interpretation. There is a definite tendency for hypothermia *per se* to cause an increase in the hydrogen ion concentration and this is more pronounced if hypercarbia is permitted to occur. However, when the whole procedure of thoracotomy, circulatory arrest and cardiotomy are added to that of hypothermia itself, acidaemia is more manifest and this is only partly explained by the added insult of stagnant anoxia. A reduction of metabolic dissimilation of "acid" metabolites by the liver caused by congestive anoxia during circulatory arrest can be prevented by the simple technique of "venous decongestion"[3].

*b. Sodium and potassium ion concentrations.* The literature is confused. SWAN et al.[24] claimed that hypothermia caused a fall of plasma sodium. SEGAR et al.[25] found no significant change of plasma sodium also in dogs, whereas MOYER et al.[26] found a consistent rise of plasma sodium in both dogs and man. MUNDAY et al.[27] obtained clear evidence of a small sustained rise in plasma sodium levels in rats, rabbits and men submitted to hypothermia.

Plasma potassium, though first reported to rise on cooling by ELLIOTT AND CRISMON[28] and by BIGELOW et al. is nowadays accepted as falling during hypothermia[24-27]. The aetiology of this fall of plasma potassium is not fully understood, although measurement of the urinary loss of potassium during hypothermia[24,26] has shown that cooling does not produce a net loss of potassium from the body. MUNDAY et al.[27] found that a very significant fall of plasma potassium concentration occurs with cooling and that circulatory occlusion causes an additional drop in the potassium level. In experiments on rats subjected to cooling during spontaneous respiration, MUNDAY et al.[27] found that hypokalaemia occurred on cooling irrespective of the gaseous acidosis which these animals revealed and drew attention to the fact that acidosis usually favours hyperkalaemia[29,30]. Similar results of hypokalaemia in hypothermic patients suffering from acidosis have been reported by AXELROD AND BASS[31] and BOERÉ[32]. MUNDAY et al.[27] found that bilateral adrenalectomy abolished the changes in plasma potassium concentration caused by cooling in normal rats. They, therefore, opine that these electrolyte changes usually seen in hypothermia—a small rise in sodium concentration of the plasma and a more dramatic fall of the plasma potassium concentration—are due to adrenal cortical hyperactivity; they believe that there is an excessive release of mineralo-corticoids, such as aldosterone. Direct evidence that adrenal activity is decreased in hypothermic dogs is provided by EGDAHL, NELSON AND HUME[33] who showed a steady fall in the 17-hydroxycorticosteroid level of adrenal venous blood with cooling which rose again on rewarming. These changes of 17-

hydroxycorticosteroid levels were not affected by infusions of ACTH which they took to indicate a direct depression of adrenal activity by cold. However, MUNDAY et al.[27] point out that although there may be direct evidence of depression of adrenal cortical activity in hypothermia, this does not necessarily mean that the supply of adrenal corticoids to the body is low relative to the requirements of the hypothermic tissues, whose metabolism may be even more depressed than is that of the adrenal cortex itself. Similar views are expressed by SAMULI-SARAJAS et al.[34], who found clear histological evidence of adrenal cortical hyperactivity in anaesthetized dogs subjected to graded hypothermia.

Lastly, it must be borne in mind that hypothermia is almost invariably accompanied by haemoconcentration. The cause of this haemoconcentration remains obscure. D'AMATO[35] has shown that water is removed from the extracellular fluid by the skeletal muscle cells in hypothermic animals in which shivering occurs, but in cooled animals in which shivering is prevented haemoconcentration still takes place and is moreover only slowly dissipated by rewarming. Suggestions that there may be sequestration of plasma-rich fluid collections in regions of low blood flow in hypothermic animals reflect credit rather on the imaginative powers of the author than on any experimental evidence advanced in support of this hypothesis.

Figs. 1, 2, 5 and 6 are reproduced by kind permission of the Editor of *Guy's Hospital Reports*.

## SUMMARY

1. [H$^+$] Hypothermia causes alterations in two of the components of the Henderson-Hasselbalch equation: (1) [H$_2$CO$_3$] is increased for any given pCO$_2$ because the solubility of CO$_2$ rises as temperature falls. (2) [HCO$_3$$^-$] rises for any given pCO$_2$ because the concentration of proteinic anions (notably haemoglobin) falls as the temperature is reduced. Hence pK' is altered and the equation of itself is more difficult to interpret. However, the use of the log pCO$_2$/pH graph of blood samples (BREWIN et al.) makes the assessment of "metabolic" or "gaseous" acidaemia simple. Spontaneously breathing animals subjected to simple cooling betray acidaemia mainly of gaseous or respiratory type. When the procedure of the cardiac surgeon (hypothermia, artificial ventilation, thoracotomy, circulatory arrest) is faithfully mimicked, metabolic acidaemia invariably accompanies the period after release of the circulation. Slow disappearance of such acidaemia during rewarming can partly be attributed to hepatic damage caused by congestion during circulatory arrest. Transfusions of citrated blood (with its extraordinary electrolyte pattern) complicate the problem.

2. [K$^+$] usually shows a fall in hypothermia, sometimes wrongly attributed to primary changes in [H$^+$]. Recent work suggests adrenal cortical stimulation may be responsible; adrenalectomized animals do not show hypokalaemia when cooled.

3. [Na$^+$] usually shows a small rise (except in adrenalectomized animals) during hypothermia.

4. A decrease in the plasma volume which is an almost constant accompaniment of hypothermia still requires a satisfactory explanation.

*References p. 152*

REFERENCES

1 W. G. BIGELOW, W. K. LINDSAY AND W. F. GREENWOOD, *Ann. Surg.*, 132 (1950) 849.
2 I. A. BOEREMA, A. WILDSCHUT, W. J. H. SCHMIDT AND L. BROCKHUYSEN, *Arch. chir. néerl.*, 3 (1951) 25.
3 E. NEIL, Metabolic, Circulatory and Respiratory Changes in Hypothermia, Review, *XXth Intern. Congr. Physiol.*, 1956.
4 K. E. COOPER, *Brit. J. Anaesthesia*, 31 (1959) 96.
5 E. J. WARBURG, *Biochem. J.*, 16 (1922) 153.
6 W. C. STADIE AND K. A. MARTIN, *J. Biol. Chem.*, 61 (1924) 523.
7 C. J. MARTIN AND E. H. LEPPER, *Biochem. J.*, 20 (1926) 45.
8 G. S. ADAIR, N. CORDERO AND T. C. SHEN, *J. Physiol. (London)*, 67 (1929) 288.
9 E. G. BREWIN, R. P. GOULD, F. S. NASHAT AND E. NEIL, *Guy's Hosp. Repts.*, 104 (1955) 177.
10 E. G. BREWIN, F. S. NASHAT AND E. NEIL, *Brit. J. Anaesthesia*, 28 (1956) 2.
11 E. NEIL AND F. S. NASHAT, *Abstr. XXth Intern. Congr. Physiol.*, 1956, p. 675.
12 J. H. AUSTIN AND G. E. CULLEN, *Medicine*, 4 (1925) 275.
13 J. P. PETERS, *J. Biol. Chem.*, 56 (1923) 745.
14 A. B. HASTINGS, D. D. VAN SLYKE, J. M. NEILL, M. HEIDELBERGER AND C. R. HARINGTON, *J. Biol. Chem.*, 60 (1924) 89.
15 W. C. STADIE AND H. O'BRIEN, *J. Biol. Chem.*, 117 (1937) 439.
16 B. GERMAN AND J. WYMAN, *J. Biol. Chem.*, 117 (1937) 533.
17 F. S. NASHAT, *Physiological Studies in Hypothermia*, Ph. D. Thesis, Univ. of London, 1956, pp. 1–177.
18 N. JOELS AND M. SAMUELOFF, *J. Physiol. (London)*, 133 (1956) 347.
19 J. R. ELKINTON, R. B. SINGER, E. S. BARKER AND J. K. CLARK, *J. Clin. Invest.*, 34 (1955) 1671.
20 R. FLEMING, *A.M.A. Arch. Surg.*, 68 (1954) 145.
21 W. I. CRANSTON, M. C. PEPPER AND D. N. ROSS, *J. Physiol. (London)*, 127 (1955) 380.
22 I. K. R. McMILLAN, D. G. MELROSE, H. C. CHURCHILL-DAVIDSON AND R. B. LYNN, *Ann. Roy. Coll. Surg. Engl.*, 16 (1955) 186.
23 R. A. DETERLING JR., E. NELSON, S. BHONSLAY AND W. HOWLAND, *A.M.A. Arch. Surg.*, 70 (1955) 87.
24 H. SWAN, I. ZEAVIN, J. H. HOLMES AND V. MONTGOMERY, *Ann. Surg.*, 138 (1953) 360.
25 W. E. SEGAR, P. A. RILEY JR. AND T. G. BARILA, *Am. J. Physiol.*, 185 (1956) 228.
26 J. H. MOYER, G. MORRIS AND M. E. DE BAKEY, *Ann. Surg.*, 145 (1957) 26.
27 K. A. MUNDAY, G. F. BLANE, E. F. CHIN AND E. S. MACHELL, *Thorax*, 13 (1958) 334.
28 H. W. ELLIOTT AND J. M. CRISMON, *Am. J. Physiol.*, 151 (1947) 366.
29 W. O. FENN AND T. ASANO, *Am. J. Physiol.*, 185 (1956) 567.
30 R. B. TOBIN, *Am. J. Physiol.*, 186 (1956) 131.
31 D. R. AXELROD AND D. E. BASS, *Am. J. Physiol.*, 186 (1956) 31.
32 L. A. BOERÉ, *Anaesthesia*, 12 (1957) 299.
33 R. H. EGDAHL, D. H. NELSON AND D. M. HUME, *Science*, 121 (1955) 506.
34 H. S. SAMULI-SARAJAS, P. NYHOLM AND P. SUOMALAINEN, *Ann. Acad. Sci. Fennicae Ser. A*, 38 (1957) 3.
35 H. E. D'AMATO, *Am. J. Physiol.*, 178 (1954) 143.

DISCUSSION

BOERÉ: Before I make any remarks I should like to thank Professor NEIL for his most interesting lecture. I appreciate his point of view very well.

A lot of totally new disturbances with respect to the acid–base balance have been described recently. In cardiac surgery release of circulation is not always the cause of metabolic acidaemia, and if we want to study these disturbances a correct biochemical control is to be kept during the surgical procedure. There are different circumstances:

(1) During the early use of hypothermia (1955) excessive hyperventilation gave a loss of bicarbonate by inhibition of the reabsorption in the tubules. This loss of bicarbonate normally led to a metabolic acidosis which was compensated and even overcompensated by a fall of $pCO_2$, followed by a higher pH. The ratio $[HCO_3^-]/[H_2CO_3]$ was higher than 20 : 1, and Fig. 1 shows that the primary respiratory alkalosis is combined with a secondary metabolic acidosis. The net result is an alkalosis.

(2) Later on, during circulatory arrest in hypothermia, a metabolic acidosis was not seen or only rarely. The first sample of blood taken 10 min after circulatory arrest had a lower pH than before and this was caused not by a fall in bicarbonate but by a rise of carbonic acid, the accumulation of carbon dioxide during cessation of ventilation. Table I gives a typical example.

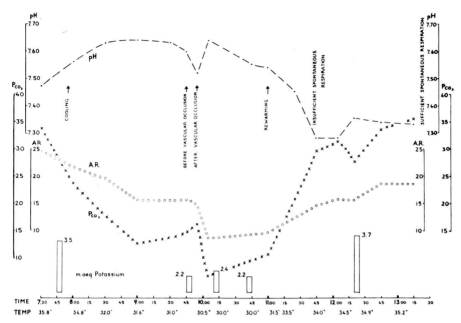

Fig. 1. Relationship between pH, alkali reserve, $pCO_2$ and potassium content in a case of valvulo-tomy for pulmonary stenosis.

TABLE I

EFFECT OF CLAMPING THE AORTA AND CAVAL VEINS IN A CASE OF REPAIR OF ATRIAL SEPTAL DEFECT

| Reg. No. (Hypothermia) | pH | | | $pCO_2$ mmHg | | | Vascular occlusion | |
| --- | --- | --- | --- | --- | --- | --- | --- | --- |
| | before | after | difference | before | after | difference | aorta V.C.S. V.C.I. | V.C.I. |
| 40 | 7.74 | 7.52 | —0.22 | 8.7 | 27.7 | +19.0 | 4′45″ | 7′30″ |
| 53 | 7.59 | 7.20 | —0.39 | 16.4 | 42.2 | +25.8 | 5′30″ | 14′ |
| 55 | 7.64 | 7.59 | —0.05 | 17.3 | 17.6 | + 0.03 | 6′20″ | 11′ |
| 56 | 7.22 | 7.44 | —0.28 | 14.7 | 20.8 | + 6.1 | 6′50″ | 10′ |
| 58 | 7.80 | 7.63 | —0.17 | 11.8 | 13.3 | + 1.5 | 3′30″ | — |
| 60 | 7.72 | 7.58 | —0.14 | — | — | — | 4′11″ | 5′20″ |
| 60 | 7.72 | 7.63 | —0.09 | — | — | — | 3′30″ | 4′ |
| 62 | 7.71 | 7.61 | —0.10 | — | 16.1 | — | — | — |
| 67 | 7.64 | 7.47 | —0.17 | 16.1 | 21.8 | + 5.7 | 4′45″ | 7′20″ |
| 69 | 7.71 | 7.48 | —0.23 | 7.4 | 15.6 | + 8.2 | 5′22″ | 7′37″ |
| 71 | 7.72 | 7.51 | —0.21 | 18.0 | 27.0 | + 9.0 | 5′30″ | 8′30″ |
| 73 | 7.66 | 7.67 | +0.01 | 12.9 | 13.6 | + 0.7 | 6′30″ | 8′ |
| 75 | 7.60 | 7.53 | —0.08 | 15.2 | 16.0 | + 0.8 | 3′55″ | 6′55″ |
| 76 | 7.79 | 7.65 | —0.14 | 10.6 | 12.0 | + 1.4 | 6′ | 8′ |

(3) In extra-corporeal circulation we have different possibilities. In 100 cases of E.C. we saw, after by-pass, 41 cases without any disturbances of the acid-base balance. In 59 cases we had a metabolic acidosis divided into 8 compensated, 23 partially compensated and 28 uncom-pensated cases. In the last group metabolic acidosis normally is dependent on the insufficient metabolism of the cells by an undersaturation of the blood. When the bloodflow is too small or an insufficient peripheral circulation occurs, anaerobic lactic acid production takes place together with loss of bicarbonate. Sometimes we have to correct the acidosis by administration of bicar-

bonate or sodium lactate as one the strongest alkalosis producing agents, as Dr. STEWART said last year. But when circulation has been restored and undersaturation disappears, acidosis disappears too. This form is called "hypoxic acidosis", a better expression than metabolic acidosis.

(4) Extra-corporeal circulation combined with deep hypothermia, to reduce the amount of blood and to reduce bloodflow, has given in dog experiments both respiratory and metabolic disturbances at the same time. In contradiction a high $CO_2$ level is, from my point of view, very favourable in the moments of lowest temperature to prevent ventricular fibrillation and to feed the brain tissue. This effect is due to the influence of $CO_2$ on the process of vascular dilations The exchange of oxygen in the cells of heart and brain tissue is easier under these circumstances.

In these cases transfusion of citrated blood is not allowed at all. Dialysed blood or heparinised blood has been advised instead. Indeed these new operations provided us with a lot of new data in the field of acid–base balance.

I should like also to make some remarks about the relationship between potassium and the influence of hydrogen ions. Normally the fall of potassium is attributed to primary changes in hydrogen ion concentration, as has been said by Professor NEIL. We too found a strong relationship between the fall of $pCO_2$ and the decrease of plasma potassium. This relationship is definitely

TABLE II

RELATIONSHIP BETWEEN CARBON DIOXIDE TENSION AND POTASSIUM CONTENT IN DIFFERENT RANGES OF TEMPERATURE

| Repair atrial septal defect | | | | | | Valvulotomy through Pulm. Art. | | | |
|---|---|---|---|---|---|---|---|---|---|
| Temp. | Resp.r | $pCO_2$ | K(mequiv.) | Reg. number | hypothermia | Temp. | Resp.r | $pCO_2$ | K(mequiv.) |
| 37 | 38 | 47 | 4.1 | | | 37 | 32 | 25 | 3.2 |
| 34 | 32 | — | 3.2 | 55 | 48 | 35 | 30 | 18 | 3.2 |
| 28 | 32 | 17 | 2.5 | | | 34 | 30 | 23 | 3.4 |
| 32 | AR | 38 | 3.5 | | | 31 | 30 | 13 | 2.9 |
| | | | | | | 30 | 30 | 15 | 2.9 |
| 35 | 30 | 36 | 3.9 | | | 29 | 30 | — | 2.8 |
| 29 | 36 | 14 | 2.2 | | | 28 | 30 | 15 | 2.3 |
| 29 | 36 | 21 | 2.9 | 56 | | 30 | 30 | 32 | 2.5 |
| 33 | SR | 35 | 3.4 | | | 39 | SR | 39 | 4.8 |
| 36 | 32 | 29 | 4.4 | | | 36 | 32 | 34 | 3.5 |
| 32 | 32 | 22 | 2.9 | | 51 | 30 | 32 | 28 | 2.4 |
| 29 | 32 | 14 | 2.6 | 58 | | 36 | SR | 56 | 3.0 |
| 28 | 32 | 17 | 2.4 | | | | | | |
| 34 | SR | 30 | 3.8 | | | 37 | 32 | 34 | 4.2 |
| | | | | | | 29 | 32 | 15 | 3.2 |
| 37 | 36 | 34 | 4.2 | | 52 | 35 | SR | 30 | 3.3 |
| 30 | 36 | 15 | 2.7 | | | | | | |
| 37 | SR | 36 | 3.8 | 60 | | 36 | 30 | 32 | 5.2 |
| | | | | | | 31 | 30 | 16 | 3.6 |
| 37 | 30 | 37 | 3.0 | | 65 | 30 | 30 | 25 | 4.9 |
| 28 | 30 | 16 | 2.4 | | | 30 | 30 | 31 | 3.9 |
| 30 | 30 | 18 | 3.2 | 62 | | 37 | SR | 35 | 5.0 |
| 37 | SR | 36 | 3.4 | | | | | | |
| | | | | | | 37 | 32 | 27 | 3.8 |
| 36 | 30 | 43 | 4.8 | | 70 | 31 | 32 | 21 | 2.2 |
| 31 | 30 | — | 2.4 | | | 30 | SR | 31 | 2.9 |
| 29 | 30 | 22 | 2.9 | | | | | | |
| 32 | 30 | 17 | 2.4 | 67 | | 36 | 30 | 38 | 3.0 |
| 35 | SR | 30 | 2.8 | | | 33 | 36 | 12 | 2.6 |
| 37 | SR | 42 | 5.2 | | | 33 | 27 | 21 | 2.5 |
| | | | | | 71 | 31 | 36 | 14 | 2.5 |
| 37 | 30 | 37 | 4.2 | | | 37 | SR | 36 | 2.6 |
| 30 | 30 | 10 | 2.5 | | | 38 | SR | — | 4.5 |
| 29 | 30 | 7 | 2.2 | | | | | | |
| 29 | 30 | 8 | 2.7 | 69 | | 35 | 30 | 33 | 3.5 |
| 27 | 30 | 8 | 2.7 | | | 31 | 30 | 15 | 2.2 |
| 34 | 30 | 32 | 2.7 | | 74 | 30 | 30 | 16 | 2.4 |
| 37 | 30 | 39 | 3.7 | | | 30 | 30 | 13 | 2.0 |
| | | | | | | 34 | AR | 36 | 3.7 |

significant in our observations (p < 0.001, Table II). We think that there is a close relationship between plasma potassium concentration and $CO_2$, especially $pCO_2$. In relation to the work of Dr. ROEGHOLT, reported in his thesis some years ago, we have seen that acute exposure of $CO_2$ to the blood is followed by a rise of the potassium level. MUNDAY, working with adrenalectomized animals, has not seen any influence in these cases. As it is impossible to study this problem in man, we have to add one more to the number of still undissolved questions in hypothermia.

VAN LEEUWEN: Is it possible that the haemoconcentration observed in hypothermia is primarily induced by the changes of the dissociation of proteins ? Since the protein-concentration is higher inside the cells than outside, the osmotic equilibrium must be disturbed, and can be restored only by a shift of water from extra- to intracellular space.

NEIL: Yes, that is one of the things, which immediately comes to mind. I wonder however that although the haemoconcentration usually disappears when the animal is rewarmed, almost always you have to get to $32°$ or $33°$, before this haemoconcentration begins to dissipate. It might be a protein factor which initiates it, but I wonder why it is then so slow to be dissipated. I don't really understand the water-shift and I still think that it might possibly be related to alterations in kidney-performance, but at $26°$ the kidney is not very predictable in what it puts out in volume. You may get an anuria, and sometimes, on the other hand, you get a diuresis, and I could find no correlation between renal loss of fluid and haemoconcentration.

VAN LEEUWEN: Is anything known on freezing-point depression of the blood after cooling ?

NEIL: Not by me.

VISSER: Professor NEIL has demonstrated that the temperature coefficient of the pH is nil when $pCO_2$ is constant. This holds for an open system when $CO_2$ in excess can enter the blood. In a closed system however, as when blood is cooled in a syringe, according to several investigators the temperature-coefficient has a negative value. Therefore it is impossible to determine acid–base equilibria using plasma if the blood is not centrifuged at body temperature. What is your opinion about the influence of centrifuging at a different temperature on the results ?

NEIL: Dr. VISSER raises an important point. It is true that when blood removed from the body at a temperature of $38°$ is cooled anaerobically to room temperature, its pH read at room temperature is more alkaline than that yielded by the original blood at $38°$. ROSENTHAL (*J. Biol. Chem.*, 173 (1948) 25) gave the relationship,

$$pH_{38}t = pH - 0.0147 (38 - t)$$

where $t$ = temperature of measurement. Hence blood with plasma pH at $38°$ = 7.40 would have a plasme pH at $18°$ = 7.694.

This state of affairs is easy to understand from what I have said previously. At the lower temperature $CO_2$ is more soluble, hence the $pCO_2$ of blood cooled anaerobically must fall. At the same time $[HCO_3^-]$ of the true plasma increases owing to the decrease in protein ionisation caused by cooling. These two changes are responsible for the increased alkalinity produced by cooling in a closed system. Hence if blood is centrifuged at a temperature other than that of its equilibration the "true plasma" which it yields will not be identical with the "true Plasma" at $38°$. PARSONS (1917) was fully aware of this and used thermos-jacketed centrifuge tubes to prevent cooling.

# EXCRETION PATTERN AND MECHANISM OF DIURESIS INDUCED BY HEPARIN*, **

C. L. H. MAJOOR, R. J. A. F. M. SCHLATMANN, A. P. JANSEN AND H. PRENEN

*Department of Medicine, St. Radboud Hospital, University of Nijmegen (The Netherlands)*

## INTRODUCTION

In 1952 RAYNAUD et al.[1] in Algeria described the disappearance of oedema during heparin treatment in a woman with severe heart failure. In the same year ENGELBERG et al.[2] independently noted the same phenomenon during heparin treatment in a young man with the Kimmelstiel-Wilson syndrome. In the following years, a diuretic action of heparin was noted in patients with a nephrotic syndrome by several French and Belgian investigators[3-8]. No determinations of urinary sodium and potassium were made during these observations.

When, in 1956, we found distinctly enhanced sodium and chloride output in a young man with a nephrotic syndrome treated with heparin for pulmonary embolism we decided to study in more detail the pattern of heparin-induced diuresis. One of our first balance studies[9] showed slight potassium retention accompanying enhanced sodium output during heparin treatment, which suggested suppression of adrenal cortical function as the mode of action of the drug.

## METHODS

### Diet

Three kinds of diet were supplied to the patients:

*a.* A diet for the study of the diurnal excretory rhythm[10]; 8 equal meals each day and urine collections every 3 h.

*b.* A diet with a constant potassium and sodium intake; 3 meals each day and urine collection over 24-h periods. This diet has been described elsewhere[11].

*c.* A diet with rigid sodium restriction (less than 20 mequiv. sodium daily). The potassium intake was not constant. Urine collections were made over 24-h periods.

### Laboratory methods

Sodium and potassium were determined flame-photometrically and creatinine by the alkaline picrate method. Haemoglobin was measured colorimetrically with an alkaline haematin method. Serum proteins were estimated by means of paper electrophoresis using the hanging strip method. Proteins were stained with amidoschwarz 10 B. Total protein was determined by the biuret method.

---

\* We are indebted to the Netherlands Organization for Health Research T.N.O. for a grant in support of this investigation.

\*\* This paper has appeared already in *Clin. Chim. Acta,* 5 (1960) 591–606.

Total urinary 17-hydroxycorticosteroids were determined according to APPLE-BY's method[12], slightly modified in some minor points.

In some patients without proteinuria, urinary titratable acidity, ammonia and

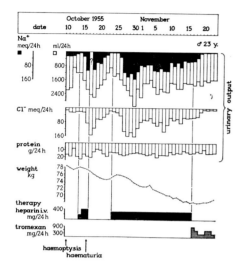

Fig. 1. Enhanced excretion of sodium, chloride and water during heparin treatment in patient A with a nephrotic syndrome.

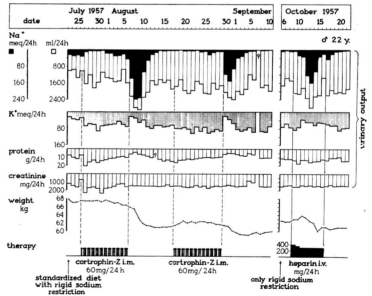

Fig. 2. The natriuretic response to heparin compared to the effect of intramuscular ACTH treatment in patient B with a nephrotic syndrome.

pH were estimated. In such cases the urine was collected in sterilized bottles containing chloramphenicol (about 10 mg per 50 ml urine) and immediately stored in a refrigerator at a temperature of 4°. Titratable acidity was determined by potentiometric titration to pH 7.4; for ammonia assay, neutralized urine (pH 7.4) was titrated potentiometrically to pH 7.4 after addition of a neutral 10% formaldehyde solution.

*References p. 171*

RESULTS

*Effect of heparin on excretion of sodium, chloride, potassium, titratable acidity and ammonia*

Our first observation on the diuretic effect of heparin is shown in Fig. 1. The patient, a young man with a severe nephrotic syndrome, not responding to repeated treatment with ACTH, showed haemoptysis from pulmonary infarction on October

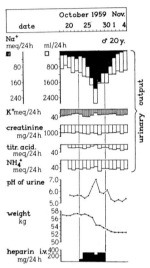

Fig. 3. The effect of heparin on the output of sodium, potassium, titratable acidity and ammonia and on urinary pH in patient C with spontaneous hypoproteinemia.

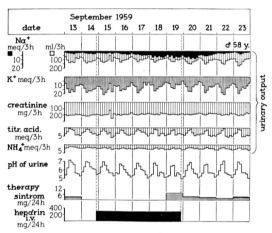

Fig. 4. Natriuresis and potassium retention with unaltered rhythmic excretion of titratable acidity and ammonia during a course of heparin injections in patient D with coronary thrombosis without heart failure.

10. Heparin was given, and to our surprise, it was followed by enhanced urinary excretion of water, sodium and chloride on the 3rd day of treatment. Heparin had to be discarded on account of haematuria, and diuresis diminished to pretreatment levels in about 4 days. A second series of heparin injections—300 mg being given during 24 successive days—resulted in diuresis of the same type with disappearance of oedema by the end of the treatment. Proteinuria was not influenced by heparin.

The assumption of diminished adrenal cortical function during heparin therapy was strengthened when we compared the effects of ACTH and heparin in a 22-year old man with chronic glomerulonephritis and severe proteinuria (Fig. 2). A depot preparation of ACTH was given in two series of 8 days. Natriuresis started during ACTH injections, but—as described earlier by many workers—sodium excretion, attended by potassium retention, became maximal only after we had stopped the drug. This pattern of response may be attributed to temporary adrenal hypofunction.

When, from October 10 until October 16, the patient was treated with heparin— 3-4 intravenous injections of 100 mg each day—a sodium output of about the same magnitude as after ACTH was noted, probably with moderate potassium retention (the potassium intake was not standardized in this part of the observation).

Natriuresis began on the second day of treatment, reaching its maximum on the 5th day. It continued for 2 days after the drug had been stopped. Just as in patient A (Fig. 1), proteinuria did not diminish during heparin therapy, in contrast to the temporary drop seen after ACTH treatment.

A natriuretic response of exactly the same type was found in a young man of 20 years with spontaneous hypoproteinaemia. His serum protein values on October 19 were: alb. 16.6 g/l, $\alpha_1$-glob. 2.8 g/l, $\alpha_2$-glob. 4.5 g/l, $\beta$-glob. 4.3 g/l, $\gamma$-glob. 3.1 g/l. During the observation the patient was on a diet of type b (sodium intake 5 mequiv. daily). Details are given in Fig. 3.

TABLE I

EFFECT OF HEPARIN ON 24-h URINARY OUTPUT OF WATER, SODIUM, POTASSIUM, TITRATABLE ACIDITY, AMMONIA AND CREATININE IN A PATIENT WITH CORONARY THROMBOSIS WITHOUT SIGNS OF HEART FAILURE
(Fig. 4)
Sodium intake 29 mequiv., potassium intake 97 mequiv. daily

| Date | Urine volumes ml/24 h | $Na^+$ mequiv./ 24 h | $K^+$ mequiv./ 24 h | Titr. acid mequiv./ 24 h | $NH^+$ mequiv./ 24 h | Creatinine mg/24 h | |
|---|---|---|---|---|---|---|---|
| 12–9–59 | 690 | 17 | 85 | 25 | 18 | 1595 | |
| 13–9 | 795 | 16 | 102 | 21 | 15 | 1570 | |
| 14–9 | 885 | 18 | 115 | 21 | 14 | 1615 | |
| 15–9 | 815 | 16 | 115 | 26 | 16 | 1535 | 75 mg of |
| 16–9 | 755 | 21 | 98 | 25 | 17 | 1500 | heparin |
| 17–9 | 750 | 33 | 93 | 22 | 17 | 1485 | i.v. |
| 18–9 | 805 | 48 | 88 | 25 | 18 | 1455 | 4 times |
| 19–9 | 780 | 49 | 75 | 23 | 18 | 1495 | daily |
| 20–9 | 940 | 57 | 90 | 25 | 16 | 1480 | |
| 21–9 | 870 | 34 | 94 | 29 | 18 | 1440 | |
| 22–9 | 895 | 14 | 102 | 28 | 18 | 1485 | |
| 23–9 | 915 | 11 | 98 | 27 | 19 | 1475 | |

The output of sodium and water again did not rise during the first 1 or 2 days of heparin therapy. Natriuresis continued for about 3 days after the drug was stopped. Potassium retention was not evident in this study, but a fall in titratable acidity and a rise in urinary pH during the period of most profuse natriuresis pointed to an action in the distal part of the nephron and again suggested that the diuretic effect might be caused by an effect of heparin on the adrenal cortical function[13].

In Fig. 4 the effect is shown of intravenous heparin injections (75 mg 4 times a day) in a man of 58 years with coronary thrombosis without heart failure. The patient was on a diet of type a. In this case, too, natriuresis began at the end of the second day of treatment and continued for 48 h after the drug was stopped.

It is interesting that during distinct natriuresis, urine volumes failed to increase in this rigorously controlled study. In other patients the same phenomenon was noted during treatment with heparin or heparinoids[11]. The rhythmic excretion of water and electrolytes, showing maxima at midday for water, sodium and potassium and maximal excretion during the night for titratable acidity and ammonia, was not disturbed during heparin treatment. The reciprocal rhythm of potassium versus $H^+ + NH_4^+$-

excretion—so clearly shown in Fig. 4—was earlier studied by MILLS AND STANBURY[14]. It is clear that a slight but definite potassium retention occurred during heparin therapy. A distinct effect on the titratable acidity and urinary pH—as was shown in Fig. 3—was however absent in this case. Ammonia excretion was also not affected.

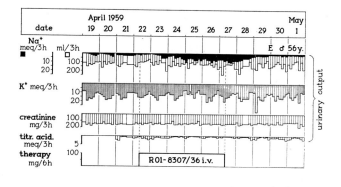

Fig. 5. Natriuresis and diminished excretion of titratable acidity with unaltered rhythmic excretion of potassium during a course of RO1-8307 injections in patient E, convalescent from pneumonia.

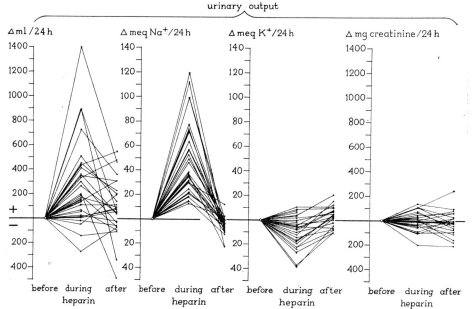

Fig. 6. Compilation of diuretic effects observed during 33 courses of heparin in patients with a great variety of clinical disorders.

In Table I, the 24-h output of sodium, potassium, titratable acidity and ammonia are included to show more clearly the retention of potassium and the unaltered output of hydrogen and ammonia in this patient.

Fig. 5 on the other hand again shows hydrogen retention without diminished potassium output during heparinoid-induced natriuresis*. The patient, a man of 56 years convalescent from pneumonia, was on the diet for the study of diurnal excretory

---

* A part of this study has already been published[11].

rhythm (diet of type a) that was also used in patient D(Fig. 4). We have not yet been able to decide what factors are responsible for the occurrence of potassium retention in some cases (Fig. 4) and hydrogen retention in others (Fig. 5) during heparin or heparinoid treatment, for the patients were on the same type of rigorously standardized diet. More work along these lines is in progress.

The last fact that deserves attention is the absence of natriuresis during treatment with bishydroxycoumarin or its substitutes; this has already been noted by us[9],[11] and is again clearly illustrated in Fig. 1, 4, 7 and 12 of this study.

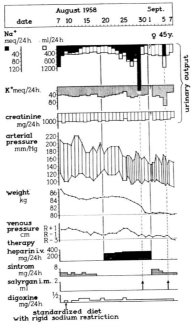

Fig. 7. The effect of heparin and salyrgan, given (a) separately and (b) simultaneously on the excretion of sodium and potassium by patient F with severe failure from rheumatic heart disease.

Fig. 6 summarizes the effects of 33 courses of heparin in 29 patients with a great variety of clinical disorders, in which heparin clearly caused natriuresis. Mean daily urinary excretion of water, sodium, potassium and creatinine was calculated over short periods before, during, and after treatment. The days with maximal urinary sodium output were selected to represent the period of treatment. In most cases they were found to be the 3rd to the 5th day of drug administration. As representative of the period after drug administration we chose the first days with pretreatment levels of sodium excretion—frequently the 3rd to 5th day after withdrawal of heparin. Results are indicated in the graph as increments or decrements of excretion compared with pretreatment output. It is evident that slight potassium retention, followed by a rebound after the drug had been stopped, appears in most patients during heparin treatment.

*The effect of combining heparin or heparinoids with other diuretics*

It is well known that treatment with organic mercurials in patients with heart failure is followed in most cases by enhanced excretion of sodium and potassium. This is illustrated in Fig. 7, which concerns a woman of 45 years with mitral incompetence and stenosis, tricuspid incompetence and severe heart failure. On September 5, this patient showed enhanced excretion of sodium and potassium after 2 ml of Salyrgan given intramuscularly. On August 29, however, during heparin-induced diuresis, the effect of Salyrgan on natriuresis had been clearly additive, but no extra excretion of potassium had been noted. This observation again illustrates the tendency of the kidneys to retain potassium during heparin treatment.

About the same course of events was seen in the study of patient M (Fig. 15). In this woman the heparinoid R01-8307 did not elicit natriuresis though aldosterone

TABLE II

EFFECTS OF COMMON DIURETICS ON EXCRETION OF Na+ AND K+, AND ON Na+/K+ RATIO
IN URINE, BEFORE AND DURING HEPARINOID TREATMENT, IN PATIENT M
(Fig. 15)

| Diuretic | Date | $Na^+$ in urine mequiv./24 h | $K^+$ in urine mequiv./24 h | $Na^+/K^+$ ratio in urine |
|---|---|---|---|---|
| Before heparinoid | | | | |
| chlorothiazide: | | | | |
| 500 mg 3 dd | Dec. 12, 1959 | 45 | 149 | 0.302 |
| hydrochlorothiazide: | | | | |
| 50 mg 3 dd | Dec. 18 | 12 | 159 | 0.075 |
| Mersalyl 1 ml | Dec. 14 | 2 | 21 | 0.095 |
| Mersalyl 2 ml | Dec. 16 | 7 | 54 | 0.130 |
| During heparinoid | | | | |
| chlorothiazide: | | | | |
| 500 mg 3 dd | Jan. 8, 1960 | 77 | 123 | 0.625 |
| idem | Jan. 14 | 68 | 94 | 0.725 |
| Mersalyl 2 ml | Jan. 6 | 77 | 76 | 1.01 |
| idem | Jan. 12 | 78 | 82 | 0.95 |

excretion fell to immeasurable values (see also below). It is clear from Fig. 15 and Table II that during this last part of our study the natriuretic effect of the common diuretics was distinctly larger than during the period when no heparinoid was given. The tendency towards potassium retention is illustrated by the urinary $Na^+/K^+$ ratios, which were largest in the period when the chlorothiazides and Mersalyl were combined with the heparinoid.

## Diuretic action of the heparinoids Thrombocid and R01-8307

Evidence has already been published[11] that the heparinoids Thrombocid and R01-8307 share the diuretic action of natural heparin.

Thrombocid* is a semisynthetic heparinoid of vegetable origin used extensively in Germany for its anticoagulant action. R01-8307** was of special interest because it has preserved part of its clearing properties but lacks almost all anticoagulant action[15,16]. It can thus be given for a number of days without causing an enhanced bleeding tendency.

Table III illustrates some chemical and physiological properties of the drugs

---

* Manufactured by Dr. Benend K.G., München-Solln.
** R01-8307 was kindly supplied by Hoffmann-La Roche, Basel, Switzerland. It is not yet commercially available.

TABLE III

CHEMICAL AND PHYSIOLOGICAL PROPERTIES OF HEPARIN, R01-8307 AND THROMBOCID

|  | Heparin | R01-8307 | Thrombocid* |
|---|---|---|---|
| Chemical composition | Mixture of mucoitin-polysulphates | N-formyl-chitosan polysulphuric acid | Xylan-polysulphuric acid |
| Source | Extracted from lungs or livers | Semisynthetic product of animal origin | Semisynthetic product of vegetable origin |
| Molecular weight | 12,000–20,000 | approx. 5000 | approx. 3000 |
| Sulphur content | 10–14% | approx. 15% | approx. 14% |
| Carbohydrate part of molecule | Glucosamine and glucuronic acid | Formyl-glucosamine | Xylose |
| Anticoagulant effect | +++ | In humans far lower than heparin (on a weight basis) | 40–45% of heparin (on a weight basis) |
| Clearing effect | +++ | About 10% of heparin in humans. About 12% of heparin in rabbits. | ++ |
| Diuretic effect | +++ | ++ | ++ |
| Daily dose necessary for diuretic action | 200–400 mg | 400–800 mg | 600–800 mg |

* Details communicated by manufacturer.

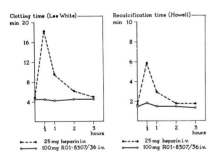

Fig. 8. Clotting time and recalcification time after 25 mg of heparin and 100 mg of the heparinoid R01-8307 in a healthy man.

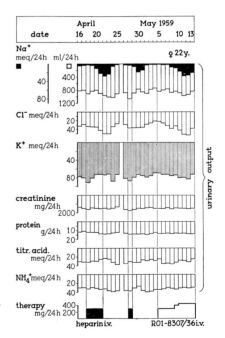

Fig. 9. Natriuretic response to heparin and R01-8307 in patient G with a nephrotic syndrome.

studied. Fig. 8 shows the negligible anticoagulant action of 100 mg of R01-8307 given intravenously, compared with 25 mg of heparin.

In Fig. 5, the natriuretic effect of R01-8307 has already been shown. It is clear that the response is of the same type and about the same magnitude as during heparin treatment. In Fig. 9 the effect of heparin and R01-8307 are compared in a girl of 22 with chronic nephritis and a severe nephrotic syndrome. The patient was on a diet of type b during this study. Though the natriuretic and chloruretic effects of both drugs are slight, in this case with severe hypoalbuminaemia, the response is of about the same magnitude during both treatment periods. No clear-cut effect on the output of potassium, protein and ammonia is seen and the influence on titratable acidity is unimpressive.

## *Heparin and the excretion of 17-hydroxycorticosteroids*

From the results so far presented it is clear that an investigation of adrenal cortical function during heparin treatment was indicated.

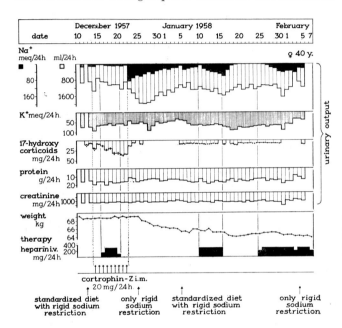

Fig. 10. The influence of heparin and ACTH given separately and simultaneously on the excretion of sodium, potassium and 17-hydroxycorticosteroids in patient H with a nephrotic syndrome.

Fig. 10 illustrates our observations in a 40-year old woman with a very severe nephrotic syndrome, and shows that during heparin treatment from January 10 until January 15, and from January 25 until the beginning of February, no influence on the excretion of 17-hydroxycorticosteroids could be noted. Natriuresis, on the contrary, was distinct, showing the typical pattern already described. Proteinuria was again not influenced by heparin.

Whereas in this patient the basal excretion of 17-hydroxycorticosteroids was on a rather low level, we gave heparin from December 16 until December 20, when the hormone output was raised by simultaneous ACTH administration. The gradual rise of 17-hydroxycorticosteroid excretion was not influenced by heparin. During this combined treatment with ACTH and heparin no natriuresis was noted.

Another study during combined administration of ACTH and heparin is shown in Fig. 11. This patient, a girl of 17, was suffering from a nephrotic syndrome of unknown origin. During the first course of heparin injections, distinct natriuresis was noted, but 17-hydroxycorticosteroid excretion was not altered. From January 20 to February 9, ACTH was given. Heparin, in this case, was not started until January 26, when the excretion of 17-hydroxycorticosteroids was on a high and fairly constant level. In this girl, unlike the preceding patient, heparin treatment during ACTH-stimulation was followed by a natriuretic response of the type now well known. During heparin injections 17-hydroxycorticosteroid excretion was somewhat irregular, but did not fall distinctly. The unmistakable rise of hormone excretion after heparin injections were stopped suggests a rebound that might have been caused by a temporary inhibiting action of the anticoagulant. We must concede, however, that this was our only observation which suggested any influence of heparin on the production of 17-hydroxycorticosteroids.

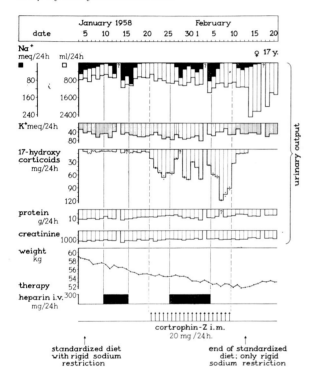

Fig. 11. The influence of heparin and ACTH given separately and simultaneously on the excretion of sodium, potassium and 17-hydroxycorticosteroids in patient I with a nephrotic syndrome.

*The influence of heparin and heparinoids on aldosterone secretion: some clinical observations*

The marked suppression of 17-hydroxycorticosteroid production observed in animal experiments after amphenone administration, can be induced in the human subject only with considerable irregularity[17]. Aldosterone production, however, is inhibited regularly and almost immediately by this drug. In most patients the inhibition is accompanied by a gradual increase of urinary sodium output[18,19]. This pattern of natriuresis resembles that seen after heparin administration, though the urinary sodium excretion increases usually on the first day of amphenone treatment. As all our patients were on a restricted salt intake during heparin administration, they probably were in a state of mild secondary hyperaldosteronism. A salt load causes a decrease in the aldosterone output. If heparin should cause natriuresis by suppressing aldosterone production in the adrenal cortex, the natriuretic effect, though distinct during a period of salt restriction, might remain absent during salt

*References p. 171*

loading. This type of response was seen in a woman of 48 years with severe left-sided phlebothrombosis. Our observations in this patient are illustrated in Fig. 12. They constituted the first evidence for the hypothesis that heparin, though its influence on the secretion of 17-hydroxycorticosteroids is questionable or absent, might act by specifically suppressing aldosterone production.

A second argument was found in the study of a 36 year old woman with Addison's disease and diabetes mellitus who was on the diet of type a. For reasons of comparison and clarity of presentation, urinary excretions in 3-h specimens were added to obtain 24-h outputs (Fig. 13). It is evident that R01-8307 did not cause a natriuretic effect, though the patient was in mineral equilibrium during the period of study*.

The slight fluctuations found in the excretion of sodium and potassium were

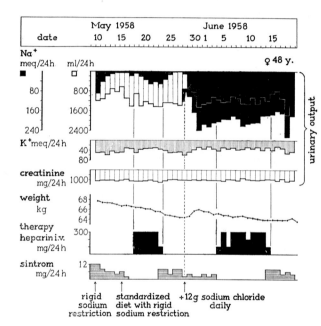

Fig. 12. Diuretic response to heparin during salt restriction and salt loading in patient J with thrombosis of left femoral vein.

probably induced by glycosuria and insulin therapy. They certainly did not show the pattern of heparin-induced diuresis, as sodium retention—so regularly seen on the 3rd or 4th day after heparin injections are stopped—is absent.

*Studies of aldosterone output in patients with secondary hyperaldosteronism*

In a preliminary communication[20] from the University Clinic of Internal Medicine in Amsterdam and this department it was shown that urinary excretion of aldosterone fell to extremely low values in 3 patients with secondary hyperaldosteronism during treatment with heparin or heparinoids. The type of response shown by one of these patients, in whom the effect of R01-8307 was studied twice with nearly identical results, is shown in Fig. 14. This patient is a 57-year old woman with concretio pericardii, who showed signs of severe heart failure notwithstanding a

---

* 9-α-Fluorohydrocortisone was kindly supplied by Merck, Sharp & Dohme, Rahway, N.J. (U.S.A.).

cardiolysis performed some years before. She was treated with salt restriction and diuretics from August 1959, resulting in a slow decrease of the central venous pressure and a loss of 11 kg of body weight. At the end of October 1959, on a diet containing an average of 15 mequiv. of sodium and receiving 0.5 g of chlorothiazide daily, she excreted hardly any sodium in the urine and her body weight increased gradually. In this period the excretion of aldosterone in the urine was 40–60 µg per day. From November 5 to November 24, the patient received R01-8307 intramuscularly in 4 doses of 100–200 mg daily. Aldosterone excretion decreased to very low values, though the fall was perhaps less rapid than commonly seen after amphenone administration[19, 21].

Sodium excretion during this and a second course of heparinoid therapy[20] started when the aldosterone output had diminished to about 20 µg/24 h. During the first course shown in Fig. 14, this happened on the 7th day of treatment, 4 days later than was seen in most other patients during heparin or heparinoid administration.

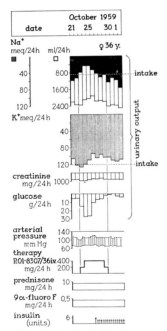

Fig. 13. The lack of natriuretic response to heparin in patient K with Addison's disease.

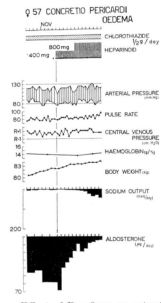

Fig. 14. Effect of R01-8307 on output of sodium and aldosterone in patient L with concretio pericardii and oedema.

Another instance of the fall of aldosterone excretion almost to zero during heparinoid treatment is presented in Fig. 15. Urinary aldosterone was still unmeasurable when the combination of heparinoid therapy with chlorothiazide and Mersalyl had caused an appreciable though partial loss of oedema on January 12 and 13.

*Failure of heparin or heparinoid therapy in causing a diuretic response*

During the past 3 years we have studied 12 patients in whom heparin or heparinoids failed to cause a diuretic effect during treatment lasting 5 to 7 days. Two had Addison's disease: one of these has been mentioned above. Of the remaining 10, 6 had severe heart failure, 3 a nephrotic syndrome with very low serum albumin values (15.2, 10.1 and 7.0 g/l respectively) and 1 was nephritic with a creatinine clearance of 20 ml/min.

From the observations illustrated in Figs. 7 and 14, it appears that the increase of sodium output can be delayed till the 4th and 7th day of heparin or heparinoid

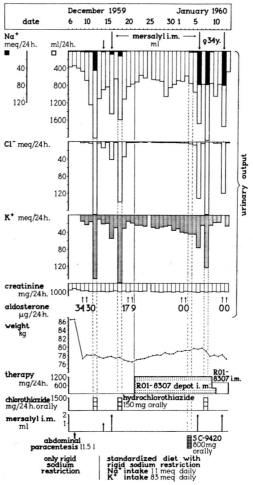

Fig. 15. Effect of R01-8307, Mersalyl and chlorothiazides on excretion of sodium, potassium and aldosterone, in patient M with severe rheumatic heart disease, cardiac cirrhosis and ascites.

treatment in patients with severe heart failure. Hence, too short a course of therapy might be the cause of failure in some of the 12 patients mentioned. It is however apparent that the failure of heparin or heparinoids to cause natriuresis can have another cause. To illustrate this point, we would refer to the study of a woman of 34 with mitral incompetence and stenosis, tricuspid incompetence and severe heart failure with cardiac cirrhosis (Fig. 15). On admission she had massive oedema and needed paracentesis of 11 litres for severe ascites. Glomerular filtration was not diminished, as endogenous creatinine clearances of 90–145 ml/min were found in frequently repeated examinations throughout this study. No natriuresis occurred during the first 13 days of Ro1-8307 therapy, a depot preparation being given in the fairly high dosage of 1200 mg/day. Aldosterone excretion, on the other hand, fell from slightly elevated or normal outputs of 9–34 $\mu$g/24 h to zero (Fig. 15)*. When 800 mg of the spirolactone SC-9420** were added orally to the heparinoid, an extremely slight natriuresis occurred; sodium excretion rose from 0.2–0.5 mequiv./24 h before SC-9420 to 2.3 and 2.2 mequiv./24 h on January 4th and 5th respectively.

As aldosterone was absent from the urine during heparinoid treatment, it is probable that the hormone was also eliminated from the blood. SC-9420 may have expelled the last remnants of aldosterone from the tubular cells of the kidneys. The stubborn retention of sodium in this patient, notwithstanding the facts that aldosterone was probably lacking and glomerular filtration rate was normal, is certainly remarkable. It suggests with new emphasis the existence of a primary renal tubular mechanism for sodium conservation; this is probably active in all circumstances in which the filling of the arterial system is insufficient.

The significance of this renal factor was surmised during recent years by Thorn et al.[21], Muller[19], Nelson and August[22] and others, but was first formulated by Borst[23] in 1948 and clearly defined in 1953 in the following words: "The circulatory diuresis mechanism is able to regulate the excretion of extracellular fluid without the mediation of alterations in glomerular filtration rate and without the mediation of changing blood levels of adrenocortical hormones"[24] (p. 280). The prevalence of this non-aldosterone-induced tubular mechanism of sodium conservation was probably the principal cause of the failure of patient M and some of our other patients to show natriuresis during heparin therapy.

*Clinical significance of the diuretic and aldosterone-inhibiting action of heparin and heparinoids*

It is clear from some of the studies described in this paper that heparin or heparinoids can cause an excellent diuretic response in some patients with intractable oedema. However failures were relatively common. This is why the major indication for these drugs in the treatment of intractable oedema is probably not to be found in their diuretic action but in the possibility which they afford, of assessing the rôle of aldosterone in oedema formation in each individual case by elimination of the hormone. Thorn et al.[19] have already suggested this rôle for amphenone, but the extreme toxicity of this drug has hampered its use.

A second indication for the clinical use of heparin or heparinoids might be the combination with mercurials and chlorothiazides. In this way excessive urinary potassium loss by the common diuretics can be limited, as is shown in Figs. 7 and 15 and Table II.

*Point of attack of heparin and heparinoids on aldosterone secretion*

At present two distinctly different mechanisms for diminution of aldosterone

---

* The aldosterone determinations were done for us by Dr. V. Cejka of the Department of Internal Medicine of the Binnen-Gasthuis in Amsterdam, using Moolenaar's method.
** SC-9420 (Aldactone) was kindly supplied by Dr. C. L. Gantt of G. D. Searle & Co., Chicago, Ill. (U.S.A.)

secretion by the adrenals are known. One—the physiological one—causes a fall of aldosterone secretion probably in all conditions in which there is an "augmentation of the filling of the arterial system"[25]. Possibly this mechanism is governed *via* nervous pathways by a centre in the neighbourhood of the pineal gland which secretes glomerulotrophic hormone[26-28]. The significance of the volume control for aldosterone production in clinical medicine has been fully demonstrated by MULLER[21]. The second mechanism, which is brought about by amphenone and related substances, is active at the level of the adrenal cell and probably exerts its action by blocking 11-, 17- and 21-hydroxylation. Both mechanisms are tentatively depicted in Fig. 16.

It would be very interesting to know by which routes heparin and the heparinoids exert their influence on aldosterone metabolism. Of the existing possibilities we can only deal with the influence of these drugs on the filling of the arterial system. Against such a supposition, several arguments can be advanced.

First, we can state that we have never seen symptoms of hypercirculation in our patients. There was no augmentation of pulse pressure, and in some cases even a decrease. The creatinine excretion remained constant in all cases. In some patients a slight and gradual rise of haemoglobin and haematocrit values during heparin

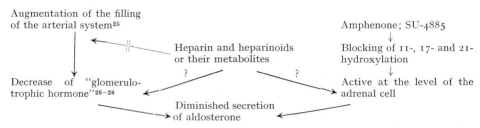

Fig. 16. Possible pathways by which heparin and heparinoids could inhibit aldosterone secretion.

therapy pointed to a slight contraction of the blood volume. The observations shown in Figs. 14 and 15 point to the same conclusion. In these patients a slight deterioration of the circulation occurred during heparinoid treatment: oedema and body weight increased and sodium excretion was extremely low. Still, urinary aldosterone fell to low or zero levels in the periods of heparinoid administration.

Secondly, the pattern of heparin-induced diuresis, with potassium retention in most patients, is clearly opposed to the one following hypercirculation, which, according to BORST's investigations[24], is never attended by decreased potassium excretion and often by slightly enhanced outputs.

Hence it may be concluded that heparin and heparinoids probably do not decrease aldosterone secretion by an augmentation of the filling of the arterial system.

As to the other possibilities, we hope that animal experiments now in progress in our department will shed some light on this intriguing problem.

### SUMMARY

1. Heparin causes increased urinary output of sodium, chloride and water in patients with all types of oedema as well as in those without sodium retention.

2. Diuresis is of a delayed type, beginning 36–48 h after the first injection and continuing for about 48 h after therapy has been stopped.

3. Sodium loss is nearly always accompanied by a slight potassium retention. In some patients diminished urinary titratable acidity occurred.

4. The diuretic action of heparin is shared by Thrombocid and a new heparinoid Ro1-8307, which has hardly any anticoagulant action.

5. Renal excretion of 17-hydroxycorticosteroids shows no or only a doubtful reduction during short courses of heparin therapy.

6. A decided diminution of aldosterone output to very low levels was found during therapy with heparin or Ro1-8307 in patients with secondary hyperaldosteronism.

7. The point of attack of heparin, heparinoids or their metabolites on aldosterone metabolism is not known. Evidence is put forward to show that the drugs studied probably do not elicit their natriuretic and aldosterone-inhibiting action by augmenting the filling of the arterial system.

## REFERENCES

[1] R. RAYNAUD, J. R. D'ESHOUGUES, P. PASQUET AND E. KAROUBI, Algérie méd., 56 (1952) 135.
[2] H. ENGELBERG, J. GOFMAN AND H. JONES, Diabetes, 1 (1952) 425.
[3] CH. SARROUY, A. RAFFI AND H. DEYME, Pédiatrie, 8 (1953) 98.
[4] P. KISSEL, G. ARNOULD AND P. HARTEMANN, Rev. méd. Nancy, 29 (1954) 252.
[5] J. SONNET AND J. HEREMANS, Bruxelles-méd., 34 (1954) 223.
[6] R. CUVELIER, L. VILEMIN-CLOG, G. MENUT, BERGER AND ANDRAUD, Presse méd., 63 (1955) 738.
[7] Y. BOQUIEN, P. HORVENO AND LUCAS, Bull. soc. méd. hôp. Paris, 71 (1955) 253.
[8] Y. BOQUIEN AND J. F. PORGE, Presse méd., 64 (1956) 692.
[9] C. L. H. MAJOOR, H. PRENEN, P. J. J. VAN MUNSTER AND R. J. A. F. M. SCHLATMANN, Ned. Tijdschr. Geneesk., 101 (1957) 1301.
[10] J. G. G. BORST AND L. A. DE VRIES, Lancet, 259 (1950) 1.
[11] R. J. A. F. M. SCHLATMANN, H. PRENEN, A. P. JANSEN AND C. L. H. MAJOOR, Lancet, 278 (1960) 314.
[12] J. I. APPLEBY, G. GIBSON, J. K. NORYMBERSKI AND R. D. STUBBS, Biochem. J., 60 (1955) 453.
[13] G. W. LIDDLE, A.M.A. Arch. Internal Med., 102 (1958) 998.
[14] J. N. MILLS AND S. W. STANBURY, Clin. Sci., 13 (1954) 177.
[15] A. STUDER, F. KOLLER, P. KAEGI, K. VOGLER, W. OBERHAENSLI AND M. KOFLER, Bull. schweiz. Akad. med. Wiss., 13 (1956) 239.
[16] K. REBER, A. STUDER, R. TOBLER AND F. KOLLER, Acta Haematol., 21 (1959) 31.
[17] R. HERTZ, J. A. PITTMAN AND M. M. GRAFF, J. Clin. Endocrinol. and Metabolism, 16 (1956) 705.
[18] A. E. RENOLD, J. CRABBÉ, L. HERNANDO-AVENDANO, D. H. NELSON, E. J. ROSS, K. EMERSON AND G. W. THORN, New Engl. J. Med., 256 (1957) 16.
[19] G. W. THORN, E. J. ROSS, J. CRABBÉ AND W. VAN 'T HOFF, Brit. Med. J., 11 (1957) 955.
[20] V. CEJKA, L. A. DE VRIES, M. E. SMORENBERG-SCHOORL, J. J. VAN DAATSELAAR, J. G. G. BORST AND C. L. H. MAJOOR, Lancet, 278 (1960) 317.
[21] A. F. MULLER, Schweiz. Med. Wochschr., 89 (1959) 1093.
[22] D. H. NELSON AND J. T. AUGUST, Lancet, 277 (1959) 883.
[23] J. G. G. BORST, Acta Med. Scand., Suppl. 27 (1948).
[24] J. G. G. BORST, Ciba Foundation Symposium on the Kidney, (1954) 255.
[25] J. G. G. BORST, Acta Med. Scand., 97 (1938) 68.
[26] C. H. ANDERSON, M. McCALLY AND G. L. FARRELL, Endocrinology, 64 (1959) 202.
[27] A. E. NEWMAN, E. S. REDGATE AND G. L. FARRELL, Endocrinology, 63 (1958) 723.
[28] F. C. BARTTER, Year Book of Endocrinology, (1958–1959) 204.

# RENAL CONCENTRATING AND WATER-EXCRETING CAPACITY IN HYPERTHYROIDISM*

P. G. A. B. WIJDEVELD AND A. P. JANSEN

*Department of Internal Medicine, St. Radboud Hospital, University of Nijmegen*
*(The Netherlands)*

This paper reports a study of renal water handling in hyperthyroidism. Interest in this problem was induced by the observation of a severe dehydration syndrome, resembling the so-called thyrotoxic crisis, in a patient suffering from hyperthyroidism with hypercalcemia. The present report deals with studies of renal water handling in 14 patients with hyperthryoidism, 4 with and 10 without hypercalcemia. Some of the findings in 2 hypercalcemic patients have been previously reported[1].

## SUBJECTS AND METHODS

### Subjects

14 patients, suffering from typical hyperthyroidism, were investigated. In 3 of them the disease was attented with temporary hypercalcemia and in one patient plasma calcium levels varied about the upper normal limit; in 3 patients the calcium level of the plasma was not determined, and they were included in the normo-calcemic group. Clinical data are given in Table I. The experimental procedures described in the following paragraph were applied to a number of "normal subjects": hospitalized patients suffering from diseases not related to cardiovascular, renal, adrenal or thyroidal function. In this group some cases of mild psychogenic polydipsia and of hyperthroidism after treatment were included. The age of the normal subjects in whom a concentration test was performed, was from 22 to 56 years.

### Experimental procedures

The effect of dehydration was studied by means of a modification of the current concentration test. The patient subsisted on a hospital diet; water and liquid food were withheld for 36 h; the experiment began at 21.00 h.

Urine was collected every 6 h; in each sample the osmolality and the excretion of urea and electrolytes were determined. All urine specimens were examined for the presence of glucose and protein. In [the s]ame period plasma levels of sodium, urea, creatinine and osmolality were dete[rmined]. The excretion of endogenous creatinine was used as a check on the correct collection of the urine; in relation to the plasma levels it served to estimate the glomerular filtration rate. A specimen of this "concentration test" is given in Fig. 1.

The effects of induced hypertonia of the plasma and of vasopressin administration were investigated by means of a modification of the procedure introduced by CARTER et al.[2]. In order to study the effects of both hypertonic saline and vasopressin in the same experiment, a high level of hydration was established by oral administra-

---

* This paper has been published already in *Clin. Chim. Acta*, 5 (1960) 618–631.

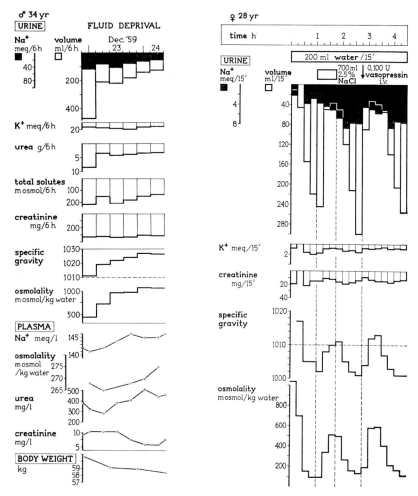

Fig. 1. The influence of fluid deprivation on some parameters of water metabolism ("concentration test") in a normal subject.

Fig. 2. The influence of administration of hypertonic (2.5%) NaCl and vasopressin on some parameters of water metabolism ("Carter test") in a normal subject

tion of 200 ml of water every 15 min throughout the test. Hypertonic saline (2.5% was given by intravenous infusion, and vasopressin* by intravenous injection. Details may be found in Fig. 2.

The effect of vasopressin over a period of time was investigated as follows. After collection of a urine portion from 8.00 to 12.00 h, 5 units of vasopressin tannate in oil* were given intramuscularly. After the injection, fluid was withheld till 24.00 h. Urine was collected every 2 h till 20.00 h, an additional collection being taken at 24.00 h. Urinary specific gravity and osmolality were determined.

The effect of hydration was studied by means of a modification of OLEESKY's[3] water diuresis test. After oral administration of 1000 ml of water within 20 min,

* Pitressin and Pitressin tannate in oil, manufactured by Parker, Davis and Co.

*References p. 184–185*

## TABLE I

### CLINICAL AND BIOCHEMICAL FINDINGS IN 14 PATIENTS SUFFERING FROM HYPERTHYROIDISM

| Pat. | Sex and age years | Thyroid gland | Eye symptoms | Cardiac rate beats/min | Arterial pressure mm Hg | BMR % | ug PBI g/100 ml | Thirst | Polyuria | Renal function | Plasma Calcium mequiv./l | Plasma Inorg. phosphate mg/100 ml | Plasma Alkaline phosphatase p-nitrophenylphosphate units |
|---|---|---|---|---|---|---|---|---|---|---|---|---|---|
| A | M 55 | slightly enlarged | pos. | 120 a.f. | 120/0 | +63 | — | + | + | $C_u$ 65% | 5.8 | 4.1 | 2.7 |
| B | F 33 | diffusely enlarged | pos. | 120 reg. | 140/60 | +67 | — | + | + | $C_e$ 94 ml/min | 6.6 | 4.6 | 4.0 |
| C | M 40 | not enlarged | neg. | 110 reg. | 170/0 | +75 | 24.6 | + | + | $C_e$ 132 ml/min | 5.9 | 4.7 | 1.8 |
| D | F 51 | diffusely enlarged | neg. | 162 a.f. | 160/80 | +46 | — | + | — | $C_e$ 107 ml/min | 5.2 to 5.7 | 5.0 | — |
| E | F 24 | diffusely enlarged | pos. | 142 reg. | 160/100 | +54 | — | ? | ? | $C_e$ 82 ml/min | 5.0 | 4.8 | 1.9 |
| F | F 32 | diffusely enlarged | pos. | 120 reg. | 160/40 | +39 | — | + | — | $C_e$ 116 ml/min | 4.9 | 4.1 | 2.1 |
| G | M 44 | not enlarged | neg. | 128 reg. | 190/95 | +60 | 17.7 | + | — | sp. gr. 1029 | 5.4 | 4.1 | 3.2 |
| H | F 50 | diffusely enlarged | neg. | 142 reg. | 180/90 | +43 | 12.5 | + | + | $C_e$ 110 ml/min | 5.3 | 3.9 | 2.5 |
| I | F 51 | diffusely enlarged | neg. | 112 a.f. | 160/95 | +35 | — | ? | ? | $C_u$ 56% | — | — | 1.9 |
| J | M 52 | slightly enlarged | neg. | 120 a.f. | 190/90 | +70 | 17.6 | + | — | $C_e$ 110 ml/min | 4.6 | 4.5 | 1.2 |
| K | M 54 | not enlarged | pos. | 84 reg. | 130/60 | +35 | 13.4 | + | ? | $C_e$ 121 ml/min | 5.2 | 3.1 | 3.1 |
| L | F 58 | nodular | pos. | 160 a.f. | 180/100 | +30 | 15.0 | ? | ? | — | — | — | — |
| M | F 63 | nodular | neg. | 120 reg. | 265/0 | +35 | 10.0 | ? | ? | sp. gr. 1030 | — | — | 3.3 |
| N | F 63 | slightly enlarged | neg. | 100 a.f. | 160/80 | +45 | — | — | — | $C_e$ 125 ml/min sp. gr. 1032 | 5.1 | 3.4 | 2.8 |

PBI  = protein-bound iodine
BMR  = basal metabolic rate

$C_e$ and $_u$ = endogenous creatinine clearance and urea clearance
sp.  = urinary specific gravity

reg.  = regular
a.f.  = atrial fibrillation.

urine was collected by an indwelling catheter every 20 min for 4 h, the patient remaining in the recumbent position. Urinary volume and specific gravity were determined. In connection with the use of this test in the investigation of adrenocortical function, it was repeated after an oral dose of cortisone (50 to 100 mg, dependent upon body weight).

*Analytical methods*

Urine and plasma osmolality were determined by the freezing point method with the apparatus described by Bowman *et al.*[4]. Urinary specific gravity was measured

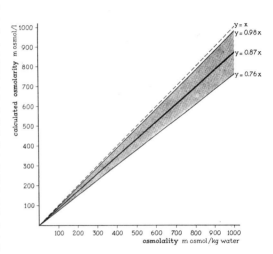

Fig. 3. Relationship of "calculated osmolarity" (see text) to cryoscopically determined osmolality of urine. The scale of the abcissa is the same as that of the ordinate, so that the line drawn at $45°$ to the abcissa ($y = x$) would show the relationship if both properties were equal. The actual relationship was investigated in 187 simultaneous observations, obtained during 17 experiments in 12 patients. Since the number of observations in each patient differed widely, the average of regression lines was calculated. The lines of least squares through the points of the 12 patients ($y = ax + b$) showed an average $y$-intercept of $+8$ with a range from $+85$ to $-46$. Therefore adaptation of the regression lines through the origin ($y = ax$) seemed justified. The mean value for the slope of the regression lines ($a$) was 0.87, the standard deviation of $a$ was 0.055. The shaded area represents the mean value of the slope $+ 2$ S.D.

with a densitometer, after the urine had been cooled to a temperature between $15°$ and $20°$, or by weighing. An approximate "calculated osmolarity" of urine was obtained by addition of the double molar value of the sodium and potassium concentrations to the molar value of the urea concentration. The relationship between specific gravity and osmolality was in general agreement with the results of Miles *et al.*[5]. The relationship between calculated osmolarity and cryoscopically determined osmolality is shown in Fig. 3; the former is lower, the average difference being 13% with a standard deviation of 5.5%. Details of the statistical analysis are given in the legend to Fig. 3. Sodium and potassium were determined by flame photometer, urea by the methods of van Slyke and Cullen (plasma) and Ambard (urine), creatinine by the alkaline picrate method, hemoglobin by an alkaline hematin method, chloride by potentiometric titration, bicarbonate by the gasometric method of van Slyke and Cullen, cholesterol according to Zlatkis and Zak, calcium by chelatometric titration, inorganic phosphate by the method of Fiske and Subbarow and alkaline phosphatase according to Bessey.

## RESULTS

*Hyperthyroidism with hypercalcemia*

In patients A, B and C hyperthyroidism was attended with hypercalcemia,; in patient D plasma calcium levels varied about the upper normal limit (Table I) before treatment; in all patients the calcium level fell to a normal value during treatment. In patients B, C and D the calcium determinations were done in the absence of dehydration; the calcium level of patient A was determined in another hospital, shortly before admission into our department.

The results of analyses on patient A induced us to investigate renal water handling in hyperthyroidism. The observations on this patient may be best discussed in relation to Fig. 4. In spite of the existence of a severe hyperthyroidism the patient showed a hyposthenic polyuria. This polyuria being originally imputed to the drinking of too much water the patient was deprived of fluid for 36 h (7–9/5/57). The maximal urinary specific gravity was 1012; the next day a value of 1017 was found. At the end of the period of fluid deprivation the patient was critically ill with delirium, vomiting, tachycardia and rise of body temperature. At this moment a severe hypernatremia and hyperchloremia were found ($Na^+$ 172 and $Cl^-$ 128 mequiv./l); the plasma levels of $K^+$ and $HCO_3^-$ were normal but the levels of hemoglobin and urea had also risen. After institution of antithyroid treatment, including iodine administration, the patient recovered quickly, and the basal metabolic rate became normal within three weeks. In this period hypotonic urine was produced in the presence of a definite

TABLE II

MAXIMAL URINARY SPECIFIC GRAVITY AND SODIUM CONTENT OF THE PLASMA AT THE END OF CONCENTRATION TESTS IN A CASE OF HYPERTHYROIDISM WITH HYPERCALCEMIA (A) IN THE COURSE OF ANTITHYROID TREATMENT

| Date | Maximal specific gravity | Plasma $Na^+$ mequiv./l |
|---|---|---|
| 9.5.57 | 1012 | 172 |
| 30.5.57 | 1010 | 150 |
| 21.8.57 | 1021 | 147 |
| 7.3.59 | 1028 | 140 |

TABLE III

INFLUENCE OF VASOPRESSIN UPON DIURESIS, URINARY SPECIFIC GRAVITY AND CALCULATED OSMOLARITY IN A CASE OF HYPERTHYROIDISM WITH HYPERCALCEMIA (B) BEFORE TREATMENT AND AFTER THYROIDECTOMY

| Time h | Urinary vol. ml | Specific gravity | Calculated osmolarity mosmol/l |
|---|---|---|---|
| 18.00–12.00 | 800 | 1009 | 255 |
| 12.00 | 5 U vasopressin tannate in oil, i.m., fluid deprival | | |
| 12.00–15.40 | 510 | 1011 | 333 |
| 15.40–17.45 | 330 | 1008 | 298 |
| 17.45–20.00 | 325 | 1006 | 316 |
| 20.00–24.00 | 440 | 1010 | 333 |
| After thyroidectomy | | | |
| 08.00–12.00 | 380 | 1008 | 326 |
| 12.00 | 5 U vasopressin tannate in oil, i.m., fluid deprival | | |
| 12.00–14.00 | 85 | 1023 | 675 |
| 14.00–16.00 | 170 | 1027 | 750 |
| 16.00–18.00 | 85 | 1023 | 724 |
| 18.00–20.00 | 70 | 1025 | 684 |
| 20.00–24.00 | 87 | 1028 | 769 |

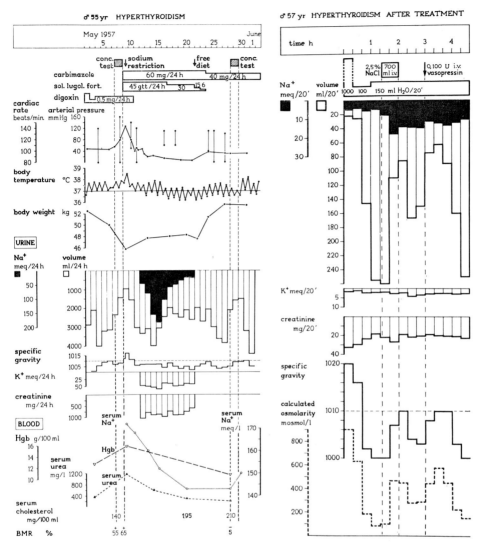

Fig. 4. Clinical events in a patient (A) with hyperthyroidism with hypercalcemia. Excretion of sodium, potassium and creatinine were only examined from 11–20.5.57. Note the effects of the two concentration tests (7–9 and 28–30.5.57) and the hypotonia of the urine between 9 and 21.5.57 in the presence of an increased plasma sodium level.

Fig. 5. Carter test in patient A, 18 months after the clinical crisis described in the text.

hypernatremia. In the course of a second concentration test (28–30/5/57) the sodium content of the plasma rose to 150 mequiv./l. The maximal urinary specific gravity was 1010. Renal concentrating capacity recovered gradually in the course of 10 months (Table II). Eighteen months after the clinical crisis a normal reaction to hypertonic saline and vasopressin was found (Fig. 5). The clinical crisis of this patient resembled descriptions of the so-called thyrotoxic crisis, whereas the objective findings pointed to an acute dehydration syndrome.

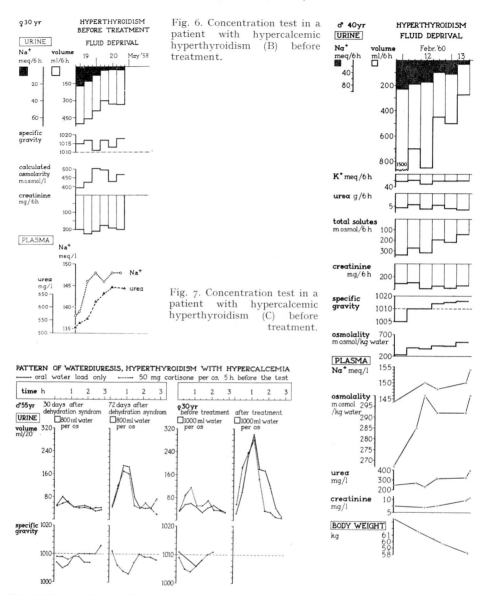

Fig. 6. Concentration test in a patient with hypercalcemic hyperthyroidism (B) before treatment.

Fig. 7. Concentration test in a patient with hypercalcemic hyperthyroidism (C) before treatment.

Fig. 8. Pattern of water diuresis in two patients with hypercalcemic hyperthyroidism (A and B). The normal pattern of reaction can be read from the left hand side of Fig. 12. Note the reestablishment of an almost normal pattern in the first patient and of a completely normal pattern in the second patient in the course of antithyroid treatment.

Patients B and C also showed a marked polyuria with low specific gravities. Their concentration tests, showing essentially the same picture as patient A, are given in Figs. 6 and 7. In both patients the effect of vasopressin tannate in oil was investigated. The results on patient B are given in Table III. Patient C. showed the same picture: the maximal urinary osmolality after vasopressin tannate in oil was 500 mosmol/kg water. Water diuresis tests in patients A and B are shown in Fig. 8; a temporary im-

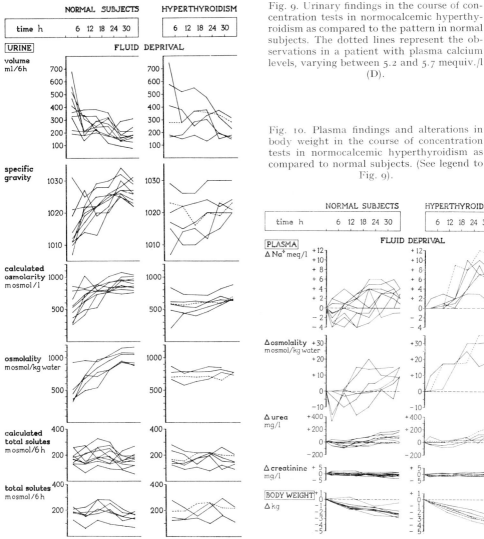

Fig. 9. Urinary findings in the course of concentration tests in normocalcemic hyperthyroidism as compared to the pattern in normal subjects. The dotted lines represent the observations in a patient with plasma calcium levels, varying between 5.2 and 5.7 mequiv./l (D).

Fig. 10. Plasma findings and alterations in body weight in the course of concentration tests in normocalcemic hyperthyroidism as compared to normal subjects. (See legend to Fig. 9).

pairment of renal water-excreting capacity was found in both. In patient C the excretion of water also failed to increase in the course of a water diuresis test.

Since the findings in patient D did not differ clearly from those in the normocalcemic patients, they are given in Figs. 9 and 10 (dotted lines).

*Normocalcemic hyperthyroidism*

Figs. 9 and 10 represent a comparison of concentration tests in 10 normal subjects and in 6 patients with hyperthyroidism, 5 of whom (E, F, H, J, K) were without hypercalcemia: the sixth (D, dotted lines) has been mentioned above. The results in the normal subjects agreed with the findings of DE WARDENER[6]. Only one of the patients (J) showed a normal pattern; in the other patients a slight but unmistakable impairment of concentrating capacity was found. There was an insufficient rise of urinary specific gravity, calculated osmolarity and osmolality (Fig. 9) in the presence of a relatively large increase of the plasma sodium content and of plasma osmolality (Fig. 10). Furthermore, the loss of body weight was larger in the patients than in the normal subjects (Fig. 10). In only one patient (E) the effect of vasopressin tannate in oil was investigated; it failed to restore the concentrating capacity. In three patients we did not perform complete concentration tests since they had produced high urinary specific gravities before: patient G reached 1029 after administration of 5 units of

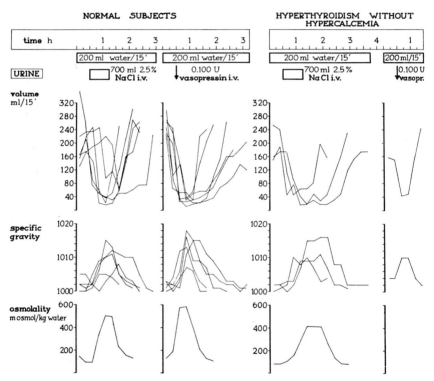

Fig. 11. Urinary findings in the course of "Carter tests" in 3 patients with normocalcemic hyperthyroidism (E, F and J) as compared to normal subjects.

vasopressin tannate in oil, patients M and N spontaneously produced 1030 and 1032. Thus in 4 out of 8 cases of normocalcemic hyperthyroidism, and in patient D an impairment of renal concentrating capacity was found. In 3 patients (D, H and K) concentration tests were repeated after treatment of hyperthyroidism, and found normal. The results in patients D and K after treatment are included in the normal group (Figs. 9 and 10).

In the hyperthyreotic patients, urinary total solute excretion was in the same range as in the normal subjects (Fig. 9). Therefore the impairment of concentrating capacity could not be explained by an increased osmotic load to the kidney. In order to rule out the possibility of neurohypophyseal insufficiency, Carter tests were performed in two hyperthyreotic patients with an impaired concentrating capacity (E and F) and in one patient with a normal concentrating capacity (J). The results, compared with the results in normal subjects, are shown in Fig. 11. The antidiuretic reaction to 700 ml of 2.5% NaCl of the patients was not less than in the normal subjects. The production of a sufficient quantity of vasopressin under the influence of this stimulus suggests an intact neurohypophyseal function. It must be stated that this procedure is not suitable for analysis of maximal concentrating capacity since submaximal urinary osmolalities are reached as a consequence of the high level of hydration. The failure of a high dose of vasopressin tannate in oil to restore the concentrating capacity in 3 hyperthyreotic patients (B, C and E) may rule out the

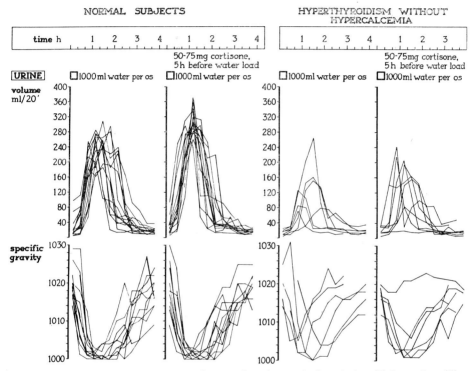

Fig. 12. Urinary findings in the course of water diuresis tests in 8 patients with hyperthyroidism (D, E, F, G, J, L, M and N) compared to normal subjects.

possibility of an accelerated destruction of vasopressin in hyperthyroidism. Therefore localization of the concentrating defect in the kidney itself seems justified.

Water diuresis tests in 8 patients with hyperthyroidism without hypercalcemia (D, E, F, G, J, L, M and N) are given in Fig. 12; for comparison, the pattern in normal subjects is included. The quantity of water excreted after an oral water load was distinctly lower in the patients. Since cortisone failed to re-establish a normal pattern, the insufficient excretion of a water load cannot be imputed to adrenocortical insufficiency. It must be stated that this impairment of water excretion does not necessarily imply a diminished capacity to dilute the urine. Some of the patients reached low specific gravities; in others high urinary volumes with low specific gravities were provoked by gradual hydration in the course of Carter tests. The pattern of water excretion recovered during treatment of hyperthyroidism. This is illustrated in one patient (I) by Fig. 13.

References p. 184–185

DISCUSSION

The findings reported in this paper indicate that renal concentrating and water-excreting capacity may be disturbed in hyperthyroidism. The concentrating defect could not be explained by a reduction of glomerular filtration rate (Table I), by an increased total solute excretion or by either a diminished production or an accelerated destruction of vasopressin. Therefore it seems to be due to an incapacity of the tubular system to establish maximal antidiuresis. The most marked defect was found

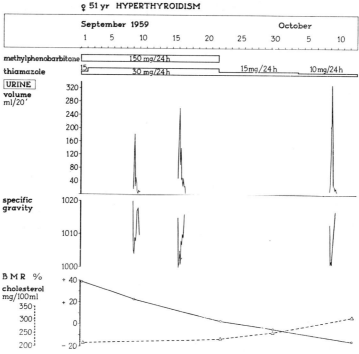

Fig. 13. The pattern of water diuresis tests in the course of treatment of hyperthyroidism (patient I).

in 3 patients, in whom hyperthyroidism was accompanied by hypercalcemia. Nevertheless, the defect also existed in a patient with calcium levels varying about the upper normal limit and in 4 out of 8 patients with normocalcemic hyperthyroidism. The clinical importance of this complication in hyperthyroidism appears from the findings in one (hypercalcemic) patient, who developed a clinical crisis, resembling the so-called thyrotoxic crisis, after a period of fluid deprival.

Parameters of renal function, particularly clearance values, have been found undisturbed in hyperthyroidism[7,8]. In these studies renal concentrating and water-excreting capacity were not investigated. Contradictory data are presented in the literature about this matter. HARE et al.[9] found a diminished response to vasopressin after administration of thyroid extract to dogs. WESTON et al.[10] described the same phenomenon in hyperthyreotic patients. In contrast, EPSTEIN et al.[11] reported a normal response to vasopressin tannate in oil in patients suffering from hyperthyroidism. A defective water-excreting capacity in hyperthyroidism can be suspected from the statement of SELYE [12] that "falsely positive" responses to the Robinson-Power-Kepler test may occur in this disease.

Polyuria and loss of renal concentrating capacity have been reported in hypercalcemia due to a number of causes. Moreover histological alterations in the distal convolute and the collecting system, combined with an impairment of concentrating capacity after induced hypercalcemia, have been described by EPSTEIN et al.[13, 14] in rats and dogs. From the existing literature we have combined 18 cases of hyperthyroidism in which hypercalcemia was found [15-27]. Some other cases in which multiple bone cysts, parathyroid adenomas or low inorganic phosphate levels were described [28-35] are not included. In 13 of the 18 cases, polyuria or symptoms of dehydration were reported [16, 18-27]. In 5 of them [18, 23-26] concentration tests were performed, combined in 3 cases [18, 23, 27] with administration of vasopressin. Maximal specific gravities varied between 1008 and 1013 in 4 of the 5 cases; in the fifth case [27], the concentration test was said to be normal in spite of the existence of a massive polyuria. In 7 cases acute clinical crises were reported, defined as thyrotoxic crisis [16, 19], impending thyrotoxic crisis [17], critical dehydration status [19], marked prostration [21] or alarming general condition [24]. In some cases [23, 24, 26], a temporary reduction of glomerular filtration rate was found, and nephrocalcinosis was reported in two of them [23, 26]. In two cases an impairment of the water diuresis pattern can be inferred from an insufficient water excretion in the first part of a Strauss test [25] and from a positive Robinson-Power-Kepler test [26] respectively. In one case [27] the dilution test was said to be normal. These data from the literature originally gave rise to the supposition that impairment of renal concentrating capacity in hyperthyroidism would be confined to those cases in which hypercalcemia was present. Our results indicate, however, that hypercalcemia is not the primary cause of concentrating inability in hyperthyroidism.

It is tempting to speculate about the possible mechanisms of an apparently intrarenal defect from the point of view of the newer concepts about urinary osmoregulation by the kidney. In this connection either a relative lowering of the renal medullary hypertonia or a defective osmotic equilibration between the renal medulla and the contents of the collecting tubules may be considered possible causes. The increase in cardiac output in hyperthyroidism [36] may increase the blood flow in the vasa recta, and thus limit the counter-current diffusion capacity of the vascular system in the renal medulla [37]. On the other hand, the disturbed utilization of oxygen in hyperthyroidism may limit the sodium transport mechanism, which is responsible for the counter-current multiplication function of Henle's loop [38-48]. Similar explanations have been proposed for the impairment of renal concentrating capacity after injection of pyrogens in dogs [41] and after heavy exercise in man [42]. A defective osmotic equilibration in the renal medulla is generally supposed to be the cause of the loss of concentrating capacity in hypercalcemia [13, 14]. As to our findings in normocalcemic hyperthyroidism, the possibility must be considered that the hypercalcuria, which is generally found in hyperthyroidism, may limit the permeability of the collecting tubules for water.

The question whether a relationship exists between the diminshed concentrating capacity and the insufficient excretion of a water load cannot be answered at the present moment. This last defect may be caused in part by the high level of insensible perspiration in hyperthyroidism. In our patients the impairment of the water-

184 P. G. A. B. WIJDEVELD, A. P. JANSEN

excreting capacity was not clearly related to the degree of concentrating inability.

Finally we have been impressed by the fact that the dehydration syndrome of patient A strikingly resembled descriptions of the so-called thyrotoxic crisis and we have wondered whether this very polymorphous clinical picture might not in fact be caused by acute dehydration.

ACKNOWLEDGEMENTS

The authors are indebted to Prof. Dr. C. L. H. Majoor for helpful criticism and advice, to the nursing and laboratory staff of the department of medicine, to Dr. H. B. Benraad for the opportunity to study patient C at his department (St. Canisius Hospital, Nijmegen), to Mr. Ph. van Elteren for aid in statistical analysis, and to Dr. S. Heijdemann (Biochemical Laboratory, Department of Medicine, "Vrije Universiteit", Amsterdam) for determinations of protein-bound iodine.

The figures were drawn at the department of medical illustration of the University of Nijmegen.

SUMMARY

In a case of hyperthyroidism combined with hypercalcemia, temporary impairment of renal concentrating and water-excreting capacity was found. A severe clinical crisis was induced in this patient by a period of fluid deprival. The clinical picture resembled the so-called thyrotoxic crisis whereas the objective findings pointed to an acute dehydration syndrome. This observation gave rise to a study of renal water handling in hyperthyroidism with and without hypercalcemia. An impairment of concentrating capacity was found in other hypercalcemic and also in some cases of normocalcemic hyperthyroidism. This concentrating defect could not be accounted for by a reduction in glomerular filtration rate, by an increased osmotic load to the kidney or by either a diminished production or an accelerated destruction of vasopressin. Therefore it must be imputed to an incapacity of the tubular system to establish maximal antidiuresis. Hypercalcemia was apparently not the primary cause of this defect. Possible causes from the point of view of modern concepts about urinary osmoregulation by the kidney are discussed. Excretion of a water load was insufficient in hyperthyroidism. There was no clear relationship between the impairment of water-excreting capacity and the degree of concentrating inability. The normal pattern of water excretion was not re-established by cortisone. The impairment of renal concentrating capacity in hyperthyroidism as well as the occurrence of a clinical picture resembling a thyrotoxic crisis after fluid deprival in one patient, gave rise to the supposition that the so-called thyrotoxic crisis may be caused in fact by acute dehydration.

REFERENCES

[1] P. G. A. B. Wijdeveld, A. P. Jansen and C. L. H. Majoor, *Ned. Tijdschr. Geneesk.*, 103 (1959) 2486.
[2] A. C. Carter and J. Robbins, *J. Clin. Endocrinol.*, 7 (1947) 753.
[3] S. Oleesky, *Lancet*, 264 (1953) 769.
[4] R. L. Bowman, H. V. Trantham and P. A. Caulfield, *J. Lab. Clin. Med.*, 43 (1954) 310.
[5] B. A. Miles, A. Paton and H. E. de Wardener, *Brit. Med. J.*, 2 (1954) 901.
[6] H. E. de Wardener, *Lancet*, 270 (1956) 1037.
[7] A. C. Corcoran and I. H. Page, *J. Clin. Endocrinol.*, 7 (1947) 801.
[8] C. J. Hlad and N. S. Bricker, *J. Clin. Endocrinol.*, 14 (1954) 1539.
[9] K. Hare, D. M. Philips, J. Bradshaw, C. Chambers and R. Hare, *Am. J. Physiol.*, 141 (1944) 187.

[10] R. W. WESTON, H. R. HOROWITZ, J. GROSSMANN, I. R. HANENSON AND L. LEITER, *J. Clin. Endocrinol.*, 16 (1956) 322.
[11] F. H. EPSTEIN AND M. J. RIVERA, *J. Clin. Endocrinol.*, 18 (1958) 1135.
[12] H. SELYE, *Textbook of Endocrinology*, 2nd ed., Acta Endocrinologica Inc., Montreal, 1950, p. 752.
[13] F. H. EPSTEIN, M. J. RIVERA AND F. A. CARONE, *J. Clin. Invest.*, 37 (1958) 1702.
[14] F. H. EPSTEIN, M. J. RIVERA AND F. A. CARONE, *J. Clin. Invest.*, 38 (1959) 1214.
[15] N. FIESSINGER, H. R. OLIVIER, D. LEROY AND R. MESSIMY, *Ann. md., (Paris)*, 38 (1935) 389.
[16] H. WIJNBLADH, *Acta Chir. Scand.*, 19 (1937) 507.
[17] D. PUPPEL, H. T. CROSS, F. K. McCORMICK AND E. HERDLE, *Surg. Gynecol. Obstet.*, 81 (1945) 243.
[18] M. M. STANLEY AND J. FAZEKAS, *Am. J. Med.*, 7 (1949) 262.
[19] E. ROSE AND R. S. BOLES, *Med. Clin. N. Am.*, 37 (1953) 1715.
[20] F. L. J. JORDAN, *Ned. Tijdschr. Geneesk.*, 98 (1954) 2406.
[21] R. A. PRIBEK AND R. C. MEADE, *A.M.A. Arch. Internal Med.*, 100 (1957) 994.
[22] C. R. KLEEMANN, S. TUTTLE AND C. H. BASSET, *J. Clin. Endocrinol.*, 18 (1958) 477.
[23] F. H. EPSTEIN, L. R. FREEDMAN AND H. LEVITIN, *New Engl. J. Med.*, 258 (1958) 782.
[24] O. SALLIN, *Acta Endocrinol.*, 29 (1958) 425.
[25] J. LEDERER AND C. LOPEZ-PINTO, *Thyroïde et exploration thyroïdienne médullo-surrénale*, Doin, Masson, Paris, 1959, p. 148.
[26] E. J. HUTH, R. L. MAYCOCK AND R. M. KERR, *Am. J. Med.*, 26 (1959) 818
[27] M. P. KÖNIG AND R. GUBLER, *Schweiz. med. Wochschr.* 89 (1959) 369.
[28] R. BALL, *Proc. Staff Meetings Mayo Clin.*, 5 (1930) 331.
[29] H. MEYER-BORSTEL, *Bruns' Beitr. klin. Chir.*, 148 (1930) 436.
[30] M. BALLIN AND P. F. MORSE, *Am. J. Surgery*, 12 (1931) 403.
[31] J. HELLSTRÖM, *Acta Chir. Scand.*, 69 (1932) 237.
[32] J. F. NOBLE AND J. B. BORG, *A.M.A. Arch. Internal Med.*, 58 (1936) 847.
[33] E. S. MILLER AND L. D. EVANS, *New Engl. J. Med.*, 227 (1942) 949.
[34] M. P. KÖNIG, D. A. SCHOLZ AND R. M. SALASSA, *Minn. Med.*, 80 (1957) 782.
[35] B. FRAME AND R. H. DURHAM, *Am. J. Med.*, 27 (1959) 824.
[36] S. HUMERFELT, O. MÜLLER AND O. STORSTEIN, *Am. Heart J.*, 56 (1958) 87.
[37] R. W. BERLINER, N. G. LEVINSKY, D. G. DAVIDSON AND M. EDEN, *Am. J. Med.*, 24 (1958) 730.
[38] B. G. HARGITAY AND W. KUHN, *Z. Elektrochem.*, 55 (1951) 539.
[39] H. WIRZ, B. G. HARGITAY AND W. KUHN, *Helv. Physiol. Pharmacol. Acta*, 9 (1951) 196.
[40] K. J. ULLRICH AND G. PEHLING, *Pfluger's Arch. ges. Physiol.*, 267 (1958) 207.
[41] J. L. BRANDT, B. ZUMOFF, L. CASTLEMAN, H. D. RUSKIN, A. JONES, S. ZUCKERMAN AND M. BIANCHI, *J. Clin. Invest.*, 35 (1956) 1080.
[42] L. G. RAISZ, W. Y. W. AU AND R. L. SCHEER, *J. Clin. Invest.*, 38 (1959) 8.

## DISCUSSION

VAN LEEUWEN: You have found an elevated blood calcium only in the two patients who showed signs of a thyrotoxic crisis. These two patients were probably dehydrated, as is suggested by the elevated Hb level. Would it be possible that the resulting elevated plasma protein concentration is responsible for the elevation of the calcium level? An increase of protein of 40% would increase total calcium by 1 mequiv./l, without a change in the ionized fraction.

WIJDEVELD: I cannot give definite information about the state of hydration of the patient with the thyrotoxic crisis at the moment of the calcium determination, since it was done in another hospital, shortly before admission into our department. As to the other hypercalcemic patients, I do not know their serum protein levels at the moment of determination of calcium. I can however say that calcium was not determined in the course of dehydration experiments and particularly that hypercalcemia was found in a period in which the sodium content of the plasma was not elevated. In patient B the sodium level was, *e.g.*, 138 mequiv./l with a calcium level of 6.6 mequiv./l. Therefore I think that the hypercalcemia cannot be explained in the way you suggest.

BORST: You are attributing some symptoms to dehydration, but according to the figures of your slides the patient must have had a massive oedema. Did he lose many liters of oedema fluid during the next days on a salt-free diet?

WIJDEVELD: As a matter of fact the patient did not have any oedema. Indeed the figure representing the clinical events in patient A shows a natriuresis in the period following the clinical crisis. In this period a rigid sodium restriction was imposed. In spite of the sodium loss the body weight of the patient increased. Therefore this natriuresis cannot be imputed to loss of oedema fluid. The most probable explanation is that it is related to the decrease of the plasma sodium level in some way.

McCANCE: You will remember the famous letter of JOHN HUNTER to JENNER urging him not to speculate but to settle the question by experiment. It would seem to me that you ought to be able to solve most of the problems raised by these interesting observations of yours by some relatively easy animal or even human experiments.

# ELECTROLYTE METABOLISM IN PERIODIC PARALYSIS

J. DE GRAEFF

*Department of Endocrinology, University Hospital, Leiden (The Netherlands)*

In periodic paralysis spontaneous attacks of flaccid paralysis of voluntary muscles occur. The frequency of these attacks varies from individual to individual and may even change in one patient in the course of the disease. The duration of paralysis may vary from a few hours to a few days. During paralysis the muscles cannot be stimulated electrically, neither directly nor indirectly. The disease is generally hereditary, but sporadic cases have been reported.

In 1933, two Dutch investigators, BIEMOND AND POLAK DANIËLS[1], described the pedigree of a family with periodic paralysis. They were the first to mention hypokal-

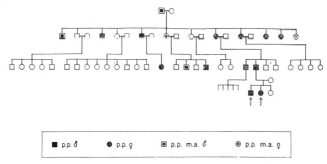

Fig. 1. Pedigree of the family with periodic paralysis[1]. The arrows indicate the patients described in this paper. p.p., periodic paralysis. m.a., muscular atrophy.

aemia during an attack of paralysis, although they did not comment on it. These and other changes in electrolyte metabolism have been found by many other investigators[2-6].

The studies to be discussed in this paper were made on two members of the same family (Fig. 1). The diagnosis of periodic paralysis with hypokalaemia thus seems to be correct by definition. The subjects were a boy aged 14, and a girl aged 13 at the time of the first examination in 1958. Both had had attacks since the age of 7. The boy had had severe attacks, generally lasting for 18 h and occurring at least once a week during the last year. The girl had a much milder form of the disease and sometimes was free from attacks for months. Nearly all studies were done on the boy.

## METABOLIC CHANGES DURING AN ATTACK

In Fig. 2 the metabolic changes during an attack in the boy are shown. The same amount of food and fluids was given every 3 h during day and night and the urine was collected every 3 h. He remained in bed during the whole study. In Fig. 2 the averages

of the excretion of different urinary constituents during the two days before an attack
are shown by an interrupted line, which proves a normal diurnal rhythm. The excretory values during an attack, which lasted from 1 a.m. to 6 p.m. are shown by an
uninterrupted line. The difference between these two lines is a rough measure of the
amounts retained or excreted during the paralysis. The serum values during paralysis
were measured at regular intervals. The following features deserve notice:

*a.* As has been known for a long time, the decrease of serum potassium and
phosphate during paralysis is accompanied by a decrease in the urinary excretion,

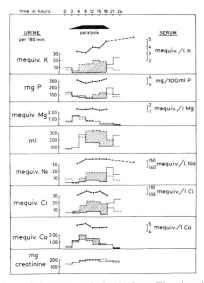

Fig. 2. Rhythm study in the boy. The time in
hours are absolute values, beginning at mid-
night. The interrupted line shows the average
excretion during the two days before an
attack. The full line indicates the excretory
values during the day of the attack.

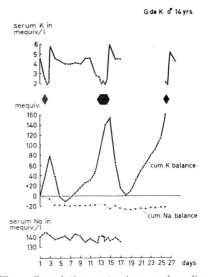

Fig. 3. Cumulative potassium and sodium
balance, and the potassium and sodium values
of the serum during a balance study on a salt-
poor diet.

which indicates a transport of these ions into the intracellular compartment. Studies
by ZIERLER[7] have shown this to be an uptake of potassium by muscle cells. The serum-
and urinary values of magnesium remain unchanged.

*b.* During paralysis sodium and chloride are retained. During this attack a slight
increase in the serum values of these ions was observed.

*c.* The urinary volume decreases during paralysis, which probably indicates
retention of water.

*d.* There is a slight decrease in serum calcium towards the end of the attack and
perhaps a slight increase in urinary calcium.

*e.* The excretion of creatinine is unchanged.

An inborn error of the metabolic process concerned with maintaining a gradient
of potassium across the cellular membrane seems to be the cause of this disease, as has
been shown by other investigators[8]. The first change is a migration of potassium and
phosphate, probably accompanied by water, into the muscle cells[7–9]. The increase in
the intra- to extracellular ratio of potassium is the cause of the paralysis.

*Building up of an attack*

If an inborn error is in fact the cause, it seems rather curious that the attacks occurred suddenly and that between the attacks everything was normal. We scrutinised the rhythm study already mentioned; it appeared that there was already some potassium retention before the attack. To get more information on this subject, another balance study was performed on the boy (Fig. 3). A constant salt-free diet was given throughout. During this study three attacks of paralysis occurred. The cumulative potassium balance was strongly positive during an attack, but returned to equilibrium rapidly. Afterwards, in the days preceding an attack, this cumulative balance had already become positive. At a certain moment a rapid increase occurred and paralysis supervened. The cumulative phosphate balance has not been drawn as the large fecal excretion prohibited this. Roughly, it followed the potassium balance.

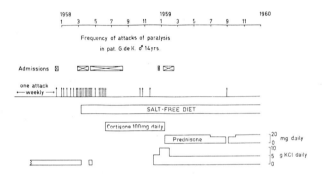

Fig. 4. Influence of therapy on the frequency of the attacks.

It seems as if the metabolic defect had always been present in this patient and had only become excessive gradually. This might perhaps be compared to the phenomenon of Wenkenbach in electrocardiology.

Incidentally, Fig. 3 shows that the sodium balance remained more or less in equilibrium throughout the whole study and that serum sodium fluctuated but did not show any definite increase during an attack.

*Na-retention*

At the time of this study a paper was published by CONN et al.[10] on periodic paralysis, in which he claimed the following points:

  1. Sodium retention precedes potassium retention.
  2. Serum sodium increases during paralysis.
  3. Sodium migrates into the cell.
  4. A salt-free diet can prevent attacks of paralysis.

We were unable to confirm these findings and would interpret our own findings in a different way.

As was shown in Fig. 2, on a salt-rich diet sodium and chloride were both retained *during* an attack. This retention certainly did not precede the migration of potassium into the muscle cells. If chloride is considered as an extracellular ion, the conclusion emerges that extracellular fluid is retained. When the amounts of sodium and chloride retained are considered, it seems probable that some sodium came from the intracellular compartment in exchange for potassium. In view of the large changes in the relation of extra- and intracellular potassium shown by pronounced changes in the electrocardiogram during these attacks, it seems rather probable that this retention of extracellular fluid is the result of cardiac failure.

As Professor Borst has contended, the occurrence of hypernatraemia (in our case up to 152 mequiv./l) in such a situation depends on the relative amounts of sodium and water available. If one considers the retention of sodium and chloride to be the *result* of the migration of potassium into the cells rather than the essential feature,

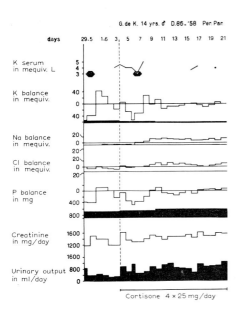

Fig. 5. Effect of cortisone during a balance study on the boy.

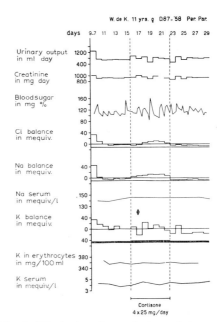

Fig. 6. Effect of cortisone during a balance study on the girl.

it is not to be expected that a salt-free diet would prevent the occurrence of attacks. Indeed, as will be shown later, even on a salt-free diet the attacks occurred with the same frequency. With this salt-free diet hypernatraemia was never found.

## TREATMENT

Therapy was necessary because the boy was very much incapacitated by his disease. In Fig. 4 it is shown that neither a salt-free diet nor supplements of potassium salts prevented the occurrence of about one attack weekly.

On very vague theoretical grounds, we decided to test cortisone. Afterwards we found a statement by Grob[8] that cortisone inhibited the transfer of potassium into muscle cells caused by the administration of glucose. The boy was started on 100 mg of cortisone daily. The salt-free diet was continued to prevent potassium-depletion by cortisone. He had one attack two days after the beginning of cortisone treatment and then remained free from attacks for 4 months. Then, three attacks occurred. We thought that this could be due to the fact that he had rather neglected his diet and that some potassium-depletion had occurred. We added 5 g of potassium chloride daily to his diet. Since then, even after changing from cortisone to prednisone, he has remained well. In September 1959, he stopped prednisone for personal reasons during a week, and immediately an attack occurred. Afterwards he remained well and has resumed full activities.

*Effects of cortisone*

The effects of cortisone were studied in detail in two balance studies in the boy and the girl. A constant salt-free diet was given throughout in both cases. In each case an attack occurred two days after the beginning of cortisone administration.

Fig. 5 shows the results of this balance study in the boy. The sodium and chloride balances are of special interest. Both were negative during cortisone administration. The relation of sodium to chloride loss was approximately that of extracellular fluid. Indeed the urinary volume increased during this period.

In Fig. 6 is shown the balance study in the girl. Here again, cortisone administration was followed by loss of sodium and chloride. Before and after this therapy the sodium and chloride balances were in equilibrium.

We were unable to find data on the effect of cortisone during a salt-free diet in normal subjects. In one control study we did not find this salt-losing effect.

It is difficult to explain this phenomenon. If one assumes that the retention of sodium and chloride is the result of a relative cardiac failure, one might suppose that cortisone, by influencing the cellular transport mechanism, improved cardiac function and that this was followed by excretion of extracellular fluid.

CONCLUSIONS

The following conclusions may be drawn:

*1.* Periodic paralysis is the result of an inborn error of metabolism affecting the cellular transport mechanism of potassium.

*2.* The retention of potassium and phosphate precedes the attacks by several days, and shows a build-up.

*3.* The retention of sodium, chloride and water is secondary to the migration of potassium into the cellular compartment and is possibly the result of relative cardiac failure.

*4.* It is thus not to be expected that changes in the salt content of the diet would affect the occurrence of attacks.

*5.* Cortisone affects the frequency of attacks, and probably has some effect on the transport mechanism cited above.

*6.* Contrary to the effects of cortisone on a salt-free diet in the normal individual, in periodic paralysis cortisone administration resulted in a loss of extracellular fluid.

SUMMARY

During an attack of paralysis, retention of sodium, chloride, potassium, phosphorus and water occurs. The serum level of potassium and phosphorus decreases, indicating transport of these ions into the cellular compartment. Sodium retention does not precede potassium retention as has been claimed. Neither does salt restriction prevent the occurrence of attacks. The balance data obtained suggest that retention of the ions mentioned starts a few days before the attack, showing a kind of building-up. In one of the patients the administration of cortisone has greatly diminished the frequency of the attacks of paralysis.

## REFERENCES

1  A. BIEMOND AND A. POLAK DANIËLS, *Brain*, 57 (1934) 91.
2  R. S. AITKEN, E. W. ALLOTT, L. I. M. CASTLEDEN AND M. WALKER, *Clin. Sci.*, 3 (1937) 47.
3  E. N. ALLOTT AND B. MCARDLE, *Clin. Sci.*, 3 (1937) 229.
4  J. W. FERREBEE, M. K. GERITY, D. W. ATCHLEY AND R. F. LOEB, *A.M.A. Arch. Neurol. Psychiat.*, 44 (1940) 830.
5  J. H. TALBOTT, *Médecine*, 20 (1941) 85.
6  T. S. DANOWSKI, J. R. ELKINTON, B. A. BURROWS AND A. W. WINKLER, *J. Clin. Invest.*, 27 (1948) 65.
7  K. L. ZIERLER AND R. ANDRES, *J. Clin. Invest.*, 36 (1957) 730.
8  D. GROB, R. J. JOHNS AND A. LILJESTRAND, *Am. J. Med.*, 23 (1957) 356.
9  E. F. VASTOLA AND C. A. BERTRAND, *Neurology*, 6 (1956) 523.
10 J. W. CONN, L. H. LOUIS, S. S. FAJANS, D. H. P. STREETEN AND R. D. JOHNSON, *Lancet*, 272 (1957) 802.

## DISCUSSION

GLYNN: Has anyone tried treating familial periodic paralysis with digoxin? On theoretical grounds this, or another cardiac glycoside, ought to work.

DE GRAEFF: I agree with your suggestion, but as far as I know nobody has tried it. I have thought about it but have not tried it because the patient was all right with cortisone. Moreover, I hesitated to give it because I do not know what would be the result of administering digoxin for a long time to a person with a normal heart.

GLYNN: In the case you described, you mentioned that there were changes in the electrocardiogram and suggested that there might have been some degree of heart failure. Was there any direct evidence for heart failure? The electrocardiographic changes might merely reflect the change in potassium distribution across the cardiac muscle membranes.

DE GRAEFF: We only proved that the sodium retention was accompanied by chloride retention and that this indicates retention of extracellular fluid. The suggestion was made that this was induced by heart failure; one would suppose that such pronounced changes in potassium distribution would be accompanied by impairment in cardiac function, but we have no definite proof for this. Another argument can be found in the literature, for it has been mentioned that during attacks the heart is enlarged as shown by radiography. Of course, other causes of retention of extracellular fluid, for example by impairment of the venous return from the paralytic muscles, cannot be excluded.

# GENERAL SUMMARY

C. P. STEWART

*Department of Clinical Chemistry, Royal Infirmary, Edinburgh (Great Britain)*

I think everyone will agree that this symposium has crammed into two days a remarkably wide range of diverse though related topics presented on a very high intellectual plane. This is, certainly, my opinion—reached after careful consideration, for I now distrust my snap judgements, having the uneasy feeling that the rate of my mental processes is being affected by the same agencies which, as Professor McCANCE has pointed out, are slowing down my glomerular filtration rate and my power of absorbing carbon monoxide.

Such a symposium is clearly very difficult to summarise adequately. With so many subjects discussed, or touched upon, the choice seems to lie between a recapitulation so brief as to amount to little more than a "Table of Contents" or a selection which can only be made on the basis of one's own personal predilections. Rightly or wrongly, I have chosen the latter course and apologise in advance to those speakers who may feel that their contributions have been passed over rather lightly—such treatment is evidence of my own limitations rather than of any lack of value in the communications.

As I mentioned in my opening remarks yesterday, scientists interested in water and electrolytes in relation to living matter are fundamentally concerned with the maintenance of the internal environment in the face of physiological and pathological variations in the external medium. I might have added—in the face also of pathological variations in cellular function, for this aspect was rightly considered by several speakers. Professor McCANCE also emphasised the importance of internal environmental stability, pointing out that in the case of complex animal organisms stability is normally maintained throughout life, from the embryonic stage to death in old age. He made the important point that this did not mean an absolute constancy of body composition from infancy to old age but did involve a progressive adjustment of the reactions—involving the kidneys, the lungs, the suprarenals, the pituitary, the brain stem and all those other factors which are concerned in growth and tissue metabolism —whose integration constitutes the stabilising mechanism.

Since life as we know it is cellular, Dr. GLYNN's theme was fundamental. He reviewed the selective movement of inorganic ions through natural (*i.e.* cell) membranes, a movement involving the power of maintaining within the cell a concentration of $Na^+$ nearly constant and much lower than that in the extracellular fluid, and a fixed concentration of $K^+$ much higher than that outside of the cell. He considered various suggested mechanisms, including that of ion-binding by proteins and the linking of ion transport to electron transfer through the cytochrome system, but clearly favoured the idea of sodium and potassium (and other) "pumps"; the sodium pump tending to expel $Na^+$ from the cell and the potassium pump tending to draw $K^+$

in. Of course such pumps, which were also invoked by McCance and by several later speakers, demand energy for their operation whatever their precise mechanism may be, and GLYNN described an extremely elegant method, involving the use of glycosidic inhibitors of adenosine phosphatase, which showed the ATP–ADP system to be closely concerned in the provision of energy for such trans-membrane pumps.

VAN LEEUWEN also considered the question of the protein binding of inorganic ions chiefly as exemplified by Ca$^{++}$ and Mg$^{++}$, of which considerable quantities seem to be bound, and Na$^+$ and K$^+$ of which only a small proportion is not free. He compared various methods of measurement with an *in vivo* ultrafiltration resulting from venous compression as the standard of reference. Whatever the role of this ion-binding in relation to transport across "membranes", it is probably of fundamental importance in maintaining the orderly sequence of enzymic reactions which is an essential part of Hopkins' dynamic equilibrium.

In discussions of the "whole man" metabolism of water and electrolytes much attention was paid to the sites of activity—the intestine, the circulation, the tissues, and the kidney—and to the mechanisms, particularly hormonal and renal, with evidence drawn from physiology, pharmacology and medicine. Actual summarization of the individual papers taken *seriatim* would be almost misleading as a means of giving a general impression of the trend of the symposium. Every paper was a valuable contribution but the nature of the subject made it inevitable that every paper would have repercussions on and from others.

Professor WIRZ gave a masterly exposition of the concept, for the introduction and development of which he himself is primarily responsible, that in man (and other mammals) the process of urine concentration is effected by a countercurrent multiplier system of the loops of HENLE. The action of this is to produce a zone of hypertonicity in the medulla, the basic process being transport of sodium out of the ascending limb —a sodium pump involving energy expenditure. The consequence is that osmotic forces are then able to withdraw water from the collecting ducts and so produce hypertonic urine. This idea, revolutionary to many besides those of us who are old enough to remember the work of CUSHNY, explains many of the facts brought to light more recently and is invoked, implicitly or explicitly, by several contributors to this symposium. Indeed it has now won general acceptance and is used by the doyen of renal physiology, HOMER SMITH.

Ion exchange, again involving reciprocating ion pumps, was also invoked by Dr. LAMBIE who emphasised that the renal excretion of K$^+$ in health and disease could be interpreted on the basis of the influence of Na$^+$ concentration at the site of Na$^+$/K$^+$ exchange in the distal tubule, the capacity of the tubular cells to absorb Na$^+$ (partly under hormonal control), and the K$^+$/H$^+$ available for exchange with Na.

The importance of hormonal control in water and electrolyte regulation, to which I have just referred, naturally received a great deal of attention, and the general situation and some of its consequences were so clearly but so succinctly reviewed by Dr. MULLER that I find myself quite unable to achieve any greater brevity. Considering principally the hormones of the adrenal cortex, but referring to others such as those of the gonads, Dr. MULLER discussed these in relation to the behaviour of water and of sodium and potassium ions. The regulatory effects of the hormones, it was pointed out, were produced not only at the site of entry (the intestine) and of exit (chiefly the kidney) but also internally by affecting inter-compartmental transfer, tissue storage etc. An analysis of the activities of these hormones was made not only in normal, but also in pathological conditions.

Dr. MULLER naturally considered the site and mode of action of certain (adrenal) hormones on the kidney tubules and this was also part of the concern of Dr. DE VRIES who reviewed the effect, on the renal excretory pattern, of various stimuli some acting directly on the renal mechanism (diuretics, adrenal hormones etc.) and some acting indirectly through circulatory changes (cardiac glycosides, changes in ECF volume caused by transfusion, dehydration etc.). He pointed out that changes in the volume and composition of the body fluids are countered by homeostatic mechanisms which lead, as a culminating event, to a renal reaction. Whatever the primary stimulus, a new steady state was reached under the combined influence of the stimulus and the counteracting homeostatic reactions.

The importance of circulatory factors in relation to electrolytes and the maintenance of stability of the one at the expense of changes in the other was discussed by Professor BORST whose work in this field began over 25 years ago, for his pioneer study was published in 1936. Since then he has contributed enormously to the therapy of conditions in which correction of water and electrolyte imbalance may determine the issue between life and death.

Professor BORST described conditions which led to the general conclusion that retention of water and of $Na^+$ (and $Cl^-$) is found in all types of circulatory failure and that, provided the cardiac reserve is not exhausted, this constitutes a valuable homeostatic function favouring an increase in circulatory blood plasma volume. Hyper- and hypo-natraemia, which reflect respectively an excess of salt and an excess of water in the fluid balance are rarely maintained if the circulation is adequate. These interesting and highly important considerations do not negate the view that hormonal influences play their part and in discussion between Professor BORST and Dr. MULLER, the "permissive role" of adrenocortical steroids was stressed.

Whilst much of the evidence advanced in elucidation of the basic mechanisms of water electrolyte control stemmed from clinical, or rather clinico-chemical investigations, many points of real clinical and therapeutic value emerged. The papers of Professor BORST and Dr. DE VRIES are an obvious example of this two-way traffic. Dr. LAMBIE, whilst contributing importantly to knowledge of the mechanism behind potassium control, provided an excellent survey of the conditions in which potassium depletion is to be expected and described a simple means of minimising it—by restricting the sodium in the tubular fluid available to the distal tubular cells for $K^+/Na^+$ exchange. She concluded that the three most important factors in the control of $K^+$ excretion are: the amount of $Na^+$ reaching the site of $Na^+/K^+$ exchange in the distal tubule, the capacity of the cells there to absorb $Na^+$, and the relative amounts of $H^+ (+ NH_4^+)$ and $K^+$ available for exchange with $Na^+$. Dr. ROBSON, besides discussing the renal factors involved in water elimination and emphasising the role of the adrenal cortex so directly concerned with $Na^+$ reabsorption, pointed out the importance of the thirst mechanism and its clinical implications. Both in his paper and in his subsequent discussion with Dr. WIRZ, Dr. ROBSON spoke of the interdependence of water excretion and sodium reabsorption—with the latter, probably, as the main mediator. He and Dr. LAMBIE made the interesting suggestion that hyperparathyroidism, classically associated with altered Ca (and P) metabolism may turn out to involve fundamentally a change in the capacity to deal with $H^+$, $K^+$ and $H_2O$.

Dr. MacGillivray reviewed a special aspect of our subject—the changes in water and salt metabolism inherent in normal pregnancy (the importance of oestrogens and especially progesterone had already been mentioned by Dr. Muller) and the more marked changes in pre-eclampsia, a study based on the use of isotope techniques.

In this category of clinically important papers founded upon and contributing to the underlying physiological and biochemical factors fall those of Professor Neil, Dr. Majoor, Dr. Wijdeveld and Dr. De Graeff.

Professor Neil reviewed the changes in acid/base equilibrium occurring in hypothermia (and during re-warming), the fall in $K^+$ and the corresponding small rise in $Na^+$, both of which could reasonably be attributed to increased adrenocortical activity, and the constant but unexplained fall in plasma volume. Professor Neil's exposition of the fundamental processes controlling plasma $[H^+]$ and of the effects of temperature variation was most illuminating. On the basis of this he emphasised the care needed in interpreting $[H^+]$ changes produced by hypothermia—the increase due to hypothermia itself, the enhancement of this increase by hypercarbia and by the circulatory arrest, thoractomy and cardiotomy of the full surgical procedure. He also pointed out the occurrence of metabolic acidosis associated with liver dysfunction during circulatory arrest, and described a simple means of abolishing or minimising this. The importance to the surgeon of an understanding of these processes can hardly be overestimated.

Dr. Majoor's discussion dealt with the electrolyte, water and hormonal effects of heparin administration, especially in oedematous (nephrotic) patients and gave some indication of its therapeutic value and limitations. Heparin (like several related compounds) stimulates loss of water and sodium with, therefore, disappearance of oedema, and, as would be expected from the exchange hypothesis, some slight retention of potassium.

Dr. Wijdeveld has observed and carefully analysed two cases of the rather rare condition of polyuria accompanying hyperthyroidism and has concluded that these may be examples of nephrogenic diabetes insipidus due to hypercalcaemia. He suggested as a further deduction from his data that thyrotoxic crises may be caused by dehydration resulting from the syndrome he described.

Finally, Dr. De Graeff gave a further example of electrolyte and water disturbances of clinical interest—a retention of $Na^+$, $Cl^-$, $K^+$, $HPO_4^{--}$ and water prior to and during attacks of periodic paralysis. He suggested that $K^+$ and $HPO_4^{--}$ were passed into the cellular compartment and he reported that in one of his patients cortisone administration was successful in diminishing the frequency of the attacks.

Let me conclude this summary, already overlong and, I feel, rather inadequate, by expressing the hope that the many omissions indicate no lack of appreciation and mean no disrespect to the authors whose papers I have truncated; they are signs of my own limitations. May I also say this—and I am sure my British colleagues will echo it—it is a particularly flattering experience to attend a Symposium on the mainland and to find every paper and every contribution to the discussion given in English. It is also a humbling experience, for throughout the English has been real English and we have at times been put to shame by the fluency and correctness of our speakers —I was about to say "foreign speakers" but it must never be forgotten that *we* are the foreigners here!

# AUTHOR INDEX

# SUBJECT INDEX